Everyday Mathematics®

The University of Chicago School Mathematics Project

Math Masters

Grade **2**

Mc Graw Hill **Wright Group**

The **McGraw·Hill** Companies

The University of Chicago School Mathematics Project (UCSMP)

Max Bell, Director, UCSMP Elementary Materials Component; Director, *Everyday Mathematics* First Edition; James McBride, Director, *Everyday Mathematics* Second Edition; Andy Isaacs, Director, *Everyday Mathematics* Third Edition; Amy Dillard, Associate Director, *Everyday Mathematics* Third Edition

Authors

Max Bell, Jean Bell, John Bretzlauf, Amy Dillard, Robert Hartfield, Andy Isaacs, James McBride, Cheryl G. Moran*, Kathleen Pitvorec, Peter Saecker

*Third Edition only

Technical Art
Diana Barrie

Teachers in Residence
Kathleen Clark, Patti Satz

Editorial Assistant
John Wray

Contributors

Librada Acosta, Carol Arkin, Robert Balfanz, Sharlean Brooks, Jean Callahan, Ann Coglianese, Mary Ellen Dairyko, Tresea Felder, James Flanders, Dorothy Freedman, Rita Gronbach, Deborah Arron Leslie, William D. Pattison, LaDonna Pitts, Danette Riehle, Marie Schilling, Robert Strang, Sadako Tengan, Therese Wasik, Leeann Wille, Michael Wilson

Photo Credits

©C Squared Studios/Getty Images, p. 155 *right;* ©Dynamic Graphics Group/Creatas/Alamy, p. 39 *third row, second from right;* ©John Henley/CORBIS, p. 376; ©Ken Karp photography, p. 347 *bottom;* ©Tom and Dee Ann McCarthy/CORBIS, p. 194; ©Ryan McVay/Getty Images, p. 39 *fourth row, left;* ©Ken O'Donoghue, pp. 223, 345, 347 *top;* ©John A. Rizzo/Getty Images, pp. 155 *left,* 225; ©Royalty-Free/Corbis, pp. *39 second row, left,* 249; ©Stockdisk Classic/Getty Images, p. 39 *fourth row, right;* ©Dana White/PhotoEdit, p. 39 *first row, center;* ©Jeremy Woodhouse/PhotoDisc, p. 118 *bottom row, right.*

www.WrightGroup.com

 **Wright Group**

Send all inquiries to:
Wright Group/McGraw-Hill
P.O. Box 812960
Chicago, IL 60681

ISBN 0-07-604558-7

2 3 4 5 6 7 8 9 QWD 12 11 10 09 08 07 06

The McGraw·Hill Companies

Contents

Unit 4

Unit 5

Unit 11

Unit 12

Project Masters

Teaching Aid Masters

Game Masters

Teaching Masters
and
Home Link Masters

Name _____ Date _____ Time _____

HOME LINK 2·3 | **Doubles Facts**

Family Note Today we worked with an Addition/Subtraction Facts Table and dominoes to practice with a special kind of addition problem called doubles facts. $3 + 3 = 6$, $4 + 4 = 8$, and $5 + 5 = 10$ are examples of doubles facts. We also worked with almost-doubles facts, such as $3 + 4 = 7$, $5 + 4 = 9$, and $7 + 8 = 15$. Review doubles facts and almost-doubles facts with your child.

Please return this Home Link to school tomorrow.

1. Write the sum for each doubles fact.

a. $2 + 2 =$ _____   b. _____ $= 5 + 5$ c. _____ $= 0 + 0$

d. $\begin{array}{r} 7 \\ + 7 \\ \hline \end{array}$ e. $\begin{array}{r} 3 \\ + 3 \\ \hline \end{array}$ f. $\begin{array}{r} 8 \\ + 8 \\ \hline \end{array}$ g. $\begin{array}{r} 6 \\ + 6 \\ \hline \end{array}$

h. $9 + 9 =$ _____   i. _____ $= 1 + 1$ j. _____ $= 4 + 4$

2. Ask someone to give you doubles facts. You say the sums. Do this for about 10 minutes or until you know all the doubles facts.

3. Write each sum. Use doubles facts to help you.

a. $5 + 4 =$ _____   b. $4 + 5 =$ _____   c. _____ $= 9 + 8$

d. $\begin{array}{r} 6 \\ + 7 \\ \hline \end{array}$ e. $\begin{array}{r} 2 \\ + 3 \\ \hline \end{array}$ f. $\begin{array}{r} 7 \\ + 8 \\ \hline \end{array}$ g. $\begin{array}{r} 6 \\ + 5 \\ \hline \end{array}$

Copyright © Wright Group/McGraw-Hill

27

Name _____ Date _____ Time _____

LESSON 6·6 | **Making a Dollar**

Work together in a small group.

Materials ☐ 20 nickels

☐ 10 dimes

☐ 4 quarters

☐ paper and pencil

Directions

1. Use the coins to find as many different ways as you can to make $1.00.

2. Before you begin, THINK about how to do this. *Hint:* First, make a dollar using 3 quarters and some other coins.

3. Plan how you will record the different ways to make $1.00.

4. On a sheet of paper, record the different ways you find to make $1.00. Use Ⓝ, Ⓓ, and Ⓠ to show the coins.

Follow-Up

◆ How many ways did you find to make $1.00? Check with other groups to see if they thought of any ways that your group didn't find.

◆ Did you have a plan to find all the combinations? Compare your plan with the plan used by another group.

175

LESSON 1·1 **Number Lines**

1. ←——|——|——|——|——|——|——|——|——→

- - - - - - - - - -

2. ←——|——|——|——|——|——|——|——|——→

- - - - - - - - - -

3. ←——|——|——|——|——|——|——|——|——→

- - - - - - - - - -

4. ←——|——|——|——|——|——|——|——|——→

- - - - - - - - - -

5. ←——|——|——|——|——|——|——|——|——→

- - - - - - - - - -

6. ←——|——|——|——|——|——|——|——|——→

- - - - - - - - - -

HOME LINK 1·1

Unit 1: Family Letter

Introduction to *Second Grade Everyday Mathematics*

Welcome to *Second Grade Everyday Mathematics*. It is a part of an elementary school mathematics curriculum developed by the University of Chicago School Mathematics Project.

Several features of the program are described below to help familiarize you with the structure and expectations of *Everyday Mathematics*.

A problem-solving approach based on everyday situations
By making connections between their own knowledge and their experiences both in school and outside of school, children learn basic math skills in meaningful contexts so the mathematics becomes "real."

Frequent practice of basic skills Instead of practice presented in a single, tedious drill format, children practice basic skills in a variety of more engaging ways. Children will complete daily review exercises covering a variety of topics, find patterns on the number grid, work with addition and subtraction fact families in different formats, and play games that are specifically designed to develop basic skills.

An instructional approach that revisits concepts regularly
To improve the development of basic skills and concepts, children regularly revisit previously learned concepts and repeatedly practice skills encountered earlier. The lessons are designed to build on concepts and skills throughout the year instead of treating them as isolated bits of knowledge.

A curriculum that explores mathematical content beyond basic arithmetic Mathematics standards around the world indicate that basic arithmetic skills are only the beginning of the mathematical knowledge children will need as they develop critical-thinking skills. In addition to basic arithmetic, *Everyday Mathematics* develops concepts and skills in the following topics—number and numeration; operations and computation; data and chance; geometry; measurement and reference frames; and patterns, functions, and algebra.

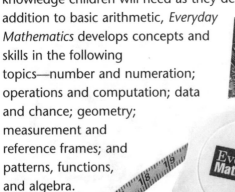

3

Second Grade Everyday Mathematics emphasizes the following content:

Number and Numeration Counting; reading and writing numbers; identifying place value; comparing numbers; working with fractions; using money to develop place value and decimal concepts

Operations and Computation Recalling addition and subtraction facts; exploring fact families (related addition and subtraction facts, such as $2 + 5 = 7$, $5 + 2 = 7$, $7 - 5 = 2$, and $7 - 2 = 5$); adding and subtracting with tens and hundreds; beginning multiplication and division; exchanging money amounts

Data and Chance Collecting, organizing, and interpreting data using tables, charts, and graphs

Geometry Exploring and naming 2- and 3-dimensional shapes

Measurement Using tools to measure length, weight, capacity, and volume; using U.S. customary and metric measurement units, such as feet, centimeters, ounces, and grams

Reference Frames Using clocks, calendars, thermometers, and number lines

Patterns, Functions, and Algebra Exploring number patterns, rules for number sequences, relations between numbers, and attributes

Everyday Mathematics provides you with many opportunities to monitor your child's progress and to participate in your child's mathematics experiences.

Throughout the year, you will receive Family Letters to keep you informed of the mathematical content that your child will be studying in each unit. Each letter includes a vocabulary list, suggested Do-Anytime Activities for you and your child, and an answer guide to selected Home Link (homework) activities.

You will enjoy seeing your child's confidence and comprehension soar as he or she connects mathematics to everyday life.

We look forward to an exciting year!

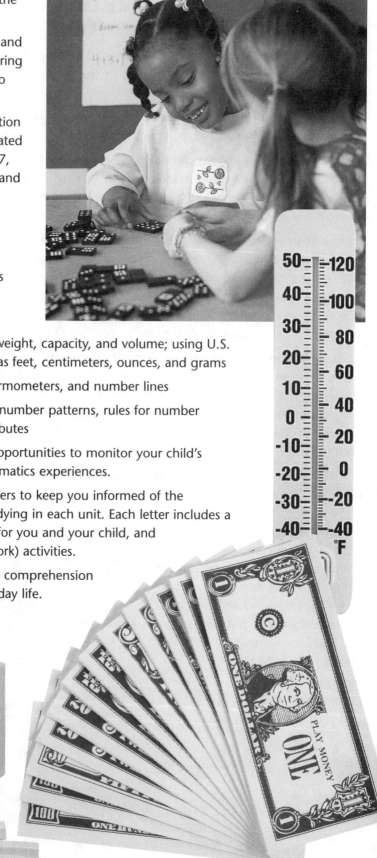

Unit 1: Numbers and Routines

This unit reacquaints children with the daily routines of *Everyday Mathematics*. Children also review and extend mathematical concepts that were developed in *Kindergarten Everyday Mathematics* and *First Grade Everyday Mathematics*.

In Unit 1, children will ...

◆ Count in several different intervals—forward by 2s from 300, forward by 10s from 64, backward by 10s from 116, and so on.

◆ Practice addition facts, such as 5 + 4 = ? and ? = 7 + 5.

◆ Review whole numbers by answering questions like "Which number comes after 57? After 98? After 234?" and "Which number is 10 more than 34? 67? 89?"

◆ Respond to prompts like "Write 38. Circle the digit in the 10s place. Put an X on the digit in the 1s place."

◆ Work with a number grid to reinforce place-value skills and observe number patterns.

−9	−8	−7	−6	−5	−4	−3	−2	−1	⓪
1	2	③	4	5	⑥	7	8	⑨	10
11	⑫	13	14	⑮	16	17	⑱	19	20
㉑	22	23	㉔	25	26	㉗	28	29	㉚

←Children use number grids to learn about ones and tens digits and to identify number patterns, such as multiples of three.

◆ Review equivalent number names, such as 10 = 5 + 5, 10 = 7 + 3, 10 = 20 − 10, and so on.

◆ Play games, such as *Addition Top-It*, to strengthen number skills.

◆ Practice telling time and using a calendar.

Do-Anytime Activities

To work with your child on the concepts taught in this unit, try these interesting and rewarding activities:

1. Discuss examples of mathematics in everyday life: television listings, road signs, money, recipe measurements, time, and so on.

2. Discuss rules for working with a partner or in a group.

- ◆ Speak quietly.   ◆ Be polite.   ◆ Help each other.
- ◆ Share.   ◆ Listen to your partner.
- ◆ Take turns.   ◆ Praise your partner.
- ◆ Talk about problems.

3. Discuss household tools that can be used to measure things or help solve mathematical problems.

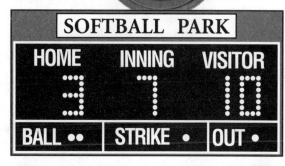

Vocabulary

Important terms in Unit 1:

math journal A book used by each child; it contains examples, instructions, and problems, as well as space to record answers and observations.

tool kits Individual zippered bags or boxes used in the classroom; they contain a variety of items, such as rulers, play money, and number cards, to help children understand mathematical ideas.

Math Message A daily activity children complete independently, usually as a lead-in to the day's lesson. For example: "Count by 10s. Count as high as you can in 1 minute. Write down the number you get to."

Mental Math and Reflexes A daily whole-class oral or written activity, often emphasizing computation done mentally.

number grid A table in which numbers are arranged consecutively, usually in rows of ten. A move from one number to the next within a row is a change of 1; a move from one number to the next within a column is a change of 10.

−9	−8	−7	−6	−5	−4	−3	−2	−1	0
1	2	3	4	5	6	7	8	9	10
11	12	13	14	15	16	17	18	19	20
21	22	23	24	25	26	27	28	29	30

Exploration A small-group, hands-on activity designed to introduce or extend a topic.

Math Boxes Math problems in the math journal that provide opportunities for reviewing and practicing previously introduced skills.

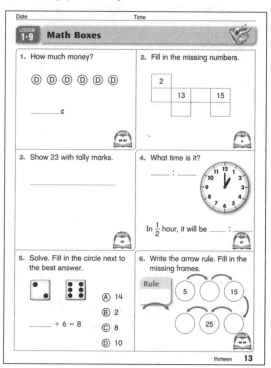

Home Links Problems and activities intended to promote follow-up and enrichment at home.

As You Help Your Child with Homework

As your child brings home assignments, you may want to go over the instructions together, clarifying them as necessary. The answers listed below will guide you through this unit's Home Links.

Home Link 1·11

1. <   **2.** >

3. >   **4.** =

5. Answers vary. **6.** Answers vary.

Home Link 1·12

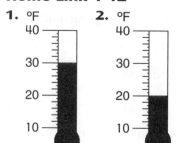

1. °F   **2.** °F   **3.** °F   **4.** °F

LESSON 1·2 | Sorting and Counting Coins

Sort your coins into piles of pennies, nickels, dimes, and quarters.

Count the number of coins you have in each pile. Record your total number of coins for each pile.

Calculate the total value for each pile of coins. Record your total value for each pile of coins.

Coin	Number of Coins	Value of Coins
Pennies		
Nickels		
Dimes		
Quarters		

Try This

Calculate the total value of all of your coins. _____

LESSON 1·3   My Activities

1. List some of the activities you do on a school day.

My Activities		
Activity	**Time**	
	From	**To**

2. Which activity takes the longest amount of time? _____

About how long does it take? _____

3. Which activity takes the least amount of time? _____

About how long does it take? _____

Try This

4. About how long do your activities take all together? _____

LESSON 1·7 **Beginning Number-Scroll Sheet**

0

LESSON 1·7

Continuing Number-Scroll Sheet

Paste/tape to here.

LESSON 1·7   Counting on the Number Grid

1. Start at 0. Count by 3s on the number grid up to 50. Color each number you land on yellow.

2. Put your finger on 12. Write an X on the number that is 10 more than 12.

3. Put your finger on 20. Count back 5. Circle the number you land on.

4. Put your finger on 37. Count back 8. Color the number you land on blue.

5. Put your finger on 74. Count back 40. Color the number you land on red.

−9	−8	−7	−6	−5	−4	−3	−2	−1	0
1	2	3	4	5	6	7	8	9	10
11	12	13	14	15	16	17	18	19	20
21	22	23	24	25	26	27	28	29	30
31	32	33	34	35	36	37	38	39	40
41	42	43	44	45	46	47	48	49	50
51	52	53	54	55	56	57	58	59	60
61	62	63	64	65	66	67	68	69	70
71	72	73	74	75	76	77	78	79	80
81	82	83	84	85	86	87	88	89	90
91	92	93	94	95	96	97	98	99	100
101	102	103	104	105	106	107	108	109	110

LESSON 1·8 — Number-Grid Pieces

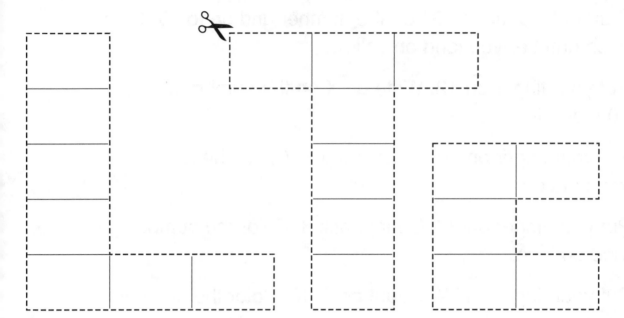

12

LESSON 1·8 — Number-Grid Pieces

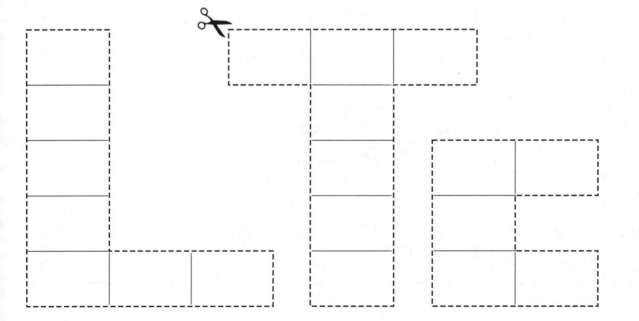

LESSON 1·8

Number-Grid Cutouts

LESSON 1·10 | **Calculator Counting**

1. Use your calculator.

2. Choose a "count by" number.

3. Enter the key sequence to start your count and press the ⊜ key three times.

4. Show your partner the calculator.

5. Slowly press the ⊜ key four times while your partner writes the display numbers on the lines.

6. Your partner then guesses your "count by" number.

7. Switch turns.

---

1. _____ _____ _____ _____

   Guess _____

2. _____ _____ _____ _____

   Guess _____

3. _____ _____ _____ _____

   Guess _____

4. _____ _____ _____ _____

   Guess _____

HOME LINK
1·11

Relations: <, >, =

Family Note

In *Second Grade Everyday Mathematics,* children "do mathematics." We expect that children will want to share their enthusiasm for the mathematics activities they do in school with their families. Your child will bring home assignments and activities to do as homework throughout the year. These assignments, called "Home Links," will be identified by the house at the top right corner of this page. The assignments will not take very much time to complete, but most of them involve interaction with an adult or an older child.

There are many reasons for including Home Links in the second grade program:

◆ The assignments encourage children to take initiative and responsibility for completing them. As you respond with encouragement and assistance, you help your child build independence and self-confidence.

◆ Home Links reinforce newly learned skills and concepts. They provide opportunities for children to think and practice at their own pace.

◆ These assignments are often designed to relate what is done in school to children's lives outside school. This helps tie mathematics to the real world, which is very important in the *Everyday Mathematics* program.

◆ The Home Links assignments will help you get a better idea of the mathematics your child is learning in school.

Generally, you can help by listening and responding to your child's requests and comments about mathematics. You also can help by linking numbers to real life, pointing out ways in which you use numbers (time, TV channels, page numbers, telephone numbers, bus routes, shopping lists, and so on). Extending the notion that "children who are read to, read," *Everyday Mathematics* supports the belief that children who have someone do math with them will learn mathematics. Playful counting and thinking games that are fun for both you and your child are very helpful for such learning.

*Please return the **second page** of this Home Link to school tomorrow.*

HOME LINK
1·11

Relations: <, >, = *continued*

Family Note This icon will often appear on the Home Links. This icon tells children where to look in *My Reference Book* to find more information about the concept or skill addressed in the Home Link. In today's lesson, we reviewed and practiced using the <, >, and = symbols. For information about relation symbols, see page 9 in *My Reference Book*.

Show someone at home your *My Reference Book.* Together find 3 things you found interesting and write them below.

1. _____

2. _____

3. _____

Explain to someone at home how to do Problems 1–4. Then write <, >, or = in each blank. Use your *My Reference Book* to look up the symbols.

1. 8 _____ 12

2. 25 _____ 18

3. 103 _____ 53

4. 79 _____ 79

Write numbers in the blanks to make up your own.

5. _____ < _____

6. _____ > _____

LESSON 1·12 | Temperature

Work in a group of 3 or 4 children.

Materials ☐ Class Thermometer Poster

☐ quarter-sheets of paper

Directions

Activity 1

1. Take turns. One person names a temperature. Another person shows that temperature on the Class Thermometer Poster.

2. Everyone in the group checks to see that the temperature is shown correctly.

3. Keep taking turns until each person has named a temperature and has shown a temperature on the Class Thermometer Poster.

Activity 2

1. Take turns showing a temperature on the Class Thermometer Poster. Everyone reads the thermometer and writes that temperature.

2. Everyone in the group compares the temperatures they wrote. Did everyone write the same temperature? Discuss any differences.

Follow-Up

Look at all the temperatures that you recorded on your quarter-sheets of paper.

◆ Were some temperatures easier to read than others? Explain.

◆ Order the temperatures from coldest to hottest.

17

Base-10 Structures

Work in a group of 3 or 4 children.

Materials   ☐ base-10 blocks (cubes, longs, and flats)

          ☐ quarter-sheets of paper

Directions

1. Each person uses base-10 blocks to make a "building." The picture shows an example.

60

2. Each block has a value.

   The value of the cube is 1.
   The value of the long is 10.
   The value of the flat is 100.

■ = 1
| = 10
☐ = 100

   What number does your building show? Use the symbols in the box above to help you.

3. Draw your building on a quarter-sheet of paper. Write the number with your drawing.

4. Have a friend help you check the number.

5. If there is time, make more buildings. Draw each building and record the number of each building.

___

Follow-Up

◆ Look at the numbers shown by your group's buildings.

◆ Order the numbers from smallest to largest.

LESSON 1·12 | **Sorting Dominoes**

Work in a group of 3 or 4 children.

Materials ☐ 1 or 2 sets of double-9 dominoes

☐ number cards 0–18 (from the Everything Math Deck, if available)

Directions

1. Lay down the number cards in order from 0 through 18.

2. Place each domino above the number card that shows the sum of the domino dots.

3. List the addition facts shown by the dominoes on a sheet of paper. Before you begin, decide how your group will record the facts.

Follow-Up

◆ Look at the list of addition facts your group made.

◆ Try to think of a better way to record the facts.

◆ Talk about why you think the new way is better.

HOME LINK 1·12

Temperatures

Family Note

In today's lesson, the class examined thermometers and practiced reading Fahrenheit temperatures. We began a daily routine of recording the outside temperature. If you have a nondigital thermometer at home (inside or outside), encourage your child to read the Fahrenheit temperatures to you. We will introduce Celsius temperatures in a later unit.

Please return this Home Link to school tomorrow.

MRB 87

1. Circle the thermometer that shows 30°F.

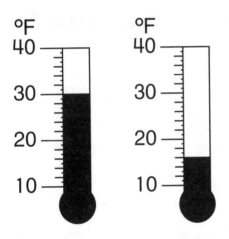

2. Circle the thermometer that shows 20°F.

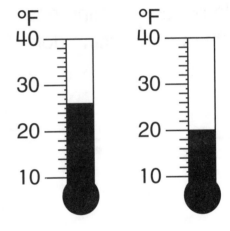

3. Circle the thermometer that shows 12°F.

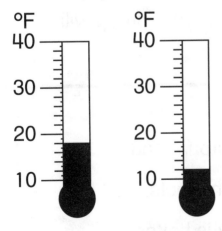

4. Circle the thermometer that shows 28°F.

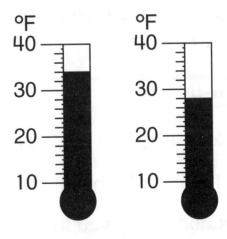

HOME LINK 1·13

Unit 2: Family Letter

Addition and Subtraction Facts

Unit 2 focuses on reviewing and extending addition facts and linking subtraction to addition. Children will solve basic addition and subtraction facts through real-life stories.

In *Everyday Mathematics*, the ability to recall number facts instantly is called "fact power." Instant recall of the addition and subtraction facts will become a powerful tool in computation with multidigit numbers, such as 29 + 92.

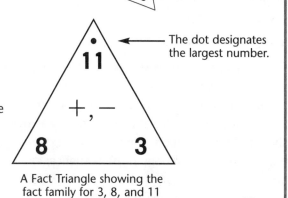

Math Tools

Your child will be using **Fact Triangles** to practice and review addition and subtraction facts. Fact Triangles are a "new and improved" version of flash cards; the addition and subtraction facts shown are made from the same three numbers, helping your child understand the relationships among those facts. The Family Note on Home Link 2-7, which you will receive later, provides a more detailed description of Fact Triangles.

The dot designates the largest number.

A Fact Triangle showing the fact family for 3, 8, and 11

Vocabulary

Important terms in Unit 2:

label A unit, descriptive word, or phrase used to put a number or numbers in context. Using a label reinforces the idea that numbers always refer to something.

unit box A box that contains the label or unit of measure for the numbers in a problem. For example, in number stories involving children in the class, the unit box would be as follows:

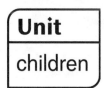

Unit
children

A unit box allows children to remember that numbers have a context without having to repeat the label in each problem.

number story A story involving numbers made up by children, teachers, or parents. Problems from the story can be solved with one or more of the four basic arithmetic operations.

number model A number sentence that shows how the parts of a number story are related. For example, 5 + 8 = 13 models the number story: "5 children skating. 8 children playing ball. How many children in all?"

fact power The ability to instantly recall basic arithmetic facts.

doubles fact The sum or product of the same two 1-digit numbers, such as 2 + 2 = 4 or 3 × 3 = 9.

turn-around facts A pair of addition (or multiplication) facts in which the order of the addends (or factors) is reversed, such as 3 + 5 = 8 and 5 + 3 = 8 (or 3 × 4 = 12 and 4 × 3 = 12). If you know an addition or multiplication fact, you also know its turn-around fact.

fact family A collection of four addition and subtraction facts, or multiplication and division facts, relating three numbers. For example, the addition/subtraction fact family for the numbers 2, 4, and 6 consists of:

$2 + 4 = 6$ $4 + 2 = 6$
$6 - 4 = 2$ $6 - 2 = 4$

The multiplication/division fact family for the numbers 2, 4, and 8 consists of:

$2 \times 4 = 8$ $8 \div 2 = 4$
$4 \times 2 = 8$ $8 \div 4 = 2$

Frames-and-Arrows diagram A diagram used to represent a number sequence, or a list of numbers ordered according to a rule. A Frames-and-Arrows diagram has frames connected by arrows to show the path from one frame to the next. Each frame contains a number in the sequence; each arrow represents a rule that determines which number goes in the next frame.

Rule
−5

35 → 30 → 25 → 20 → 15 → 10

"What's My Rule?" problem A problem in which number pairs are related to each other according to a rule or rules. A rule can be represented by a **function machine.**

in	out
3	8
5	10
8	13

"What's My Rule?" table

Function machine In *Everyday Mathematics,* an imaginary device that receives input numbers and pairs them with output numbers according to a set rule.

Do-Anytime Activities

To work with your child on the concepts taught in this unit and in previous units, try these interesting and rewarding activities:

1. Talk with your child about why it is important to learn basic facts.

2. Create addition and subtraction stories about given subjects.

3. Have your child explain how to use a facts table.

4. As you discover which facts your child is having difficulty mastering, make a Fact Triangle using the three numbers of that fact family.

5. Name a number and ask your child to think of several different ways to represent that number. For example, 10 can be represented as $1 + 9$, $6 + 4$, $12 - 2$, and so on.

10	
ten	$12 - 2$
$1 + 9$	$6 + 4$
diez	$10 - 0$

Building Skills through Games

In Unit 2, your child will practice addition facts and find equivalent names for numbers by playing the following games.

Beat the Calculator

A "Calculator" (a player who uses a calculator to solve the problem) and a "Brain" (a player who solves the problem without a calculator) race to see who will be first to solve addition problems.

Domino Top-It

Each player turns over a domino and finds the total number of dots. The player with the larger total then takes both dominoes from that round.

Doubles or Nothing

Each player adds numbers across each row, down each column, and along each diagonal in a grid for each round, circles identical sums, and finds the total of doubles as a score for the round.

Name That Number

Each player turns over a card to find a number that must be renamed using any combination of five faceup cards.

6 = 8 − 2
6 = 10 − 4
6 = 4 + 2

As You Help Your Child with Homework

As your child brings home assignments, you may want to go over the instructions together, clarifying them as necessary. The answers listed below will guide you through this unit's Home Links.

Home Link 2·1

2. 8   **3.** 18   **4.** 7   **5.** 16

Home Link 2·2

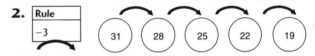

Home Link 2·3

1. a. 4   **b.** 10   **c.** 0   **d.** 14   **e.** 6
f. 16   **g.** 12   **h.** 18   **i.** 2   **j.** 8

3. a. 9   **b.** 9   **c.** 17   **d.** 13   **e.** 5
f. 15   **g.** 11

Home Link 2·4

1. a. 7   **b.** 11   **c.** 7   **d.** 7   **e.** 11   **f.** 7

2. a. 8   **b.** 5   **c.** 6   **d.** 3   **e.** 7   **f.** 9

3. a. 11   **b.** 15   **c.** 16   **d.** 10   **e.** 14   **f.** 15
    g. 17   **h.** 14   **i.** 18   **j.** 16   **k.** 13   **l.** 17

Home Link 2·5

Home Link 2·6

2. 9 + 6 = 15; 6 + 9 = 15; 15 − 6 = 9; 15 − 9 = 6

3. 8 + 7 = 15; 7 + 8 = 15; 15 − 7 = 8; 15 − 8 = 7

4. 5 + 9 = 14; 9 + 5 = 14; 14 − 9 = 5; 14 − 5 = 9

5. 13   **6.** 14   **7.** 12   **8.** 16

Home Link 2·10

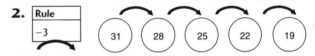

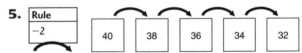
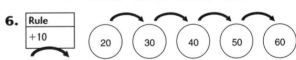

1. Rule +6 : 3, 9, 15, 21, 27

2. Rule −3 : 31, 28, 25, 22, 19

3. Rule +5 : 7, 12, 17, 22, 27

4. Rule +3 : 8, 11, 14, 17, 20

5. Rule −2 : 40, 38, 36, 34, 32

6. Rule +10 : 20, 30, 40, 50, 60

Home Link 2·11

1. Rule +9

in	out
1	10
4	13
6	15
8	17
5	14

2. Rule −8

in	out
10	2
12	4
9	1
14	6
8	0

3. Rule +6

in	out
4	10
6	12
3	9
9	15
0	6

4. Rule +5

in	out
8	13
4	9
13	18
5	10

Answers vary.

5. 18; 5

HOME LINK 2·1 | **Addition Number Stories**

Family Note

Before beginning this Home Link, review the vocabulary from the Unit 2 Family Letter with your child: **number story, label, unit box,** and **number model.** Encourage your child to make up and solve number stories and to write number models for the stories. Stress that the answer to the question makes more sense if it has a label.

Please return this Home Link to school tomorrow.

MRB
108

1. Tell someone at home what you know about number stories, labels, unit boxes, and number models. Write an addition number story for the picture. Write the answer and a number model.

Unit
lions

Story: _____

_____

_____

_____

_____

Answer the question: _____
                         (unit)

Number Model: __ + __ = ____

Practice

2. 6 + 2 = ___

3. 11 + 7 = ___

4.   4
       + 3
      ____

5.   10
       + 6
      ____

Addition Facts

Family Note In class today, we continued working with addition stories. We reviewed shortcuts when adding 0 or 1 to a number. We also stressed the importance of memorizing the sum of two 1-digit numbers. Then we reinforced addition facts by playing a game called *Beat the Calculator.*

Please return this Home Link to school tomorrow.

Solve these addition fact problems.

2 + 4	0 + 0	5 + 4	1 + 4	2 + 5	3 + 2	1 + 9	3 + 6	4 + 4	1 + 1
2 + 0	3 + 5	5 + 1	1 + 4	9 + 2	0 + 7	2 + 3	2 + 2	7 + 2	3 + 4	2 + 8
6 + 2	1 + 6	5 + 5	0 + 6	4 + 3	0 + 5	1 + 8	4 + 6	5 + 3	4 + 0	3 + 1
0 + 8	6 + 6	8 + 2	9 + 0	3 + 3	7 + 1	2 + 6	1 + 3	5 + 2	6 + 1	0 + 4
2 + 1	2 + 9	6 + 2	6 + 4	0 + 1	4 + 2	6 + 3	0 + 2	5 + 1	1 + 2	2 + 7
4 + 5	7 + 0	6 + 2	9 + 3	1 + 5	0 + 9	1 + 7	1 + 5	7 + 3	0 + 6	6 + 5
9 + 1	8 + 0	6 + 2	8 + 3	1 + 0	6 + 0	3 + 3	0 + 3	3 + 8	3 + 7	

Name	Date	Time

Doubles Facts

> **Family Note** Today we worked with an Addition/Subtraction Facts Table and dominoes to practice with a special kind of addition problem called doubles facts. $3 + 3 = 6$, $4 + 4 = 8$, and $5 + 5 = 10$ are examples of doubles facts. We also worked with almost-doubles facts, such as $3 + 4 = 7$, $5 + 4 = 9$, and $7 + 8 = 15$. Review doubles facts and almost-doubles facts with your child.
>
> *Please return this Home Link to school tomorrow.*

1. Write the sum for each doubles fact.

   a. $2 + 2 =$ _____   **b.** _____ $= 5 + 5$ **c.** _____ $= 0 + 0$

   d.   7   **e.**   3   **f.**   8   **g.**   6
       $+ 7$ $+ 3$ $+ 8$ $+ 6$

   h. $9 + 9 =$ _____   **i.** _____ $= 1 + 1$ **j.** _____ $= 4 + 4$

2. Ask someone to give you doubles facts. You say the sums. Do this for about 10 minutes or until you know all the doubles facts.

3. Write each sum. Use doubles facts to help you.

   a. $5 + 4 =$ _____   **b.** $4 + 5 =$ _____   **c.** _____ $= 9 + 8$

   d.   6   **e.**   2   **f.**   7   **g.**   6
       $+ 7$ $+ 3$ $+ 8$ $+ 5$

HOME LINK 2·4 | **Turn-Around, Doubles, and +9**

Family Note It is important for children to have instant recall of addition facts. They use shortcuts to help them learn the facts. For example, *turn-around facts* are facts that have the same sum, but the numbers being added are reversed or turned around. *Doubles facts* are facts in which the same number is added. When solving *+9 facts,* children are encouraged to think of the easier +10 combinations and then subtract 1 from the sum.

Please return this Home Link to school tomorrow.

1. Write the sums. Tell someone at home what you know about turn-around facts.

    a. 6 + 1 = _____   **b.** _____ = 3 + 8   **c.** 5 + 2 = _____

    d. 1 + 6 = _____   **e.** _____ = 8 + 3   **f.** 2 + 5 = _____

2. Fill in the missing numbers. Tell someone at home what you know about doubles facts.

    a. _____ + 8 = 16   **b.** 5 + _____ = 10   **c.** 12 = _____ + 6

    d. 6 = _____ + 3   **e.** _____ + 7 = 14   **f.** _____ + 9 = 18

3. Write the sums. Tell someone what you know about +9 facts.

    a. 10 + 1 = _____   **b.** _____ = 5 + 10   **c.** 6 + 10 = _____

    d. 1 + 9 = _____   **e.** _____ = 9 + 5   **f.** 6 + 9 = _____

    g. 10 + 7 = _____   **h.** _____ = 4 + 10   **i.** 8 + 10 = _____

    j. 7 + 9 = _____   **k.** _____ = 9 + 4   **l.** 8 + 9 = _____

HOME LINK 2·5 Addition Facts Maze

Family Note For homework, your child will review addition facts like the ones we have been working on in class. To help identify the path from the child to the ice-cream cone, have your child circle the sums of 9, 10, and 11.

Please return this Home Link to school tomorrow.

Help the child find the ice-cream cone. Answer all the problems. Then draw the child's path by connecting facts with sums of 9, 10, or 11. You can move up, down, left, or right as you move between boxes.

	2 + 6	2 + 5	1 + 6	0 + 8	5 + 7	3 + 9	7 + 0	4 + 4	1 + 5	4 + 3
2 + 7	6 + 5	1 + 7	3 + 5	6 + 3	1 + 8	8 + 2	5 + 3	2 + 4	3 + 3	8 + 7
4 + 4	5 + 4	9 + 3	0 + 9	4 + 6	7 + 1	5 + 5	8 + 0	5 + 9	6 + 7	6 + 1
6 + 2	3 + 8	7 + 4	9 + 2	5 + 3	4 + 4	2 + 9	4 + 8	4 + 9	1 + 1	5 + 2
3 + 4	6 + 6	8 + 4	7 + 5	7 + 0	6 + 2	7 + 3	3 + 6	4 + 7	6 + 8	5 + 6
8 + 5	3 + 6	4 + 7	5 + 2	1 + 6	3 + 5	6 + 7	5 + 7	8 + 3	7 + 7	9 + 4
6 + 1	8 + 4	2 + 6	7 + 7	4 + 2	1 + 4	0 + 7	3 + 9	4 + 5	6 + 4	

29

LESSON 2·5   Calculator Doubles

You can program the calculator to solve doubles problems.

1. First clear your calculator.

2. Enter ②, ⊠, ⊠, ⊟. (The calculator will display a 4).

Do NOT clear your calculator again while you work on this page.

3. Guess what the sum is for double 6 (6 + 6). _____

4. Now enter ⑥ and press ⊟. What does the calculator display? _____

5. Guess what the sum is for double 9 (9 + 9). _____

6. Now enter ⑨ and press ⊟. What does the calculator display? _____

7. Make up your own doubles problems for the calculator to solve. Record your number sentence and the sum the calculator displays.

Example:

6 + 6 = 12

_____

_____

_____

| **Try This** |

8. Why do you think you entered ② ⊠ ⊠ ⊟ on the calculator to program it to solve doubles problems?

_____

_____

HOME LINK
2·6

Domino Facts

Family Note

Today we learned that addition problems and subtraction problems are related. For example, 5 + 3 = 8 can be rewritten to show two related subtraction facts: 8 − 5 = 3 and 8 − 3 = 5.

Each domino shown below can be used to write 2 addition facts and 2 related subtraction facts.

Please return this Home Link to school tomorrow.

MRB
25

Write 2 addition facts and 2 subtraction facts for each domino.

1.

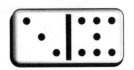

$$\begin{array}{r} 7 \\ + 3 \\ \hline 10 \end{array} \quad \begin{array}{r} 3 \\ + 7 \\ \hline \end{array} \quad \begin{array}{r} 10 \\ - 3 \\ \hline 7 \end{array} \quad \begin{array}{r} 10 \\ - 7 \\ \hline \end{array}$$

2.

3.

4.

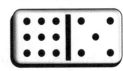

Write the sums. Tell someone at home what you know about doubles-plus-1 and doubles-plus-2 facts.

Unit

5. 6 + 7 = _____

6. _____ = 8 + 6

7. 5 + 7 = _____

8. 7 + 9 = _____

LESSON 2·6 — Domino Facts

Fill in the missing dots and missing numbers for each problem below. Hint: You can look at dominoes to help you figure out what the dots look like.

1. _____

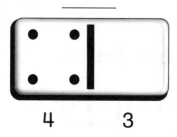

4   3

2. _____

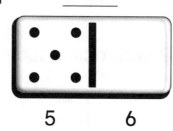

5   6

3. _____

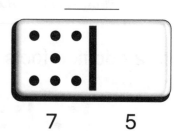

7   5

4. _10_

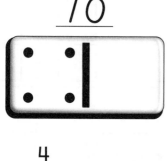

4   _____

5. _12_

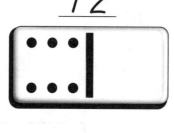

6   _____

6. _15_

9   _____

Make up one of your own.

7. _____

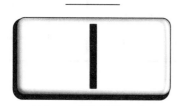

_____   _____

Try This

Explain when you think subtraction facts might help you solve the problems above. _____

_____

LESSON 2·6 | **Dice Subtraction**

For each problem below:

1. Roll two dice.

2. Record the numbers you rolled.

3. Write two subtraction number models for the numbers you rolled.

4. Use a number line to solve your problems. (Hint: Sometimes your answers will be negative numbers.)

Example:

I rolled 4 and 5.

$5 - 4 = 1$ and $4 - 5 = -1$.

1. I rolled _____ and _____.

    _____ – _____ = _____   _____ – _____ = _____

2. I rolled _____ and _____.

    _____ – _____ = _____   _____ – _____ = _____

3. I rolled _____ and _____.

    _____ – _____ = _____   _____ – _____ = _____

Try This

Each time you roll the dice, how could you use one of your subtraction problems to help you solve the other?

_____

_____

HOME LINK 2·7 | Fact Triangles

Family Note

Fact Triangles are tools used to help build mental arithmetic skills. You might think of them as the *Everyday Mathematics* version of flash cards. Fact Triangles are more effective for helping children memorize facts, however, because of their emphasis on fact families. A **fact family** is a collection of related addition and subtraction facts that use the same 3 numbers. The fact family for the numbers 2, 4, and 6 consists of $2 + 4 = 6$, $4 + 2 = 6$, $6 - 4 = 2$, and $6 - 2 = 4$.

To use Fact Triangles to practice addition with your child, cover the number next to the large dot with your thumb.

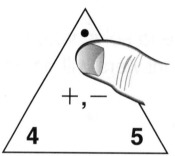

Your child tells you the addition fact: $4 + 5 = 9$ or $5 + 4 = 9$.

To use Fact Triangles to practice subtraction, cover one of the numbers in the lower corners with your thumb.

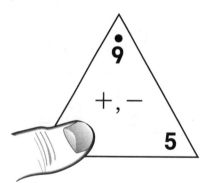
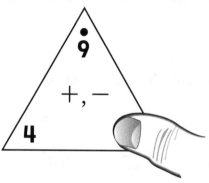

Your child tells you the subtraction facts: $9 - 5 = 4$ and $9 - 4 = 5$.

If your child misses a fact, flash the other two fact problems on the card and then return to the fact that was missed.

Example: Sue can't answer $9 - 5$. Flash $4 + 5$, then $9 - 4$, and finally $9 - 5$ a second time.

Make this activity brief and fun. Spend about 10 minutes each night over the next few weeks or until your child masters all of the facts. The work that you do at home will help your child develop an instant recall of facts and will complement the work that we are doing at school.

MRB
26 27

HOME LINK
2·7

Fact Triangles *continued*

Cut out the Fact Triangles. Show someone at home how you use them to practice adding and subtracting.

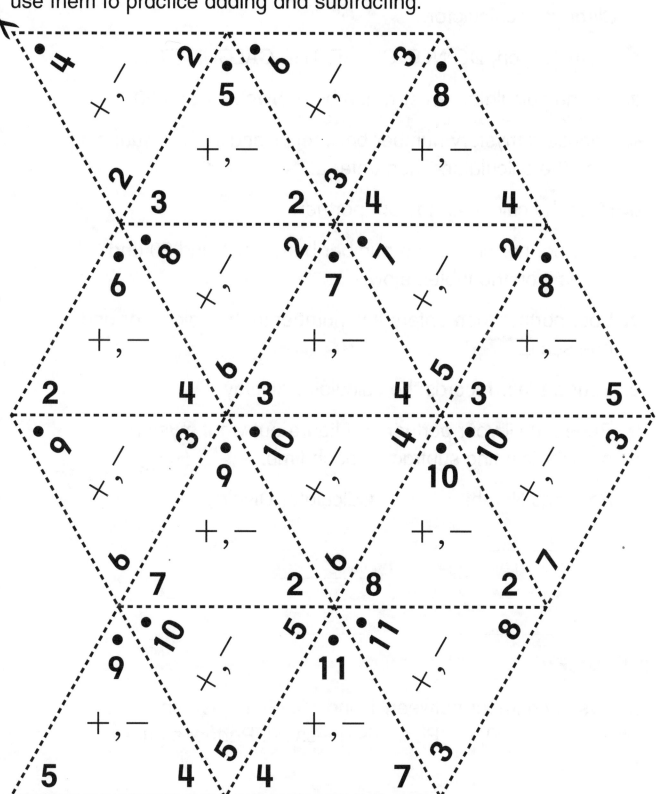

LESSON 2·7 Subtraction Mystery Numbers

Calculator A:

1. Clear your calculator.

2. From now on, DO NOT CLEAR THE CALCULATOR.

3. On the calculator, enter a number between 1 and 20.

4. Choose a mystery number between 1 and 10 and subtract it on the calculator. Then enter ▭.

5. Pass the calculator to your partner.

6. Your partner chooses a number between 1 and 20 and writes it on the table below.

7. Your partner then enters this number in the calculator and presses ▭.

8. Your partner records the calculator display.

9. Repeat until your partner can figure out what mystery number is being subtracted each time.

Partner's Number	Calculator Display
_____	_____
_____	_____
_____	_____
_____	_____

Calculator B:

▭, Mystery number between 1 and 10, ▭, ▭, Number between 1 and 20, ▭, Partner's guess ▭, Partner's guess ▭. . . , ▭

LESSON 2·8   Egg Nests

Work with a partner.

Materials
- ☐ 1 six-sided die
- ☐ 1 sheet of plain paper
- ☐ 36 counters (for example, pennies, centimeter cubes, or dried beans)
- ☐ 6 quarter-sheets of paper

Directions

Pretend that the quarter-sheets of paper are birds' nests.

Pretend that the pennies, cubes, or beans are eggs.

1. Roll the die twice.

- ◆ The first roll tells how many nests to use.
- ◆ The second roll tells how many eggs to put in each nest.

2. Work together to set up the nests and eggs for the numbers you rolled. How many eggs are there in all of the nests?

3. Use your sheet of plain paper and draw a picture.

- ◆ Show all the nests.
- ◆ Show all the eggs in each nest.

4. Start again. Repeat Steps 1–3.

37

HOME LINK 2·8 | Weighing Things

Family Note Today we worked with a pan balance to compare the weights of objects. We used a spring scale to weigh objects up to 1 pound. We introduced the word *ounce* as a unit of weight for light objects.

*Please return the **second page** of this Home Link to school tomorrow.*

1. Tell someone at home about how you used the pan balance to compare the weights of two objects.

2. Tell someone at home how you used the spring scale to weigh objects.

HOME LINK 2·8 **Weighing Things** *continued*

3. Look at the pairs of objects below. In each pair, circle the object that you think is heavier.

a.

Shoe

Marble

b.

Sock

Brick

c.

Feather

Tape Measure

4. Look at the objects below. Circle the objects that you think weigh less than 1 pound.

Pattern-Block Template

Scissors

Egg

Chair

Television

Pencil

Glasses

39

HOME LINK 2·9

Name-Collection Boxes

Family Note

Beginning in *First Grade Everyday Mathematics*, children use **name-collection boxes** to help them collect equivalent names for the same number. These boxes help children appreciate the idea that numbers can be expressed in many different ways.

A name-collection box is an open box with a tag attached. The tag identifies the number whose names are collected in the box. In second grade, typical names include sums, differences, tally marks, and arrays. At higher grades, names may include products, quotients, and the results of several mathematical operations.

10 ← Tag for box

Name-collection box

10 ‖‖‖ ‖‖‖

ten

12 − 2

6 + 4   •••••
••••

Items in the name-collection box above represent the number 10. Some names contain numbers, and some do not.

9

19 − 10

(15 − 7)   x x x

3 + 3 + 3   x x x
x x x

(8 + 0)

(5 + 4 + 1)   1 less
than 10

(‖‖‖ |||)

Sometimes children must circle names that do not belong in the box.

6 + 6   x x x

12 − 0   x x x
x x x

twelve   x x x

15 − 1 − 2   1 less
than 13

18 − 6

12 − 0   ‖‖‖ ‖‖‖ ||

Sometimes children must fill in the tag for the numbers shown in the box. The tag here should read 12.

Encourage your child to name a number in different ways—for example, use tally marks, write addition and subtraction problems, or draw pictures of objects.

*Please return the **second page** of this Home Link to school tomorrow.*

HOME LINK 2·9 | **Name-Collection Boxes** *continued*

1. Give the Family Note to someone at home. Show that person the name-collection box below. Explain what a name-collection box is used for.

8		
2 + 6	4 + 4	x x x x
eight	12 − 4	x x x x
ocho	10 − 2	8 − 0
8 + 0	3 + 5	ⵌ ///

2. Write 10 names in this 10-box.

10

3. Make up your own name-collection box. Write at least 10 names in the box.

LESSON 2·9 | **Many Names for Facts**

Below are pictures of two ten-frame cards.

Each one is filled in with 5 counters.

For each ten-frame card, Maria has written ways she thinks about the number 5 when she looks at the picture.

Names for 5

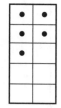

3 + 2
1 less than 3 doubled
Double 2 plus 1 more
1 less than 6

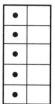

5 + 0
1 more than 4
Half of ten
10 − 5

Draw 8 counters two different ways in the ten-frame cards below.

Underneath the ten-frame cards, write numbers or words to show how each picture makes you think of the number 8.

Names for 8

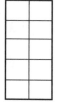

_____

_____

_____

_____

_____

_____

_____

_____

LESSON 2·10 | **Frames and Arrows**

1. | **Rule** Add 2

5 | | | |

2. | **Rule** Add 5

◯ | ◯ | ◯ 20 | ◯ | ◯

3. | **Rule**

⬠ 15 | ⬠ 12 | ⬠ 9 | ⬠ 6 | ⬠ 3

4. | **Rule**

⬡ | ⬡ | ⬡ 25 | ⬡ | ⬡ 35 | ⬡

5. | **Rule**

| | 10 | | 6 |

HOME LINK 2·10

Frames-and-Arrows Problems

Family Note

Today your child used **Frames-and-Arrows diagrams.** These diagrams show sequences of numbers—numbers that follow one after the other according to a rule. Frames-and-Arrows diagrams are made up of shapes called *frames* and arrows that connect the frames. Each frame contains one of the numbers in the sequence. Each *arrow* stands for a rule that tells which number goes in the next frame. Here is an example of a Frames-and-Arrows diagram. The arrow rule is "Add 2."

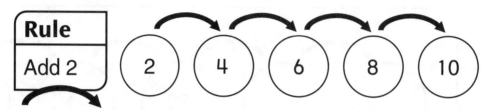

In a Frames-and-Arrows problem, some of the information is left out. To solve the problem, you have to find the missing information.

Here are two examples of Frames-and-Arrows problems:

Example 1: Fill in the empty frames according to the rule.

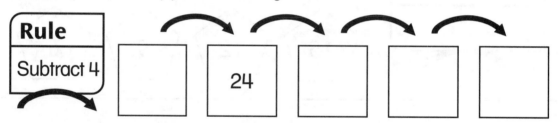

Solution: Write 28, 20, 16, and 12 in the empty frames.

Example 1: Write the arrow rule in the empty box.

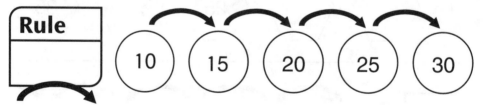

Solution: The arrow rule is Add 5, or +5.

Ask your child to tell you about Frames-and-Arrows diagrams. Take turns making up and solving Frames-and-Arrows problems like the examples above with your child.

*Please return the **second page** of this Home Link to school tomorrow.*

44

Frames-and-Arrows *continued*

Tell someone at home what you know about Frames and Arrows. Fill in the empty frames and rule boxes.

1.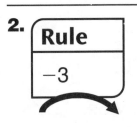
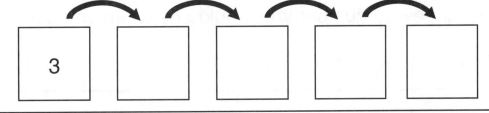

Rule: +6 | 3 | | | |

2.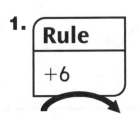
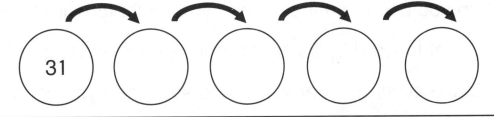

Rule: −3 | 31 | | | |

3.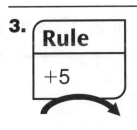
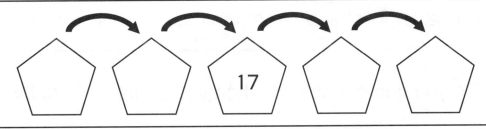

Rule: +5 | | | 17 | |

4.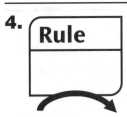
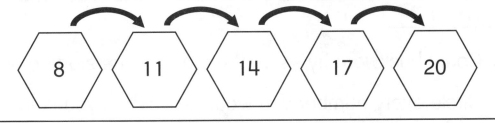

Rule: | 8 | 11 | 14 | 17 | 20

5.
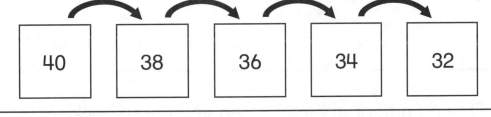

Rule: | 40 | 38 | 36 | 34 | 32

6.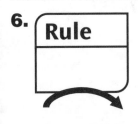
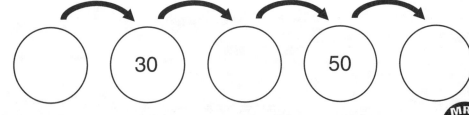

Rule: | | 30 | | 50 |

Now write your own Frames-and-Arrows problem on the back of this sheet. Ask someone at home to solve it.

LESSON 2·10 | **Counting Patterns on the Number Line**

Follow the directions for each number line below.

1. Count forward by 3s on the number line starting with 0.

Circle every number you would say when you count by 3s.

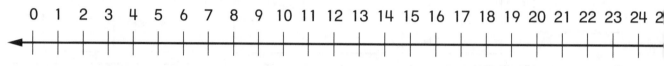

Do you add or subtract when you count forward by 3s?

2. Count forward by 5s on the number line starting with 0.

Circle every number you would say when you count by 5s.

Do you add or subtract when you count forward by 5s?

Try This

3. Count backward by 4s on the number line starting with 20.

Circle every number you would say when you count
backward by 4s.

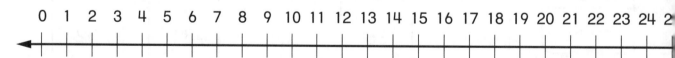

Do you add or subtract when you count backwards by 4s?

HOME LINK 2·11

"What's My Rule?"

Family Note

Today your child learned about a kind of problem you may not have seen before. We call it "What's My Rule?" Please ask your child to explain it to you.

Here is a little background information: Imagine a machine with a funnel at the top and a tube coming out of the bottom. The machine can be programmed so that if a number is dropped into the funnel, the machine does something to the number, and a new number comes out of the tube. For example, the machine could be programmed to add 5 to any number that is dropped in. If you put in 3, 8 would come out. If you put in 7, 12 would come out.

We call this device a *function machine*.

You can show the results of the rule "+5" in a table:

in	out
3	8
7	12
15	20

```
      ┌───┐
      │ 3 │
      └───┘
       in
        ↓
      ╲___╱
    ┌─────────┐
    │ Rule    │
    ├─────────┤
    │  +5     │
    └─────────┘
      ╲___╱
        ↓
       out
      ┌───┐
      │ 8 │
      └───┘
```

In a "What's My Rule?" problem, some of the information is missing. To solve the problem, you have to find the missing information. The missing information could be the numbers that come out of a function machine, the numbers that are dropped in, or the rule for programming the machine. *For example:*

Rule
Add 6

in	out
3	
5	
8	

Missing: out numbers

Rule

in	out
6	3
10	5
16	8

Missing: rule

Rule
+4

in	out
	6
	16
	11

Missing: in numbers

Like Frames-and-Arrows problems, "What's My Rule?" problems help children practice facts (and extended facts) in a problem-solving format.

*Please return the **second page** of this Home Link to school tomorrow.*

MRB
102

47

HOME LINK 2·11 | **"What's My Rule?"** *continued*

Give the Family Note to someone at home. Show that person how you can complete "What's My Rule?" tables. Show that person how you can find rules.

1. Fill in the table.

Rule
+9

in	out
1	10
4	13
6	
8	
5	

2. Find the rule.

Rule

in	out
10	2
12	4
9	1
14	6
8	0

3. Fill in the table.

Rule
+6

in	out
4	10
	12
	9
	15
	6

Try This

4. Find the rule.

Rule

in	out
8	13
4	9
13	
	10

5. Al read 5 more pages than Cindy.

If Cindy read 13 pages, how many pages did Al read? _____ pages

If Al read 10 pages, how many pages did Cindy read? _____ pages

48

HOME LINK 2·12 Subtraction Maze

Family Note For homework, your child will practice subtraction facts like the ones we have been working on in class. To help identify the path from the dog to the ball, have your child circle the differences of 3, 4, and 5.

Please return this Home Link to school tomorrow.

Help the dog find her ball. Solve all of the problems. Then draw the dog's path by connecting facts with answers of 3, 4, or 5. You can move up, down, left, right, or diagonally as you move between boxes.

	8 −4	12 −6	8 −8	4 −0	5 −4	9 −7	10 −3	5 −2	6 −0	18 −9
	8 −7	16 −8	6 −1	7 −3	4 −2	12 −3	5 −1	9 −8	8 −6	6 −3	7 −6
	5 −1	3 −3	9 −2	11 −0	7 −2	3 −2	12 −6	8 −3	3 −1	8 −0	6 −4
	10 −2	5 −0	7 −1	9 −3	11 −2	10 −5	12 −1	7 −0	4 −3	14 −7	3 −0
	5 −3	12 −0	2 −1	8 −1	6 −5	12 −2	6 −2	2 −2	7 −5	10 −9	9 −0
	11 −3	4 −1	9 −1	2 −0	10 −1	9 −9	8 −5	3 −0	11 −1	10 −7	11 −8
	10 −0	5 −5	10 −9	8 −2	10 −8	11 −9	6 −6	12 −3	9 −6	7 −4	

HOME LINK 2·13

Addition/Subtraction Facts

Family Note   For homework, your child will practice addition and subtraction facts like the ones we have been working on in class. Help your child solve the problems and identify the path from the bird to the seeds by circling all the cells with the answer 6.

Please return this Home Link to school tomorrow.

The bird wants to eat the seeds. Solve all of the problems below. Then draw the bird's path by connecting facts with an answer of 6. There are addition and subtraction facts. Watch for + or −.

	7 +3	5 +9	6 +3	16 −8	4 +3	5 +6	6 +6	6 +7	4 +6	11 −9
14 −8	7 +4	4 +5	8 +4	9 −0	6 +8	12 −8	6 +1	4 +4	5 +7	2 +5
15 −9	5 +3	5 +5	6 +4	15 −8	5 +0	7 +8	11 −8	4 +9	18 −9	5 +8
6 +9	8 −2	12 −9	7 +7	3 +6	10 −8	5 +4	13 −9	2 +2	7 +9	2 +7
7 +5	3 +4	11 −5	3 +8	13 −7	8 +8	6 +5	5 +3	8 +1	3 +9	17 −8
1 +3	7 +3	6 +2	12 −6	16 −9	9 −3	7 −1	9 +9	1 +9	3 +3	8 +2
17 −9	4 +2	4 +7	14 −9	7 +6	5 +2	13 −8	10 −4	6 +0	8 −0	

50

HOME LINK 2·13 | Addition/Subtraction Facts *continued*

Cut out the Fact Triangles. Show someone at home how you use them to practice adding and subtracting.

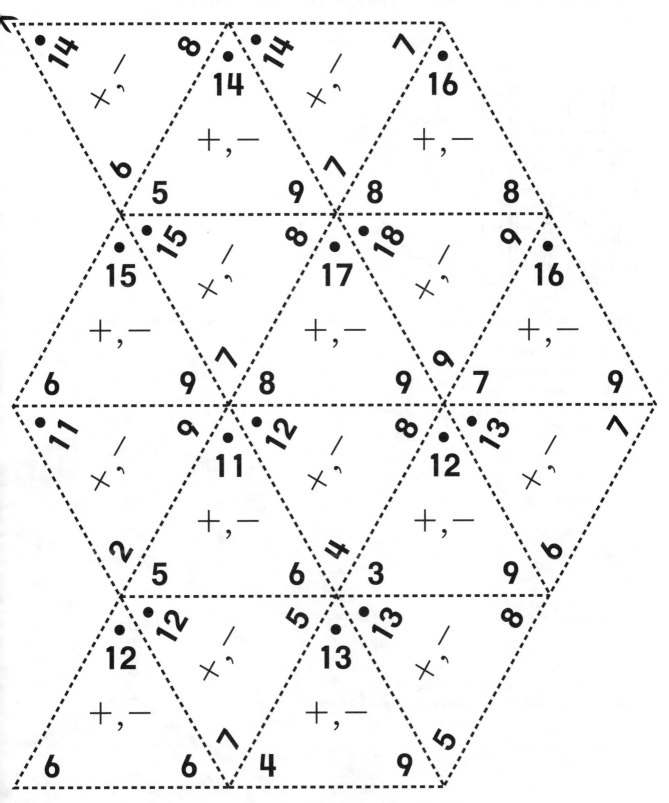

Unit 3: Family Letter

Place Value, Money, and Time

In Unit 3, children will read, write, and compare numbers from 0 through 999, working on concepts and skills built upon since *Kindergarten Everyday Mathematics.* Your child will review *place value,* or the meaning of each digit in a number. For example, in the number 52, the 5 represents 5 tens, and the 2 represents 2 ones.

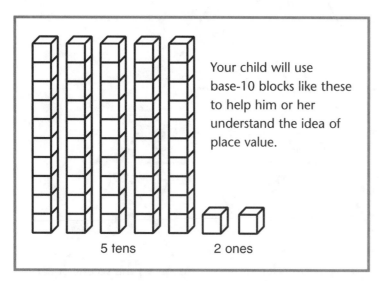

Your child will use base-10 blocks like these to help him or her understand the idea of place value.

5 tens   2 ones

Your child will also review money concepts, including finding the values of coins, identifying different coin combinations for the same amount, and making change.

43¢

43¢

43¢

Your child will read and record time using the hour and minute hands on an analog clock.

Vocabulary

Important terms in Unit 3:

analog clock A clock that shows time by the position of the hour and minute hands.

analog clock

digital clock A clock that shows time with numbers of hours and minutes, usually separated by a colon.

digital clock

data A collection of information, usually in the form of numbers. For example, the following data show the ages (in years) of six second graders: 6, 7, 6, 6, 7, 6.

middle number (median) The number in the middle of a list of data ordered from least to greatest or vice versa. For example, 5 is the middle number in the following ordered list:

2   3   ⑤   8   10

two-rule Frames and Arrows A Frames-and-Arrows diagram with two rules instead of just one, such as the following example.

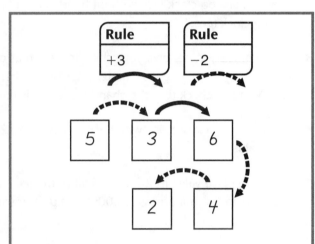

To go from the first square to the second square, use the rule for the dashed arrow.

$$5 - \mathbf{2} = 3$$

To go from the second square to the third square, use the rule for the solid arrow.

$$3 + \mathbf{3} = 6$$

53

Do-Anytime Activities

To work with your child on the concepts taught in this unit and in previous units, try these interesting and rewarding activities:

1. Have your child tell the time shown on an analog clock.

2. Draw an analog clock face without hands. Say a time and have your child show it on the clock face.

3. At the grocery store, give your child an item that costs less than $1.00. Allow your child to pay for the item separately. Ask him or her to determine how much change is due and to check that the change received is correct.

4. Gather a handful of coins with a value less than $2.00. Have your child calculate the total value.

5. Reinforce place value in 2- and 3-digit numbers. For example, in the number 694, the digit 6 means 6 hundreds, or 600; the digit 9 means 9 tens, or 90; and the digit 4 means 4 ones, or 4.

As You Help Your Child with Homework

As your child brings home assignments, you may want to go over the instructions together, clarifying them as necessary. The answers listed below will guide you through this unit's Home Links.

Home Link 3·1

1. a. 374   **b.** 507   **2.** 740

3. 936   **4.** 8; 0; 6   **5.** 2; 3; 1

Home Link 3·3

2. 6:30   **3.** 2:15   **4.** 9:00   **5.** 1:30

6.    **7.**

8.    **9.**

10. 13   **11.** 16   **12.** 6   **13.** 8

Home Link 3·4

1. Rule | Add 12   *Sample answers:*

In	Out	Out in a different way
I	II ..	I ::... .....
II	III	II ::::: :....
II	III	II ::::: :::..

2. Rule | Add 16

In	Out	Out in a different way
IIII .	IIIII	IIII ::::: ::....
......	I :....	II .

Home Link 3·6

1. 40¢; 50¢; 55¢   **2.** 50¢; 45¢; 55¢

Home Link 3·7

5. 12   **6.** 14

7. 13   **8.** 10

Home Link 3·8

5¢; 35¢; 16¢; 5¢; 2¢; 52¢

1. 3.   **2.** 8   **3.** 7   **4.** 13

Building Skills through Games

In this unit, your child will practice addition and money skills by playing the following games:

Digit Game

Players turn over two cards and call out the largest number that can be made using those cards. The player with the higher number takes all the cards from that round.

Spinning for Money

Players "spin the wheel" to find out which coins they will take from the bank. The first player to exchange his or her coins for a dollar bill wins!

Dollar Rummy

Instead of three-of-a-kind, players of *Dollar Rummy* look for two cards that will add up to $1.00.

LESSON 3·1   Place-Value Mat

hundreds	tens	ones

HOME LINK 3·1

Place Value

1. Which number do the base-10 blocks show?

a.

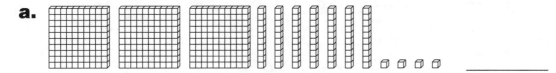

_____

b.

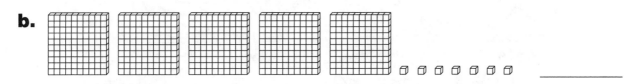

_____

2. Write a number with
7 in the hundreds place,
0 in the ones place, and
4 in the tens place.

_____

3. Write a number with
3 in the tens place,
6 in the ones place, and
9 in the hundreds place.

_____

4. In 806, how
many hundreds? _____

How many tens? _____

How many ones? _____

5. In 231, how
many hundreds? _____

How many tens? _____

How many ones? _____

LESSON 3·2   Fruit and Vegetables Stand Poster

HOME LINK 3·2 How Much Does It Cost?

Family Note In this activity, your child looks through advertisements, selects items that cost less than $2.00, and shows how to pay for those items in more than one way. For example, your child could pay for an item that costs 79¢ by drawing 3 quarters and 4 pennies or by drawing 7 dimes and 9 pennies. If you do not have advertisements showing prices, make up some items and prices for your child.

Please return this Home Link to school tomorrow.

Look at newspaper or magazine advertisements. Find items that cost less than $2.00. Write the name and price of each item.

Show someone at home how you would pay for these items with coins and a $1 bill. Write Ⓟ, Ⓝ, Ⓓ, Ⓠ, and $1. Try to show amounts in more than one way.

1. I would buy _____. It costs _____.

This is one way I would pay: _____

This is another way: _____

2. I would buy _____. It costs _____.

This is one way I would pay: _____

This is another way: _____

3. I would buy _____. It costs _____.

This is one way I would pay: _____

This is another way: _____

LESSON 3·3

Demonstration Clock

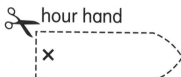

a brad

✂ hour hand

5-Minute Clock

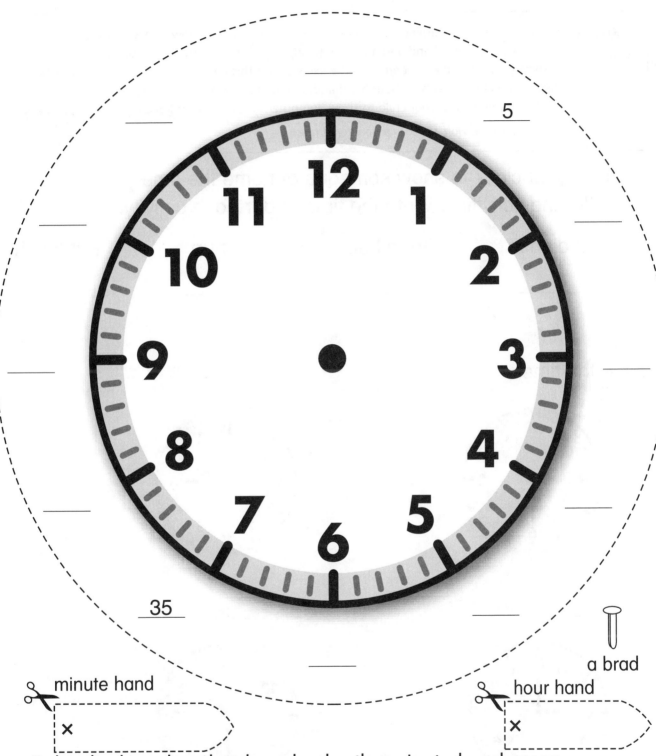

5

35

minute hand

hour hand

a brad

◆ Color the hour hand red, and color the minute hand green.

◆ Cut out the clock face and hands.

◆ Punch a hole through the center of the clock face and through the
Xs on the hands. Fasten the hands to the clock face with a brad.

61

HOME LINK 3·3   Times of Day

Family Note   Your child has been learning how to tell time by writing times shown on an analog clock (a clock with an hour hand and a minute hand) and by setting the hands on an analog clock to show a specific time. To complete the exercises on this page, your child will need a paper clock or a real clock with an hour hand and a minute hand. You can make a clock from *Math Masters*, page 61. Ask your child to show you other times on his or her clock.

Please return this Home Link to school tomorrow.

MRB 80 81

1. Use your clock to show someone at home the time you do the following activities. Write the time under each activity.

Eat dinner	Go to bed	Get up	Eat lunch
____:____	____:____	____:____	____:____

Write the time.

2.

____:____

3.

____:____

4.

____:____

5.

____:____

HOME LINK 3·3 | Times of Day continued

Draw the hands to match the time.

6.

4:00

7.

9:30

8.

12:45

9.

10:15

Practice

10. $\begin{array}{r} 7 \\ +\ 6 \\ \hline \end{array}$

11. $7 + 9 = $ _____

12. $11 - 5 = $ _____

13. $\begin{array}{r} 16 \\ -\ 8 \\ \hline \end{array}$

LESSON 3·3 **Clock Faces**

_____

_____

_____

_____

LESSON 3·4 Build a Number

Do this activity with a partner.

Materials
☐ *Math Journal 1*, p. 61

☐ *Math Masters*, 427 (Place-Value Mat)

☐ base-10 blocks: 9 flats (optional), 9 longs, and 30 cubes

☐ number cards 0–9 (from the Everything Math Deck, if available)

1. Mix the cards and stack them facedown.

2. Take 2 cards.

3. Place the first card in the tens column of your Place-Value Mat. (If the card is a 0, put it back and take another.) Then put the second card in the ones column.

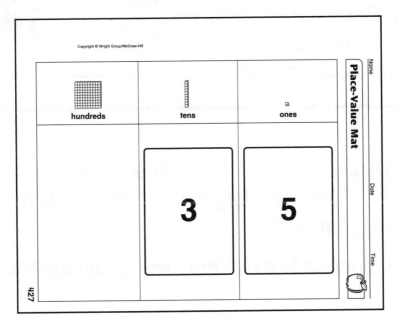

LESSON 3·4 | Build a Number *continued*

4. Build the number.

- ◆ Place longs in the tens column to show the tens digit.

- ◆ Place cubes in the ones column to show the ones digit.

5. Record your work in the table on journal page 61. Draw pictures of the longs and cubes you used.

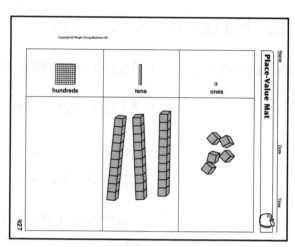

6. Use the Place-Value Mat and blocks to build the same number in a different way. Draw the longs and cubes you used.

7. Build 3 or 4 more numbers in the same way. Record your numbers and draw pictures to show the two ways you built each number.

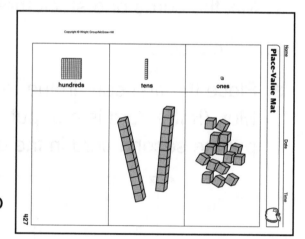

Try This

Take 3 cards instead of 2. Put 1 card in each column of the Place-Value Mat. Draw flats, longs, and cubes on journal page 61 to show your number.

Build the same number in a different way. Draw the blocks you used.

LESSON 3·4 | **A Clock Booklet**

Do this activity with a partner.

Materials ☐ at least 2 sheets of plain paper   ☐ scissors

                 ☐ clock-face rubber stamp   ☐ stapler

                 ☐ stamp pad

1. Each partner folds a sheet of paper into 4 parts.

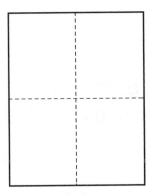

2. Cut each sheet along the folds.

3. Set aside 2 of the small pieces of paper.
You will use them for covers later.

4. Stamp a clock face on each side of the other small pieces.

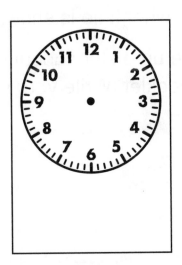

LESSON 3·4   **A Clock Booklet** *continued*

5. For each clock face:

♦ Think of a time. Help each other draw the hour and minute hands to show that time.

♦ Write the time as you would see it on a digital clock.

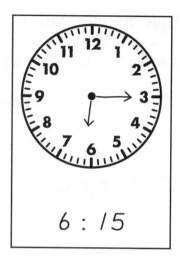

6 : 15

6. Stack the pieces. Put a piece without a clock face on the top. Put the other piece without a clock face at the bottom.

♦ Staple the left side of the pieces together to make a book.

♦ Write a title and your names on the front cover.

Follow-Up Activities

You and your partner can use your book to do these activities:

♦ Take turns. One partner covers the digital time on a page. The other partner tells what time is shown on the clock face.

♦ Work together to make up a story about one or more of the times shown in your booklet. Write your story on another piece of paper.

LESSON 3·4 | Geoboard Shapes

Materials per child ☐ *Math Journal 1,* p. 62

☐ geoboard ☐ rubber bands

Number of children 1, 2, 3, or 4

Do this activity on your own:

1. Make at least 4 shapes, designs, or pictures on your geoboard. Make things like a house, a boat, or a car.

2. Record your favorites on the geoboard dot paper on journal page 62.

Do this activity with a partner:

1. Make an easy shape on a geoboard. Make sure your partner can't see it.

2. Tell—but don't show—your partner how to make the shape.

3. Your partner makes the shape on another geoboard.

4. Compare the two shapes. How are they alike? How are they different? Did you give good directions?

5. Repeat the activity. This time your partner makes the shape first.

Do this activity in a small group:

1. Agree on a shape that everyone will make. Describe the shape in words, but don't draw it.

2. Everyone in your group makes the shape on his or her own geoboard.

3. Compare results. How are your shapes the same? How are they different?

"What's My Rule?" with Blocks

1. Draw simple pictures of base-10 blocks to complete the table.

Rule
Add 12

In	Out	Out in a Different Way
▪ ▪ ▪	| ▪ ▪ ▪ ▪ ▪	▪▪ ▪▪ ▪▪ ▪▪ ▪▪ ▪
|	|| ▪ ▪	
|| ▪ ▪ ▪ ▪		
|| ▪ ▪ ▪ ▪ ▪ ▪ ▪		

2. Write the rule. Then complete the table.

Rule

In	Out	Out in a Different Way
||||| ▪ ▪ ▪	|||||| ▪ ▪ ▪ ▪ ▪ ▪ ▪ ▪ ▪	||||| ▪▪ ▪▪ ▪▪ ▪▪ ▪▪ ▪▪ ▪
| ▪ ▪ ▪ ▪ ▪ ▪ ▪ ▪	|| ▪▪ ▪▪ ▪ ▪ ▪ ▪ ▪	| ▪▪ ▪▪ ▪▪ ▪▪ ▪ ▪ ▪ ▪ ▪
|||| ▪		
▪ ▪ ▪ ▪ ▪		

70

LESSON 3·5 | **Counting Pockets**

Name _____

**Math Message:
Counting Pockets**

1. How many pockets
are in the clothes
you are wearing now?

2. Count the pockets
on your shirt,
on your pants or skirt,
and on anything else
that you are wearing.

3. Complete the diagram.

Total		
Shirt	**Pants or Skirt**	**Other**

4. Write your total number
of pockets very large
on the back of this sheet.

Name _____

**Math Message:
Counting Pockets**

1. How many pockets
are in the clothes
you are wearing now?

2. Count the pockets
on your shirt,
on your pants or skirt,
and on anything else
that you are wearing.

3. Complete the diagram.

Total		
Shirt	**Pants or Skirt**	**Other**

4. Write your total number
of pockets very large
on the back of this sheet.

LESSON 3·5   Pockets Data Table

Pockets	Children	
	Tallies	Number
0		
1		
2		
3		
4		
5		
6		
7		
8		
9		
10		
11		
12		
13 or more		

Graphing Pockets Data

LESSON 3·5

How Many Pockets?

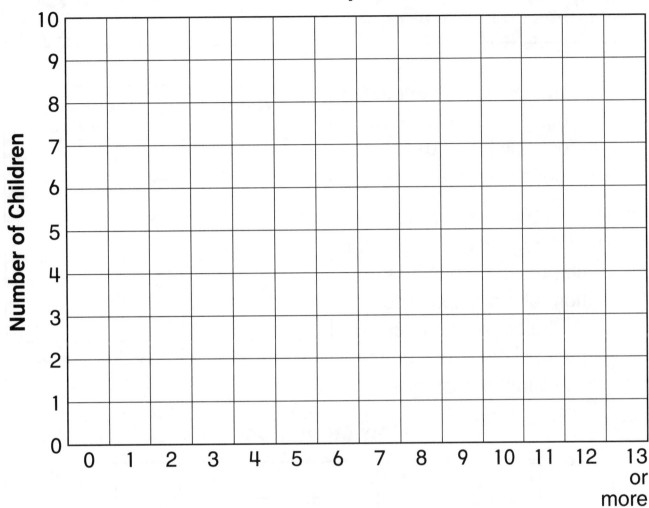

Number of Children (vertical axis, 0–10)

Number of Pockets (horizontal axis, 0–13 or more)

HOME LINK 3·5

Pockets Bar Graph

Family Note Help your child fill in the table below. Then display the data by making a **bar graph**. Please return this Home Link to school tomorrow.

MRB 44

1. Pick five people. Count the number of pockets that each person's clothing has. Complete the table.

2. Draw a bar graph for your data. First, write the name of each person on a line at the bottom of the graph. Then color the bar above each name to show how many pockets that person has.

Name	Number of Pockets

How Many Pockets?

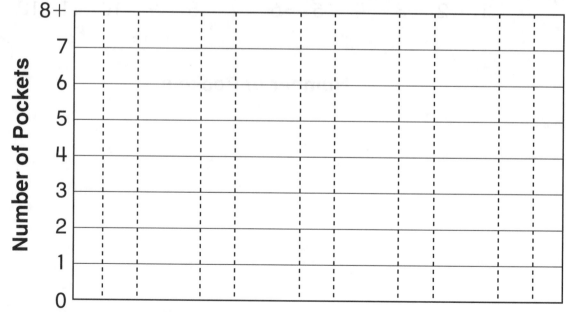

Number of Pockets

8+
7
6
5
4
3
2
1
0

Names

LESSON 3·6   Frames-and-Arrows Diagrams

Rule

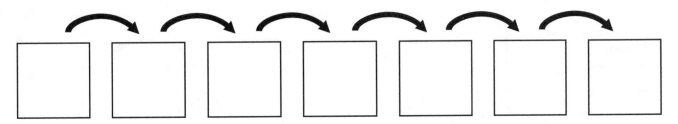

LESSON 3·6   Frames-and-Arrows Diagrams

Rule

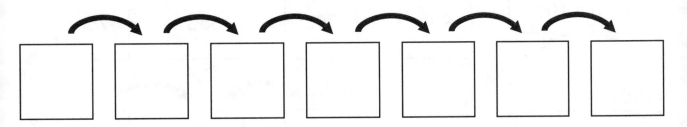

LESSON 3·6

Two-Rule Frames and Arrows

Example:

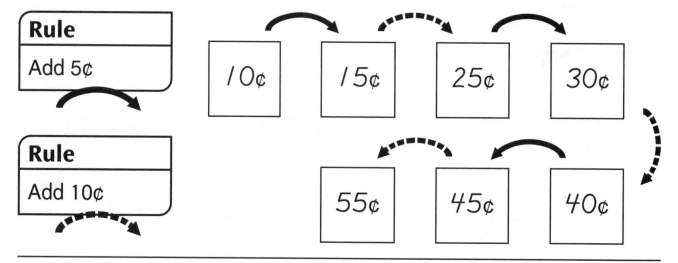

Rule Add 5¢

Rule Add 10¢

10¢   15¢   25¢   30¢

55¢   45¢   40¢

1.

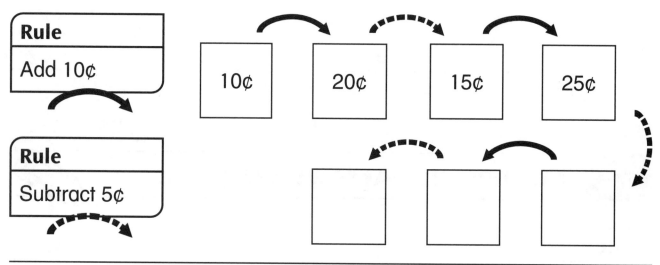

Rule Add 10¢

Rule Subtract 5¢

10¢   20¢   15¢   25¢

2.

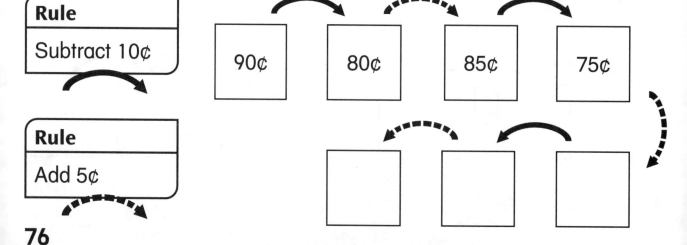

Rule Subtract 10¢

Rule Add 5¢

90¢   80¢   85¢   75¢

LESSON 3·6 **Two-Rule Frames and Arrows** *cont.*

3.

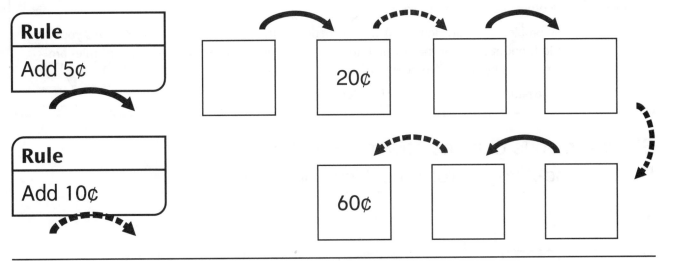

Rule
Add 5¢

Rule
Add 10¢

20¢   60¢

4.

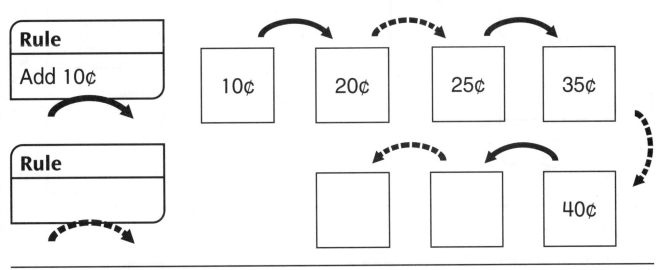

Rule
Add 10¢

Rule

10¢   20¢   25¢   35¢   40¢

5.

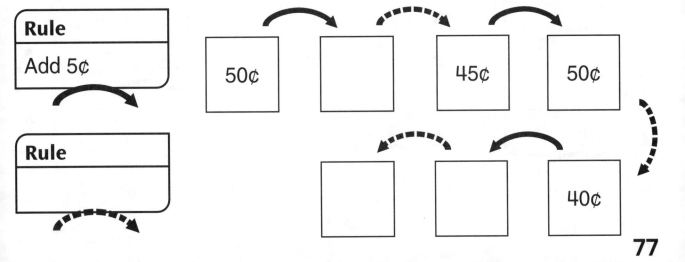

Rule
Add 5¢

Rule

50¢   45¢   50¢   40¢

77

HOME LINK 3·6

Frames-and-Arrows Problems

Family Note

Frames-and-Arrows diagrams show sequences of numbers—numbers that follow one after the other according to a rule.

The problems on this Home Link are a variation of the Frames-and-Arrows problems your child brought home in the last unit. In each of the problems below, two different rules are represented by two different arrows.

Please return this Home Link to school tomorrow.

MRB
98 99

Show someone at home how to solve these
Frames-and-Arrows problems. Use coins to help you.

1.

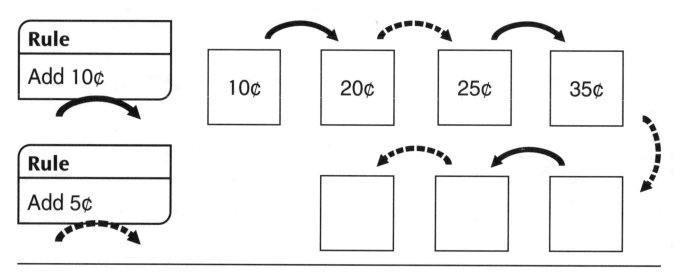

2.

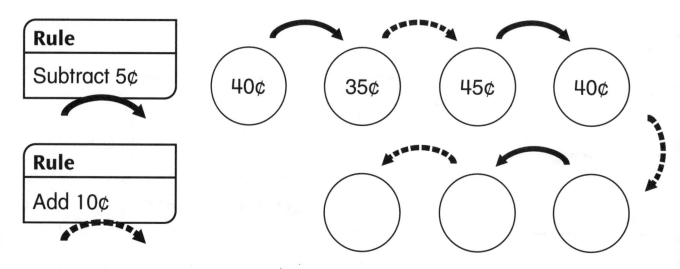

LESSON 3·6

Counting on the Number Line

1.

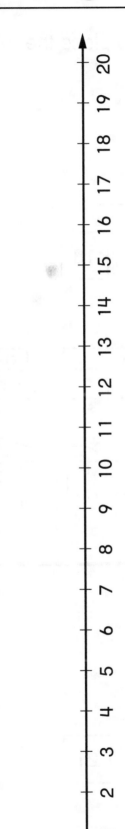

2. Start at 3. Red rule is Add 2. Blue rule is Add 4.

3. Start at 1. Red rule is Add 4. Blue rule is Add 2.

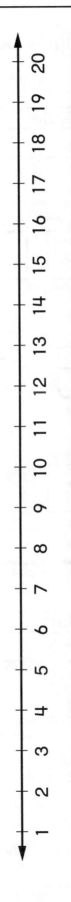

Try This

4. Start at 19. Red rule is Subtract 4. Blue rule is Subtract 2.

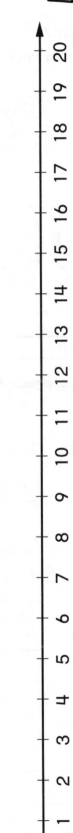

LESSON 3·6 | **Frames-and-Arrows Puzzles**

Each puzzle has 2 rules. Figure out where to place the rules to solve the problems.

1.

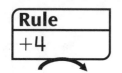

Rule +4   Rule +1

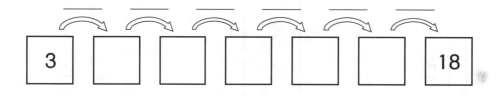

| 3 | | | | | | 18 |

2.

Rule −10   Rule −3

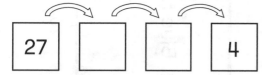

| 27 | | | 4 |

3.

Rule +8   Rule −5

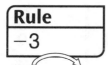 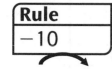 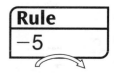

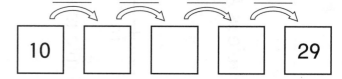

| 10 | | | | 29 |

Try This

4.

Rule +5   Rule −3

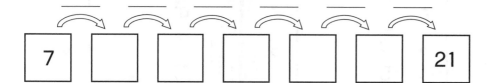

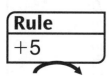 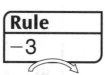

| 7 | | | | | | 21 |

HOME LINK 3·7 Change at a Garage Sale

Family Note

Encourage your child to make change by counting up. Using real coins and dollar bills will make this activity easier. *For example:*

◆ Start with the cost of an item—65 cents.

◆ Count up to the money given—$1.00.

One way to make change: Put down a nickel and say "70." Then put down 3 dimes and say "80, 90, 1 dollar." *Another way:* Put down 3 dimes and say "75, 85, 95." Then put down 5 pennies and say "96, 97, 98, 99, 1 dollar."

The Practice section in the Home Link provides a review of previously learned skills.

Please return this Home Link to school tomorrow.

Pretend you are having a garage sale. Do the following:

◆ Find small items in your home to "sell."

◆ Give each item a price less than $1.00.
   Give each item a different price.

◆ Pretend that customers pay for each item with a $1 bill.

◆ Show someone at home how you would make change by counting up. Use Ⓟ, Ⓝ, Ⓓ, and Ⓠ.

◆ Show another way you can make change for the same item.

Example:

The customer buys ___*a pen*___ for ___65¢___.

One way I can make change: _____ Ⓝ Ⓓ Ⓓ Ⓓ _____

Another way I can make change: _____ Ⓓ Ⓓ Ⓓ Ⓟ Ⓟ Ⓟ Ⓟ Ⓟ _____

HOME LINK
3·7

Change at a Garage Sale *continued*

1. The customer buys _____ for _____.

   One way I can make change: _____

   Another way I can make change: _____

2. The customer buys _____ for _____.

   One way I can make change: _____

   Another way I can make change: _____

3. The customer buys _____ for _____.

   One way I can make change: _____

   Another way I can make change: _____

4. The customer buys _____ for _____.

   One way I can make change: _____

   Another way I can make change: _____

Practice

5. $7 + 5 =$ ___

6. $8 + 6 =$ ___

7. $\begin{array}{r} 4 \\ + 9 \\ \hline \end{array}$

8. $\begin{array}{r} 3 \\ + 7 \\ \hline \end{array}$

LESSON 3·7 **Coin Puzzles**

Use the clues to solve the coin puzzles.

Example:

> **Clue 1:** I have two coins.
>
> **Clue 2:** Together they are worth 30¢.
>
> **Clue 3:** One is not a nickel.
>
> **Coin Puzzle:** What are the coins? *A quarter and a nickel*

---

1. Clue 1: I have 46¢.

> **Clue 2:** I have 7 coins.
>
> **Coin Puzzle:** Which coins do I have?

---

2. Clue 1: I have 49¢ in one pocket.

> **Clue 2:** I have 16¢ in another pocket.
>
> **Clue 3:** When I put all my coins on the table, I count 10 pennies.
>
> **Clue 4:** None of the coins is a nickel.
>
> **Coin Puzzle:** What are the coins?

---

3. Clue 1: I have 5 coins.

> **Clue 2:** I have a total of 46¢.
>
> **Clue 3:** Three of the coins are not nickels.
>
> **Coin Puzzle:** Which coins do I have?

Milk and Juice Vending Machine

HOME LINK 3·8 Counting Up to Make Change

Family Note   Help your child identify the amount of change that he or she would receive by "counting up" from the price of the item to the amount of money that was used to pay for the item. It may be helpful to act out the problems with your child using real coins and bills.

Please return this Home Link to school tomorrow.

Complete the table.

I buy:	It costs:	I pay with:	My change is:
a bag of potato chips	70¢	Q Q Q	_____ ¢
a box of crayons	65¢	$1	_____ ¢
a pen	59¢	Q Q Q	_____ ¢
an apple	45¢	D D D D D	_____ ¢
a notebook	73¢	Q Q D D N	_____ ¢
a ruler	48¢	$1	_____ ¢
	_____	_____	_____ ¢
	_____	_____	_____ ¢

Practice

1. 12 − 9 = _____   **2.** 15 − 7 = _____   **3.** 13
− 6

4. 17
− 4

Unit 4: Family Letter

Addition and Subtraction

In Unit 4, children will use addition and subtraction stories to develop mental-arithmetic skills. Mental arithmetic is computation done in one's head or by drawing pictures, making tallies, or using manipulatives (counters, money, number lines, and number grids—no calculators, though). Children can also use their own solution strategies.

A second grader uses a number grid to solve 5 + 9.

1	2	3	4	⑤	6	7	8	9	10
11	12	13	⑭	⑮	16	17	18	19	20
21	22	23	24	25	26	27	28	29	30

> I started at 5 and jumped ahead 10 to 15. But the problem said to add only 9, so I moved back 1 to 14.

Addition has two basic meanings: *putting together* and *changing to more.* In this unit, children will use **parts-and-total diagrams** and **change diagrams** to help them organize information in addition stories that either "put together" or "change to more." See the vocabulary section on page 87 to learn more about these diagrams.

Parts-and-Total Diagram

Total	
?	
Part	**Part**
20	16

Change Diagram
Change

Start		End
20	+6	?

Children will also develop estimation skills by solving problems that involve purchases. For example, your child will estimate whether $5.00 is enough to buy a pen that costs $1.69, a notebook that costs $2.25, and a ruler that costs 89¢.

In the last part of this unit, children will learn paper-and-pencil strategies for addition and will continue to gain hands-on experience with thermometers, money, tape measures, and rulers. Home Links 4-8 and 4-9, which you will receive later, will give you more information on the paper-and-pencil strategies that your child will be learning.

Please keep this Family Letter for reference as your child works through Unit 4.

Vocabulary

Important terms in Unit 4:

change-to-more number story A number story having a starting quantity that is increased so the ending quantity is more than the starting quantity.

For example: *Nick has 20 comic books. He buys 6 more. How many comic books does Nick have now?*

change diagram A device used to organize information in a change-to-more or change-to-less number story. The change diagram below organizes the information in Nick's comic book story above.

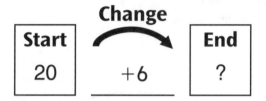

mental arithmetic Computation done totally or partially in one's head, using a variety of strategies.

parts-and-total number story A number story in which two or more quantities (parts) are combined to form a total quantity. For example: *Carl baked 20 cookies. Sam baked 16 cookies. How many cookies did Carl and Sam bake in all?*

parts-and-total diagram A diagram used to organize information in a parts-and-total number story. The parts-and-total diagram below organizes the information in Carl's cookie story.

Total	
?	
Part	**Part**
20	16

estimate (1) An answer close to, or approximating, an exact answer. (2) To make an estimate.

algorithm A step-by-step set of instructions for doing something—for example, for solving addition or subtraction problems.

Building Skills through Games

In Unit 4, your child will practice addition and subtraction skills by playing the following games:

Addition Spin

A "Spinner" and a "Checker" take turns adding two numbers and checking the sum. After five turns, each player uses a calculator to find the sum of his or her scores. The player with the higher total wins.

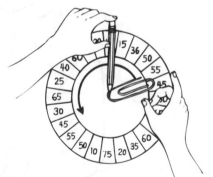

Name That Number

Each player turns over a card to find a number that must be renamed using any combination of five faceup cards.

Fact Extension Game

Players find sums of 2-digit numbers and multiples of ten.

Do-Anytime Activities

To work with your child on the concepts taught in this unit and in previous units, try these interesting and rewarding activities:

1. Encourage your child to show you addition and subtraction strategies as these concepts are developed during the unit.

2. Make up number stories involving estimation. For example, pretend that your child has $2.00 and that he or she wants to buy a pencil marked 64¢, a tablet marked 98¢, and an eraser marked 29¢. Help your child estimate the total cost of the three items (without tax) and determine whether there is enough money to buy them. If appropriate, you can also ask your child to estimate the amount of change due.

3. Look at weather reports in the newspaper and on television and discuss differences between high and low temperatures. Also note the differences between the Fahrenheit and Celsius scales.

As You Help Your Child with Homework

As your child brings home assignments, you may want to go over the instructions together, clarifying them as necessary. The answers listed below will guide you through this unit's Home Links.

Home Link 4·1

1. 18 grapes; 11 + 7 = 18

2. 38 cards; 30 + 8 = 38

3. 52 pounds; 42 + 10 = 52

4. 27	**5.** 80	**6.** 83
7. 10	**8.** 17	**9.** 70
10. 30	**11.** 66	**12.** 80

Home Link 4·2

1. 47 pounds; 17 + 30 = 47

2. 75 pounds; 45 + 30 = 75

3. 60 pounds; 15 + 45 = 60

4. 92 pounds; 17 + 45 + 30 = 92

Home Link 4·3

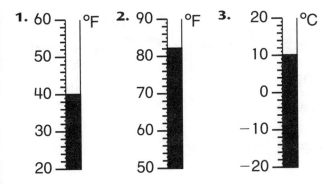

4. a. 14	**b.** 13	**c.** 6	**d.** 15

Home Link 4·4

1. 20°F	**2.** 34°F	**3.** 52°F
4. 96°F	**5.** 48°F	**6.** 73°F

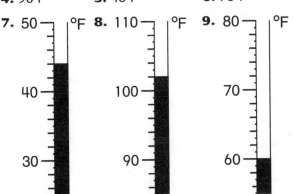

13. 70	**14.** 35	**15.** 97
16. 26	**17.** 50	**18.** 68

Home Link 4·5

1. no	**2.** yes	**3.** no	**4.** yes
5. 100	**6.** 46	**7.** 47	

Home Link 4·6

1. 30 marbles; 20 + 10 = 30

2. 54 cookies; 30 + 24 = 54

3. 100	**4.** 140	**5.** 79	**6.** 83
7. 94	**8.** 77		

Home Link 4·7

2. About 20 inches

Home Link 4·8

1. 76	**2.** 100	**3.** 83	**4.** 120
5. 98	**6.** 90	**7.** 93	**8.** 85
9. 71	**10.** 83	**11.** 169	**12.** 544

Home Link 4·9

1. 89	**2.** 108	**3.** 83	**4.** 94
5. 185	**6.** 363		

HOME LINK 4·1 | **Change Number Stories**

> **Family Note** Your child has learned about a device called a "change diagram" shown in the example below. Diagrams like this can help your child organize the information in a problem. When the information is organized, it is easier to decide which operation (+, −, ×, ÷) to use to solve the problem. Change diagrams are used to represent problems in which a starting quantity is increased or decreased. For the number stories on this Home Link, the starting quantity is always increased.
>
> *Please return the **second page** of this Home Link to school tomorrow.*
>
> **MRB** 116–118

Do the following for each number story on the next page:

◆ Write the numbers you know in the change diagram.

◆ Write "?" for the number you need to find.

◆ Answer the question.

◆ Write a number model.

Example: Twenty-five children are riding on a bus.
At the next stop, 5 more children get on.
How many children are on the bus now?

The starting number of children has been increased.

Answer: There are 30 children on the bus now.

Possible number model: 25 + 5 = 30

HOME LINK 4·1 | **Change Number Stories** *continued*

1. Becky ate 11 grapes.
Later in the day she ate
7 more grapes.
How many grapes did she

eat in all? ____ grapes

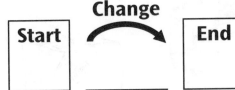

Start	**Change**	End
	_____	

Number model: _____

2. Bob has 30 baseball cards.
He buys 8 more.
How many baseball
cards does Bob

have now? ____ cards

Start	**Change**	End
	_____	

Number model: _____

3. A large fish weighs
42 pounds.
A small fish weighs
10 pounds.
The large fish swallows the
small fish.
How much does the large

fish weigh now? ____ pounds

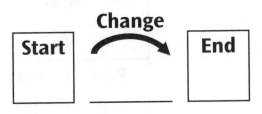

Start	**Change**	End
	_____	

Number model: _____

Practice

Add or subtract.

4. $20 + 7 =$ _____

5. _____ $= 40 + 40$

6. $3 + 80 =$ _____

7. $30 - 20 =$ _____

8. $47 - 30 =$ _____

9. $50 + 20 =$ _____

10. _____ $= 90 - 60$

11. $86 - 20 =$ _____

12. _____ $= 83 - 3$

HOME LINK 4·2

Parts-and-Total Number Stories

Family Note
Today your child learned about another device to use when solving number stories. We call it a parts-and-total diagram. Parts-and-total diagrams are used to organize the information in problems in which two or more quantities (parts) are combined to form a total quantity.

*Please return the **second page** of this Home Link to school tomorrow.*

MRB 109

Large Suitcase
45 pounds

Small Suitcase
30 pounds

Backpack
17 pounds

Package
15 pounds

Use the weights shown in these pictures. Then do the following for each number story on the next page:

◆ Write the numbers you know in each parts-and-total diagram.

◆ Write "?" for the number you want to find.

◆ Answer the question.

◆ Write a number model.

Example: Twelve fourth graders and 23 third graders are on a bus. How many children in all are on the bus?

The parts are known. The total is to be found.

Answer: 35 children

Possible number model: 12 + 23 = 35

Total	
?	
Part	**Part**
12	23

92

HOME LINK
4·2

Number Stories *continued*

1. You wear the backpack and carry the small suitcase. How many pounds do you

carry in all? ____ pounds

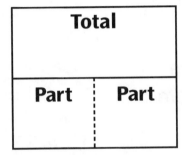

Total	
Part	**Part**

Number model:

_____

2. You carry the large suitcase and the small suitcase. How many pounds do you

carry in all? ____ pounds

Total	
Part	**Part**

Number model:

_____

3. You carry the package and the large suitcase. How many pounds do you

carry in all? ____ pounds

Total	
Part	**Part**

Number model:

_____

Try This

4. You wear the backpack and carry both of the suitcases. How many pounds do you

carry in all? ____ pounds

Total		
Part	**Part**	**Part**

Number model:

_____

MRB
109

LESSON 4·2 Solving Parts-and-Total Problems

Solve. Record what you did.

Example:

Serena had 3 marbles, Sonya had 4 marbles. When they put them together, how many did they have? _____7 marbles_____

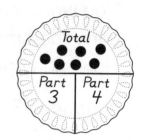

1. 6 birds were sitting in a tree. 3 birds were sitting on the ground. How many birds were there all together? _____

2. There are 8 red flowers and 7 blue flowers. How many flowers are there all together? _____

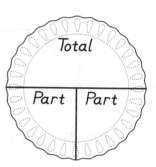

3. Marco had 29¢ and Jamila had 46¢. How much money did they have all together? _____

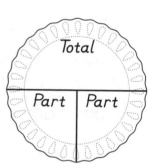

4. Yuri wants to buy a pencil for 18¢ and an eraser for 33¢. How much money does she need? _____

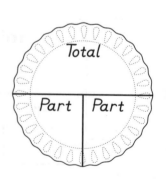

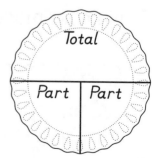

LESSON 4·3   Coin-Stamp Booklets

Work with a partner.

Materials   □ coin stamps   □ stamp pad   □ stapler

         □ scissors   □ sheets of plain paper   □ slates

1. Each partner folds a sheet of paper into 4 parts.

2. Cut the sheet along the folds.

3. Put aside 2 pieces of paper. Use them later for a book cover.

4. Stamp a group of coins on one side of each of the other six pieces of paper.

5. Write the total value of the coins on the other side of the paper. Use a dollar sign and a decimal point: $0.00. Check your partner's work.

6. Stack the pieces. Put the sides with the coins faceup.

   ◆ Put 1 blank piece of paper on top of the stack.

   ◆ Put the other blank piece at the bottom.

   ◆ Staple the pieces together to make a small book.

   ◆ Write your names on the cover of the book.

Follow-Up

◆ Take turns. One partner counts the value of the coins on a page and writes the total value on a slate. The other partner checks that the value is correct.

◆ Work together. Make up a story about the coins on a page and write it on a piece of paper.

LESSON 4·3 | **Attribute Sorts**

Work in a small group.

Materials ☐ set of attribute blocks

          ☐ paper for recording

1. Work together to sort the blocks by color.

  ◆ One way to do the sorting is to use a different sheet of paper for each color. Label each sheet with a different color.

  ◆ Record how you sorted the blocks. On each sheet, write words or draw pictures to show which blocks belong with that color.

2. Sort the blocks again. Sort them by size.

  ◆ Remember to label each sheet with a different size.

  ◆ Record how you sorted the blocks by writing words or drawing pictures.

3. Sort the blocks once more. This time sort them by shape.

  ◆ Did you label each sheet with a different shape?

  ◆ Did you make a record of your work?

HOME LINK 4·3 Reading a Thermometer

Family Note

In today's lesson, your child read temperatures on a real thermometer and on a thermometer pictured on a poster. The thermometers on this page show three different-size degree marks. The longest marks show 10-degree intervals, the medium-size marks show even-number degree intervals, and the shortest marks show odd-number degree intervals.

Help your child find the temperature shown by each thermometer by starting at a degree mark showing tens, counting the medium-size marks by 2s, and, if the temperature is at a short mark, counting 1 more.

Please return this Home Link to school tomorrow.

Circle the thermometer that shows the correct temperature.

1. 40°F

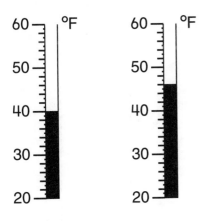

2. 82°F

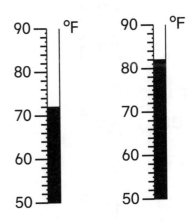

3. 10°C

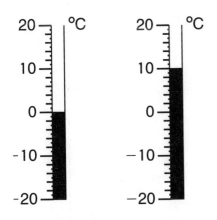

Practice

4. a. 6 + 8 = _____

b. 7 + 6 = _____

c. 9 + _____ = 15

d. _____ = 8 + 7

LESSON 4·3 · Thermometer

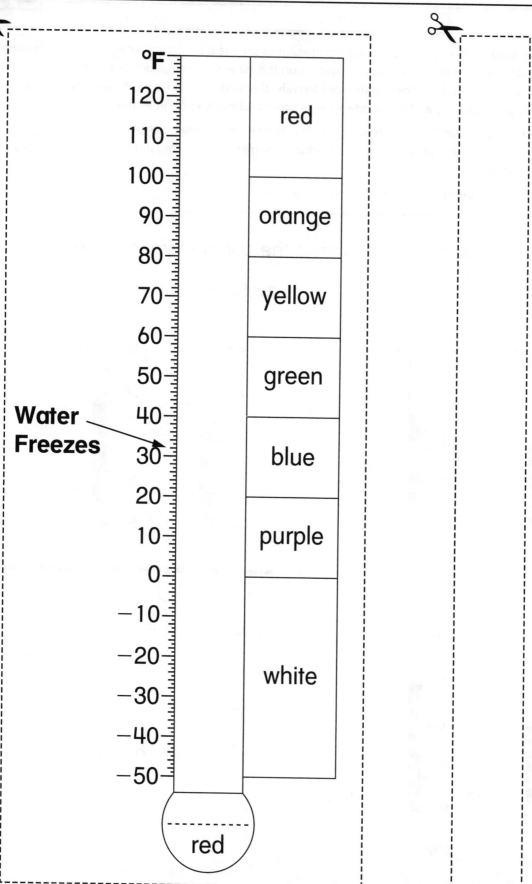

°F

120
110
100
90
80
70
60
50
40
30
20
10
0
−10
−20
−30
−40
−50

red

orange

yellow

green

blue

purple

white

Water Freezes

red

Color this red.

HOME LINK 4·4

Temperature

Family Note

In today's lesson, your child solved problems involving temperatures. On the thermometers on this Home Link, the longer degree marks are spaced at 2-degree intervals. Point to these degree marks while your child counts by 2s; 40, 42, 44, 46, 48, 50 degrees.

Problems 6 and 12 involve temperatures that are an odd number of degrees. Help your child use the shorter degree marks to get the correct answers.

Please return this Home Link to school tomorrow.

Write the temperature shown on each thermometer.

1.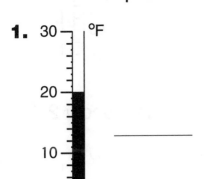

2.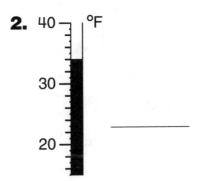

3.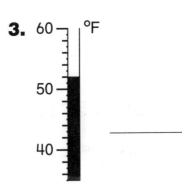

4.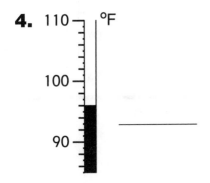

5.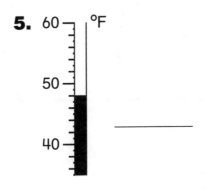

6.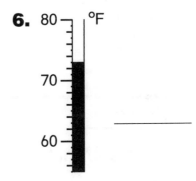

Temperature continued

Fill in each thermometer to show the temperature.

7. Show 44°F.

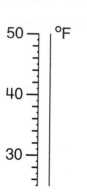

8. Show 102°F.

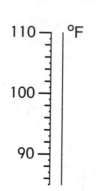

9. Show 60°F.

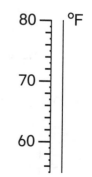

10. Show 56°F.

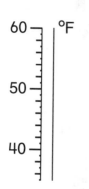

11. Show 38°F.

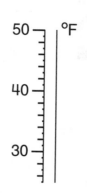

12. Show 27°F.

Practice

Add or subtract.

13. $30 + 40 =$ _____

14. $75 - 40 =$ _____

15. _____ $= 7 + 90$

16. _____ $= 46 - 20$

17.
$$
\begin{array}{r}
53 \\
-3 \\
\hline
\end{array}
$$

18.
$$
\begin{array}{r}
60 \\
+8 \\
\hline
\end{array}
$$

LESSON 4·4 **Comparing Temperatures**

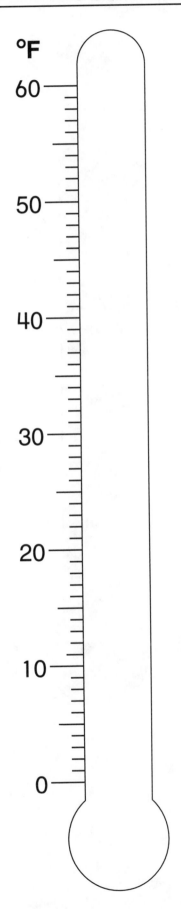

°F

60 —

50 —

40 —

30 —

20 —

10 —

0 —

LESSON 4·4 | **Thermometer**

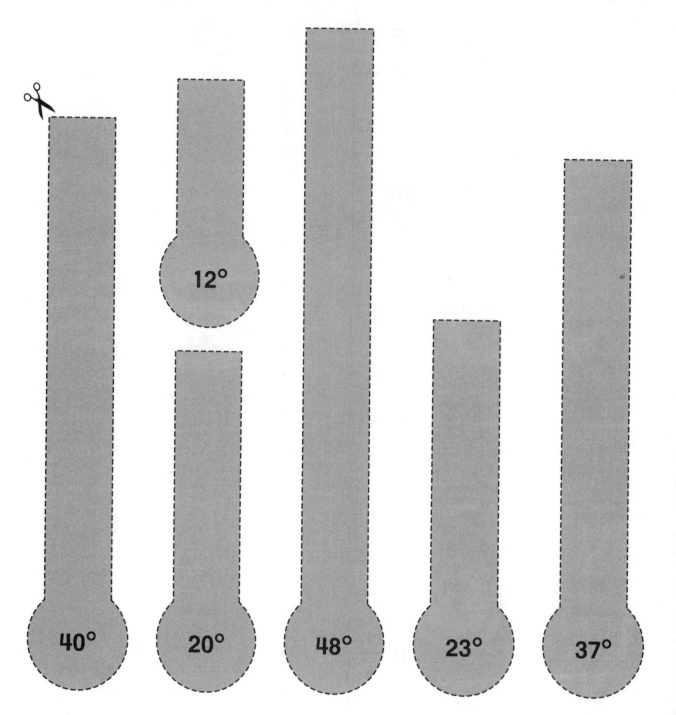

12°

40°   20°   48°   23°   37°

LESSON 4·4 | Comparing Temperatures

Solve the following problems. Use the thermometer and temperature bars to help you.

1. Find the difference between 20° and 50°. _____

2. Find the difference between 12° and 30°. _____

3. Find the difference between 23° and 60°. _____

4. If it was 37° in the morning and 43° by lunch time, how much did the temperature go up? _____

- ✂

Name   Date   Time

LESSON 4·4 | Comparing Temperatures

Solve the following problems. Use the thermometer and temperature bars to help you.

1. Find the difference between 20° and 50°. _____

2. Find the difference between 12° and 30°. _____

3. Find the difference between 23° and 60°. _____

4. If it was 37° in the morning and 43° by lunch time, how much did the temperature go up? _____

HOME LINK 4·5 | **Shopping at the Grocery Store**

> **Family Note**   Many problems in and out of the classroom require estimates rather than exact answers. In Problems 1–5 below, you need to know only whether the total cost is greater than $1.00 or less than $1.00; you do not need to know the exact total cost. In Problem 1, for example, help your child notice that the price of the can of frozen orange juice (98¢) is almost $1.00. Since a lemon is 10¢, your child could not buy both items.
>
> *Please return this Home Link to school tomorrow.*

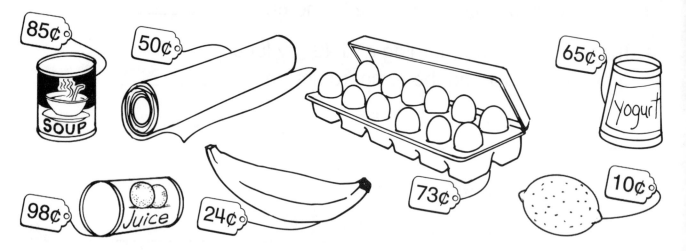

You have $1.00 to spend at the grocery store. Use estimation to answer each question.

Can you buy: Circle *yes* or *no*.

1. a can of frozen orange juice and a lemon?   yes   no

2. a banana and a dozen eggs?   yes   no

3. a container of yogurt and a roll of paper towels?   yes   no

4. a lemon and a can of soup?   yes   no

Practice

Add or subtract.

5. $50 + 50 =$ _____   **6.** _____ $= 6 + 40$ **7.** _____ $= 67 - 20$

LESSON 4·6

Shopping Cards

Calculator
$17

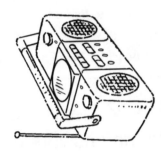

Radio
$38

CD Player
$25

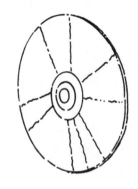

CD
$14

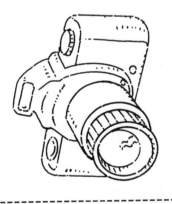

Camera
$43

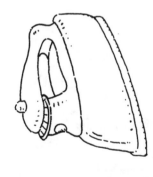

Iron
$32

Telephone
$46

Toaster
$29

HOME LINK 4·6 | **Addition Number Stories**

> **Family Note** In today's lesson, your child solved problems by adding 2-digit numbers mentally. For example, to find 34 + 23, you might first add the tens: 30 + 20 = 50. Then add the ones: 4 + 3 = 7. Finally, combine the tens and ones: 50 + 7 = 57.
>
> *Please return this Home Link to school tomorrow.*
>
> **MRB** 108 109 116 117

Try to solve Problems 1 and 2 mentally. Fill in the diagrams.
Then write the answers and number models.

1. Ruth had 20 marbles in her collection. Her brother gave her 10 more. How many marbles does Ruth have now?

Start	Change →	End

Answer: _____
  (unit)

Number model:

_____

2. Tim baked 30 ginger snaps and 24 sugar cookies. How many cookies did he bake?

Total

Part	Part

Answer: _____
  (unit)

Number model:

_____

Practice

Try to do each problem mentally. Then write the answer.

Unit

3. _____ = 40 + 60

4. 90 + 50 = _____

5. _____ = 70 + 9

6. 80 + 3 = _____

7. 30 + 64 = _____

8. _____ = 27 + 50

LESSON 4·7 | What's My Attribute?

Work with a small group.

Materials ☐ *Math Journal 1*, p. 103

☐ Attribute Rule Cards (*Math Masters*, p. 109)

☐ scissors

☐ 2 sheets of paper

☐ 1 set of attribute blocks: triangles, circles, squares (large and small; red, yellow, and blue)

☐ red, yellow, and blue crayons

Directions

1. Cut apart the Attribute Rule Cards on *Math Masters,* page 109.

2. Mix the cards. Stack them facedown.

3. Label one sheet of paper "These Fit the Rule."

4. Label another sheet "These Do Not Fit the Rule."

5. Take turns being the Rule Maker.

6. The Rule Maker takes the top card from the stack.

7. The Rule Maker puts the card faceup for everyone to see.

8. Group members take turns choosing a block.

LESSON 4·7 **What's My Attribute?** *continued*

9. If the block fits the rule on the card, place it on the paper that says "These Fit the Rule."

10. If the block does not fit the rule, place it on the paper that says "These Do Not Fit the Rule."

11. Repeat Steps 6–10 until everyone has been the Rule Maker.

Follow-Up

◆ Write one of the rules on journal page 103.

◆ Draw or describe all of the blocks that fit the rule.

◆ Draw or describe all of the blocks that do not fit the rule.

Try This

Make up two rules of your own. Write them on the two blank cards given on *Math Masters,* page 109.

_____

_____

_____

LESSON 4·7   **Attribute Rule Cards**

small blue shapes	large red shapes	large shapes, but not triangles	circles, but not red
blue and yellow shapes, but not circles	red and yellow small shapes	not triangles or squares	large triangles, but not yellow
large circles, but not red	large circles or squares		

HOME LINK 4·7 **Measuring to the Nearest Inch**

> **Family Note** In today's lesson, your child measured the length, width, or height of objects to the nearest inch and centimeter. In later lessons, your child will make more precise measurements (such as measuring to the nearest half-inch).
>
> Ask your child to show you how to measure the sections of the path on this page. Encourage your child to measure objects in your home.
>
> *Please return this Home Link to school tomorrow.*

1. The ant will take this path to get to the picnic. Measure each part of the path to the nearest inch. If you do not have a ruler at home, cut out and use the ruler at the bottom of the page.

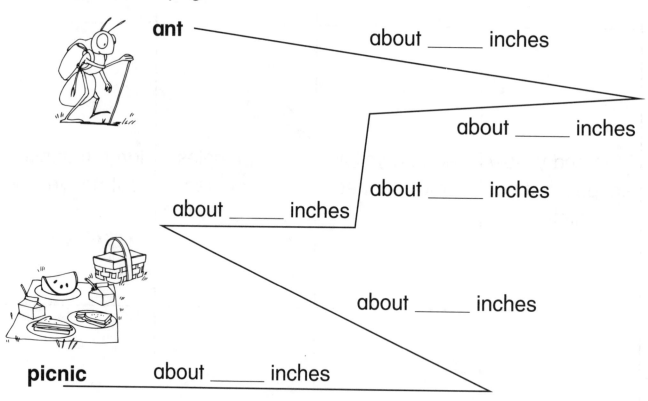

ant — about _____ inches

about _____ inches

about _____ inches

about _____ inches

about _____ inches

picnic about _____ inches

2. What is the total length of the path? about _____ inches

```
0       1       2       3       4       5       6
inches
```

110

HOME LINK 4·8

Addition Strategies

Family Note

Everyday Mathematics encourages children to use a variety of strategies to solve computation problems. By doing so, children are developing a sense for numbers and operations rather than simply memorizing a series of steps.

We suggest that you give your child an opportunity to explore and choose addition strategies that he or she feels comfortable using. At some point, you may want to share the method that you know from your own school experience; please allow your child some time to use his or her own methods before doing so.

Below are three examples of methods that your child might use to solve 2-digit addition problems.

Counting On

$47 + 33 = ?$ ⟵—————— "My problem"

47 57 67 77 ⟵—————— "Start at 47. Count up 30 more."

$\underline{+\ 3}$ ⟵—————— "Add on 3 more."

80 ⟵—————— "The answer is 80."

Combining Groups (1s, 10s, ...) Separately

$29 + 37 = ?$ ⟵—————— "My problem"

$20 + 30 = 50$ ⟵—————— "Add the tens."

$9 + 7 = \underline{16}$ ⟵—————— "Add the ones."

66 ⟵—————— "Put these together. The answer is 66."

Adjusting and Compensating

$52 + 29 = ?$ ⟵—————— "My problem"

30 ⟵—————— "30 is close to 29, just 1 more."

$52 + 30 = 82$ ⟵—————— "52 plus 30 is 82."

$\underline{-\ 1}$ ⟵—————— "Take away 1, because I added 30 instead of 29."

81 ⟵—————— "The answer is 81."

Encourage your child to use a ballpark estimate as a way to check whether an answer to a computation problem makes sense. For example, in $34 + 59$, 34 is close to 30 and 59 is close to 60. $30 + 60 = 90$ is your ballpark estimate. "90 is close to my answer 93, so 93 is a reasonable answer."

*Please return the **second page** of this Home Link to school tomorrow.*

111

HOME LINK 4·8   Addition Strategies *continued*

Practice

Unit

Add.

1. $40 + 36 = $ _____   **2.** $20 + 80 = $ _____   **3.** _____ $ = 53 + 30$

4. $60 + 60 = $ _____   **5.** _____ $ = 50 + 48$ **6.** _____ $ = 70 + 20$

Write a number model to show your ballpark estimate.

Add. Show your work in the workspaces.

Check your work.

7. Ballpark estimate: _____ $\begin{array}{r} 34 \\ + 59 \\ \hline \end{array}$	**8.** Ballpark estimate: _____ $17 + 68 = $
9. Ballpark estimate: _____ $46 + 25 = $	**10.** Ballpark estimate: _____ $56 + 27 = $
11. Ballpark estimate: _____ $123 + 46 = $	**12.** Ballpark estimate: _____ $\begin{array}{r} 318 \\ + 226 \\ \hline \end{array}$

HOME LINK 4·9   **Place Value**

Family Note   Your child is learning a method for addition that focuses on place value. The child is asked to first find a ballpark estimate. (For more on ballpark estimates see page 92 in the *My Reference Book*.)

Find 68 + 24

Ballpark estimate: 70 + 20 = 90

10s	1s
6	8
+ 2	4
8	0
+ 1	2
9	2

Add the tens (60 + 20 = 80) and write the sum.

Add the ones (8 + 4 = 12) and write the sum.

Combine the tens and ones (80 + 12 = 92) to find the final sum.

Encourage your child to use the correct place-value language when using this method. For example, when adding tens in the example, say "60 + 20 = 80," not "6 + 2 = 8." We only recently introduced this method, so allow plenty of time for practice before expecting your child to be able to use it easily.

Please return this Home Link to school tomorrow.

MRB
10

Write a number model for your ballpark estimate.
Find each sum.

Unit

1. Ballpark estimate:

_____

```
  53
+ 36
```

2. Ballpark estimate:

_____

```
  27
+ 81
```

3. Ballpark estimate:

_____

```
  45
+ 38
```

Try This

4. Ballpark estimate:

_____

```
  18
+ 76
```

5. Ballpark estimate:

_____

```
  154
+  31
```

6. Ballpark estimate:

_____

```
  126
+ 237
```

LESSON 4·9 | Base-10 Blocks

For each problem, draw a new set of base-10 blocks that uses
the fewest possible number of flats, longs, and cubes.

1. ‖‖‖ ∷∷∷ ∶∷∷	
2. ‖‖‖‖‖ ∶∷∷∷ ∷∷∷	
3. ‖‖ ∷∷∷∷ ∷∷∷∷∷	
4. ‖‖‖‖ ∷∷∷∷ ∷∷∷∷	
5. ☐ ‖‖‖‖‖ ‖‖‖‖‖ ‖ ∷∷∷ ∷∷∷	
6. ☐ ‖‖‖‖‖ ‖‖‖‖‖ ‖‖‖‖ ∷∷∷∷ ∷∷∷∷	

LESSON 4·9 | Addition Strategies

Addition Strategies

Look at the two addition strategies below. See if you can figure out how they work.

Louisa's Strategy

$37 + 44 = ?$

$37 + 40 = 77$

$77 + 4 = 81$

$37 + 44 = 81$

Li's Strategy

$37 + 44 = ?$

$40 + 44 = 84$

$84 - 3 = 81$

$37 + 44 = 81$

Now try to use either Louisa's Strategy or Li's Strategy to solve the problems below.

$29 + 56 = ?$ $65 + 27 =$

Which strategy do you think is easier? Explain. _____

_____

_____

Unit 5: Family Letter

3-D and 2-D Shapes

Geometry is an important component of *Everyday Mathematics.* Studying geometry helps develop spatial sense and the ability to represent and describe the world. Instead of waiting until ninth or tenth grade, *Everyday Mathematics* introduces geometric fundamentals in Kindergarten and develops them over time. Children are thus prepared to study more advanced geometric topics later.

In Unit 5, children will consider five basic kinds of 3-dimensional shapes: prisms, pyramids, cylinders, cones, and spheres. To sort the shapes, children will explore similarities and differences among them. They will become familiar with both the names of shapes and the terms for parts of shapes.

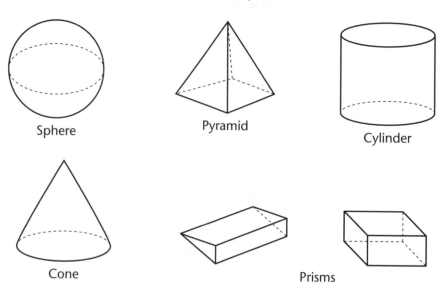

Sphere   Pyramid   Cylinder

Cone   Prisms

Children will also study **polygons,** or 2-dimensional shapes that form the flat surfaces of prisms and pyramids, as they look for examples in real life.

Later in the unit, children will explore **line symmetry** as they experiment with folding 2-dimensional shapes and matching the halves. Children will also cut out shapes and look for lines of symmetry in each shape. When children are given half of a shape, they will draw the missing half. Children will be asked to find symmetrical objects at home and in other places.

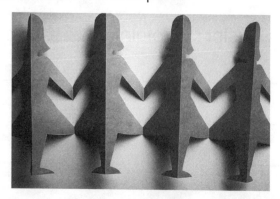

Please keep this Family Letter for reference as your child works through Unit 5.

Unit 5: Family Letter *cont.*

Vocabulary

The purpose of introducing children to the various shapes is to explore the characteristics of the shapes, not to teach vocabulary. This list is presented simply to acquaint you with some of the terms your child will be hearing in context in the classroom.

line segment A straight line joining two points. The two points are called endpoints of the segment.

Line segment *AB* or *BA*

angle A figure formed by two rays or two line segments with a common endpoint called a vertex. The rays or segments are called the sides of the angle. The sides of a polygon form angles at each vertex.

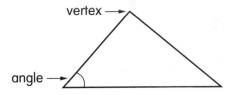

parallel lines Lines in plane that never meet. Two parallel lines are always the same distance apart.

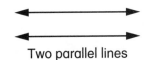

Two parallel lines

polygon A 2-dimensional figure formed by three or more line segments (*sides*) that meet only at their end points (*vertices*) to make a closed path. The sides may not cross one another.

polyhedron A 3-dimensional shape formed by *polygons* with their interiors (*faces*) and having no holes. Plural is *polyhedrons* or *polyhedra.* The following shapes are regular polyhedrons:

Tetrahedron

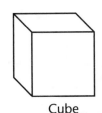
Cube

Octahedron

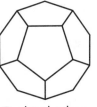
Dodecahedron

Icosahedron

face In *Everyday Mathematics* a flat surface on a 3-dimensional shape.

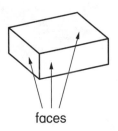

faces

vertex (corner) The point at which the ray of an angle, the sides of a polygon, or the edges of a polyhedron meet.

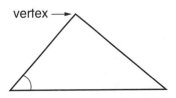

vertex

line symmetry A figure has line symmetry if a line can be drawn through it so that it is divided into two parts that are mirror images of each other. The two parts look alike but face in opposite directions.

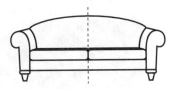

ray A part of a line starting at the ray's endpoint and continuing forever in one direction.

117

HOME LINK 4·10 | **Unit 5: Family Letter** *cont.*

Do-Anytime Activities

To work with your child on the concepts taught in this unit and in previous units,
try these interesting and rewarding activities:

1. Together, look for 2-dimensional and 3-dimensional shapes in your home and
neighborhood. Explore and name shapes and brainstorm about their characteristics.
For example, compare a soup can and a tissue box. Talk about the differences
between the shapes of the surfaces.

2. Use household items, such as toothpicks and marshmallows, straws and twist-ties,
sticks, and paper to construct shapes like those shown below.

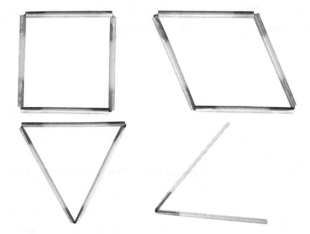

3. Look for geometric patterns in tile floors, quilts, buildings, and so on.

Unit 5: Family Letter *cont.*

As You Help Your Child with Homework

As your child brings home assignments, you may want to go over the instructions together, clarifying them as necessary. The answers listed below will guide you through this unit's Home Links.

Home Link 5·1

1.

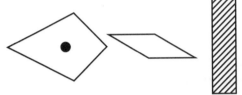

2. The shapes all have 4 sides.   **3.** Answers vary.

4. 66   **5.** 104   **6.** 58

Home Link 5·2

1.   **2.** 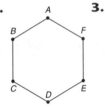   **3.**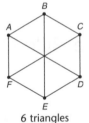

6 triangles

4. Answers vary.   **5.** 43   **6.** 44   **7.** 75

Home Link 5·3

1. 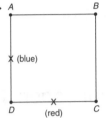   **2.** 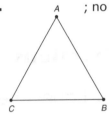 ; no

Home Link 5·5

1. the square   **2.** the rectangle

3. 9   **4.** 14   **5.** 3   **6.** 3

7. 20   **8.** 6   **9.** 97   **10.** 91

Home Link 5·6

1. 18   **2.** 27   **3.** 62   **4.** 96

Home Link 5·8

1.–3. Answers vary.   **4.** 12   **5.** 15

6. 16   **7.** 3   **8.** 5   **9.** 3

Building Skills through Games

In Unit 5, your child will practice addition and money skills by playing the following games:

Addition Spin

Players "spin the wheel" twice and add the two selected numbers. Players check their partners' addition with a calculator.

Dollar Rummy

Instead of three-of-a-kind, players look for two cards that will add up to $1.00.

Beat the Calculator

A "Calculator" (a player who uses a calculator to solve a problem) and a "Brain" (a player who solves the problem without the calculator) race to see who will be the first to solve addition problems.

LESSON 5·1 | "What's My Attribute Rule?"

Work with a small group.

Materials
- ☐ set of attribute blocks
- ☐ Attribute Rule Cards (*Math Masters*, p. 109)
- ☐ 1 six-sided die

Directions

1. Label one sheet of paper: **These fit the rule.**

2. Label another sheet of paper: **These do NOT fit the rule.**

3. Take turns. Roll the die once. The person with the lowest number is the first "Rule Maker."

4. The Rule Maker mixes the Attribute Rule Cards and then stacks them facedown.

5. The Rule Maker picks up the top Attribute Rule Card but does not show it to the other group members or tell them what the rule is.

large shapes,
but not
triangles

Sample Attribute Rule Card

120

LESSON 5·1 "What's My Attribute Rule?" *continued*

6. The Rule Maker chooses 3 or 4 attribute blocks that fit the rule on the card. The Rule Maker puts them on the sheet labeled "These fit the rule."

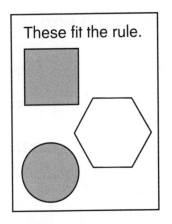

These fit the rule.

7. The Rule Maker chooses 3 or 4 blocks that do NOT fit the rule. The Rule Maker puts them on the sheet labeled "These do NOT fit the rule."

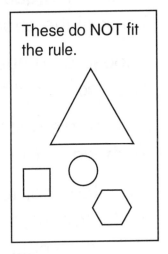

These do NOT fit the rule.

8. The other group members are the "Guessers." The Guessers take turns. Each one chooses a block that he or she thinks might fit the rule.

9. The Rule Maker tells each Guesser "yes" or "no." The Guesser puts the block on the correct sheet. The Guesser suggests what the rule might be. The Rule Maker tells the Guesser if his or her rule is correct.

10. The Guessers continue until someone figures out the rule. Then that person becomes the Rule Maker for the next round.

LESSON 5·1 | **Sharing Equally**

Work with a partner.

Materials ☐ quarter-sheets of paper   ☐ plain paper

☐ 1 six-sided die or number cube

☐ centimeter cubes, pennies, or dried beans

Directions

1. Think of the quarter-sheets of paper as "nests."
Think of the cubes, pennies, or beans as "eggs."

2. Choose a number between 8 and 32.
Then count out that many eggs.

3. Roll the die once. The number that lands faceup tells how
many nests (quarter-sheets) to lay out.

4. Work together to share the eggs equally among all the
nests. When you finish, count the eggs in each nest.
Make sure each nest has the same number of eggs.

5. Make a record of your work on the sheet of plain paper.

◆ Show the number of eggs you started with.

◆ Show the nests and the eggs in each nest.

◆ Show any eggs that were left over.

6. Choose a different number of eggs.
Then follow Steps 1–5 again.

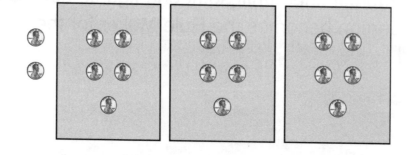

LESSON 5·1 **Making Clock Concentration Cards**

Materials
- ☐ 10 index cards
- ☐ clock-face stamp
- ☐ stamp pad
- ☐ envelope
- ☐ scissors

Directions

Make a set of Clock Concentration cards.

1. Fold each index card in half. Then unfold it.

2. Stamp a clock face on one half of the card. Then draw an hour hand and a minute hand on the face to show a time.

3. Write the matching digital time on the other half. Check one another's work.

4. Cut the card in half.

5. Write **C** on the back of each card with a clock face.

6. Write **T** on the back of each card with a time.

7. Choose a mark your group will use to identify your cards. Make that mark in the same corner on the back of every card.

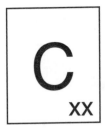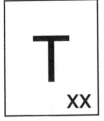

123

LESSON 5·1 | **Clock Concentration** *continued*

Materials ☐ 1 set of Clock Concentration Cards

Directions

1. Shuffle the cards and place them facedown in an array.

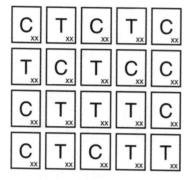

2. Take turns. For each turn, turn a **C** card and a **T** card faceup. If the cards match, pick up both cards and take another turn.

3. If the cards do not match, put them back in the array facedown. Then the next person takes a turn.

4. Continue until time is up or until all the cards have been matched.

5. Store your group's cards in an envelope.

LESSON 5·1

Clock Concentration Cards

Name _____ Date _____ Time _____

 HOME LINK 5·1 | **"What's My Attribute Rule?"**

> **Family Note** Your child has been classifying shapes according to such rules as *only large shapes, only small red shapes,* or *only triangles.* Help your child determine which shapes in Problem 1 fit the rule by checking those shapes against the shapes below. What do all the shapes that fit the rule have in common? (They all have 4 sides.) Once your child thinks she or he knows the rule, check that rule against the shapes that do NOT fit the rule. Do any of those shapes follow the proposed rule?
>
> *Please return this Home Link to school tomorrow.*

These shapes fit the rule.

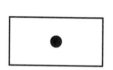 

These shapes do NOT fit the rule.

   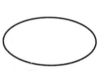

1. Which of these shapes fit the rule? Circle them.

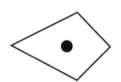 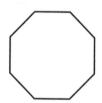  

2. What is the rule? _____

3. Draw a new shape that fits the rule.

Practice

4. 46 + 20 = _____   **5.** 74 + 30 = _____   **6.** 27 + 31 = _____

126

HOME LINK 5·2 — Line Segments

Family Note

In this lesson, your child learned to name points and line segments with capital letters. Using a straightedge, your child drew line segments to create shapes. Provide your child with a ruler, a piece of stiff cardboard, or another object having a straight edge. Observe as your child draws line segments. Ask your child to name the shapes that he or she draws in Problems 1 and 2 below (a 6-pointed star and a hexagon).

Please return this Home Link to school tomorrow.

MRB
50

Use a straightedge to draw line segments.

1. Draw these line segments:

$\overline{AC}$
$\overline{CE}$
$\overline{EA}$
$\overline{BF}$
$\overline{BD}$
$\overline{DF}$

A
B   F
C   D   E

2. Draw these line segments:

$\overline{AB}$
$\overline{BC}$
$\overline{CD}$
$\overline{DE}$
$\overline{EF}$
$\overline{FA}$

A
B   F
C   D   E

3. Draw the following line segments:

$\overline{AB}, \overline{BC}$
$\overline{CD}, \overline{DE}$
$\overline{EF}, \overline{FA}$
$\overline{AD}, \overline{FC}$
$\overline{BE}$

B
A   C
F   E   D

How many triangles are there? _____

4. Draw points on the back of this page. Label each point with a letter. Use a straightedge to connect the points with line segments to make polygons.

Practice

5. 23 + 20 = _____

6. 14 + 30 = _____

7. 45 + 30 = _____

127

LESSON 5·2

Geoboard Designs

1. Use 3 rubber bands to make a design. Record your design.

2. Use 6 rubber bands to make a design. Record your design.

3. Use 8 rubber bands to make a design. Record your design.

4. Make up your own. I used _____ rubber bands to make a design. Record your design.

LESSON 5·2   A Line Segment Design

Use a straightedge and a crayon.

Connect the dots below according to the following pattern:
A→B→C→D→E→F→A

A
•

F•

•B

E•

•C

•
D

What shape did you make with line segments? _____

Use a different color. Connect the dots again in a different
way. Follow this pattern:
A→C→E→A

What shape did you make with line segments? _____

Use a different color. Connect the dots one more time. Follow
this pattern:
B→D→F→B

What shapes do you see in your design?

_____

Color your design.

HOME LINK 5·3 Parallel Line Segments

> **Family Note** Parallel line segments are always the same distance apart. They would never meet, even if they were extended forever in either or both directions. In Problem 1, line segment *DC* is parallel to line segment *AB,* and line segment *AD* is parallel to line segment *BC.* There are no parallel line segments in Problem 2.
>
> *Please return the **top part** of this Home Link to school tomorrow.*
>
> **MRB** 51

1. Draw line segments *AB, BC, CD,* and *DA.*

A •   • B

Put a red **X** on the line segment that is parallel to line segment *AB.*

Put a blue **X** on the line segment that is parallel to line segment *BC.*

D •   • C

2. Draw line segments *AB, BC,* and *CA.*

A
•

Is any line segment in your drawing parallel to line segment *AB*? _____

C •   • B

- -

> **Special Family Note** In Lesson 5-6, your child will be studying 3-dimensional shapes. Help your child gather 3-dimensional objects for a class collection that we call the "Shapes Museum." You and your child might want to separate the objects you collect according to shape.

Shapes Museum

For the next few days, your class will collect things to put into a Shapes Museum. Starting tomorrow, bring items like boxes, soup cans, party hats, pyramids, and balls to school. Ask an adult for permission before bringing in these items. Make sure that the things you bring are clean.

LESSON 5·3 Drawing Line Segments

Draw the line segments. Use a straightedge.

$A \rightarrow B$ $B \rightarrow C$ $C \rightarrow J$ $J \rightarrow A$ $A \rightarrow I$ $I \rightarrow J$ $C \rightarrow D$

$D \rightarrow E$ $E \rightarrow F$ $F \rightarrow N$ $N \rightarrow M$ $M \rightarrow G$ $F \rightarrow G$ $G \rightarrow H$

$H \rightarrow I$ $K \rightarrow L$ $O \rightarrow P$ $P \rightarrow Q$ $Q \rightarrow R$ $R \rightarrow O$ $J \rightarrow E$

A   B

I   J   C

O   P

K   L
M   N

R   Q

□

H   G   F   E   D

131

LESSON 5·3 | # Parallel Line Segment Puzzles

1. Use 2 pattern blocks together to make a shape that has exactly two pairs of parallel line segments.

   Use your Pattern-Block Template to record your solution at the right.

2. Use 2 pattern blocks together to make a shape that has exactly one pair of parallel line segments.

   Use your Pattern-Block Template to record your solution at the right.

3. Use 2 pattern blocks together to make a shape that has no parallel line segments.

   Use your Pattern-Block Template to record your solution at the right.

Try This

If you have time, try to solve each problem using 3 pattern blocks.

LESSON 5·4   Geoboard Polygons

Work in a small group.

Materials   ☐ geoboard   ☐ rubber bands   ☐ straightedge

Directions Each person uses the square side of a geoboard to make the following polygons. Copy each polygon below.

1. Make a triangle in which each side touches exactly 3 pins.

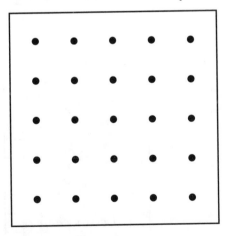

2. Make a square in which each side touches exactly 4 pins.

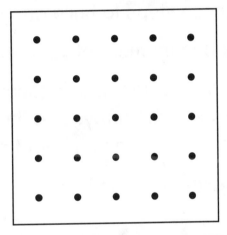

3. Make a pentagon that touches at least 5 pins.

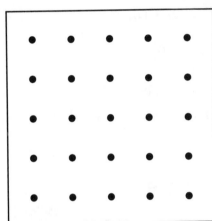

4. Make a hexagon whose sides touch exactly 6 pins in all.

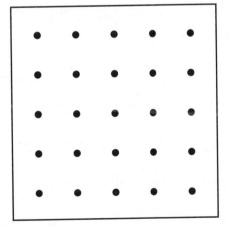

5. Compare your polygons with those of others in your group. Talk about how they are alike and how they are different.

LESSON 5·4 Cube Arrays

Work with a partner or a small group.

Materials   ☐ centimeter grid paper from *Math Masters*, p. 434

☐ 2 six-sided dice

☐ about 40 centimeter cubes

Directions

Follow these steps to build arrays with centimeter cubes:

1. Pick one member of your group to roll the dice.

2. Use the number that is faceup on one die for the number of rows in the array. Use the number that is faceup on the other die for the number of cubes in each row.

Example: If you roll this: You can make either array:

3. Work together. Use centimeter cubes to build the array.

4. On grid paper, fill in squares to show your array. Underneath the array, write

   ◆ how many rows are in the array

   ◆ how many cubes are in each row

   ◆ how many cubes there are in all

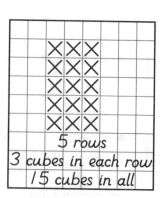

5 rows
3 cubes in each row
15 cubes in all

5. Take turns rolling the dice. Together, make at least five different arrays. Record each array on grid paper.

134

LESSON 5·4 | Attributes

Work with a small group.

Materials
- ☐ attribute blocks
- ☐ sheet of paper
- ☐ red, yellow, and blue crayons or pencils

Directions

Solve each problem. On a separate sheet of paper, trace and color the blocks to show your answers.

1. Find 2 blocks that are NOT the same size, NOT the same shape, and NOT the same color.

2. Find 2 blocks that have the same shape, but are NOT the same size and NOT the same color.

3. Find 3 blocks that are the same size and the same color, but are NOT the same shape.

4. Find 4 small blocks that are the same color, but are NOT the same shape.

Polygons

Family Note In this lesson, your child has been learning the names of different polygons. A polygon is a closed figure made up of straight sides, and you can trace and come back to where you started without retracing or crossing any part. Different types of polygons are shown below. Examples of polygons can be found in real-life objects. For example, a stop sign is an octagon and this page is a rectangle. As your child cuts out pictures of polygons, discuss each shape. Count the sides and angles and try to name the polygons. Talk about how the polygons are alike and different.

Please return this Home Link to school tomorrow or as requested by the teacher.

MRB
52–55

1. Cut out pictures from newspapers and magazines that show triangles, quadrangles, and other polygons. Ask an adult for permission first.

2. Paste each picture on a sheet of paper.

3. Write the names of some of the polygons under the pictures.

4. Bring your pictures to school.

Triangles	**Quadrangles or Quadrilaterals**
Pentagons	**Hexagons**
Heptagons	**Octagons**

These are NOT polygons.

LESSON 5·4 # Pattern-Block Template Shapes

1. Use your template to draw each shape.

square	large triangle	small hexagon
trapezoid	small triangle	wide rhombus
large circle	narrow rhombus	large hexagon

Pattern-Block Template Shapes *cont.*

2. Draw the shapes that have exactly 4 sides and 4 corners.
Write their names.

_____   _____

_____   _____

LESSON 5·5   Make Shapes

1. Cut out the triangles and rectangles.

2. Make some of the shapes listed below. Use at least 2 triangles or rectangles to make each new shape. You may have to turn some of the pieces over.

3. Paste the shapes on sheets of paper.

4. Write the names of the shapes.

Shapes to Make
square
rectangle
triangle
rhombus
kite
trapezoid
parallelogram
4-pointed star
any shape you choose

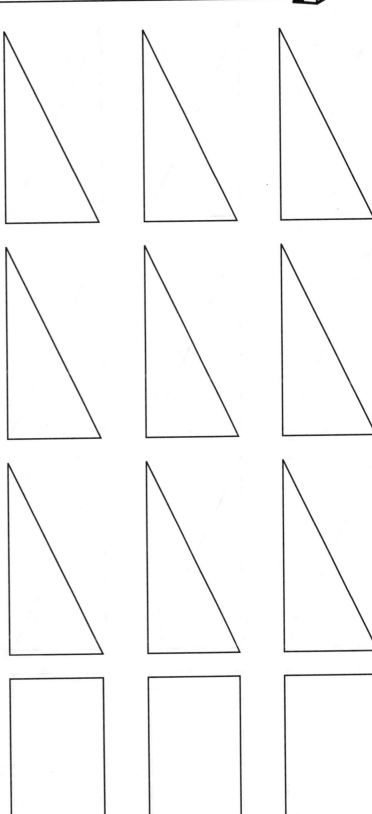

139

LESSON 5·5 Make Shapes *continued*

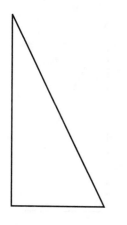
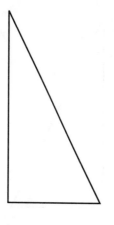
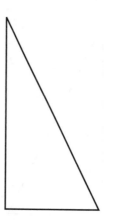
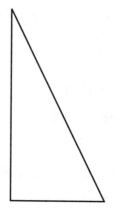
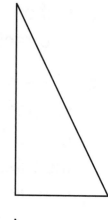

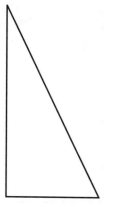

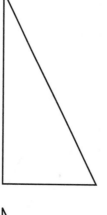
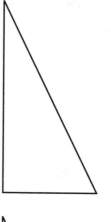
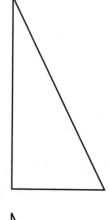

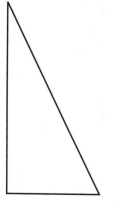
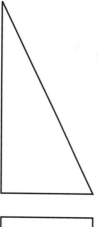

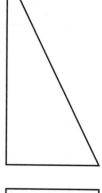

HOME LINK 5·5

Quadrangles

Family Note

In this lesson, your child has been learning about different types of quadrangles, or polygons that have 4 sides. Quadrangles are also called *quadrilaterals*. In Problems 1 and 2 below, three shapes have a common attribute that the fourth shape does not have. In Problem 1, the square is different, because it is the only quadrangle with 4 square corners. In Problem 2, the rectangle is different, because it is the only quadrangle that doesn't have 4 equal sides.

Please return this Home Link to school tomorrow.

MRB
55

1. Look at the number of square corners. Which quadrangle is different from the other three?

_____

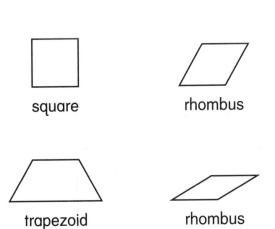

square   rhombus

trapezoid   rhombus

2. Look at the lengths of the sides. Which quadrangle is different from the other three?

_____

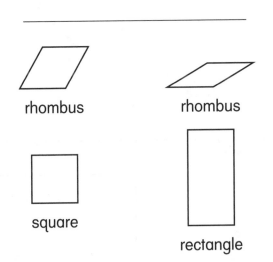

rhombus   rhombus

square

rectangle

Practice

3. $6 + 3 =$ _____

4. $5 + 9 =$ _____

5. $6 - 3 =$ _____

6. $8 - 5 =$ _____

7. $24 - 4 =$ _____

8. $56 - 50 =$ _____

9. $35 + 62 =$ _____

10. $25 + 66 =$ _____

LESSON 5·5 — Tangram Puzzle

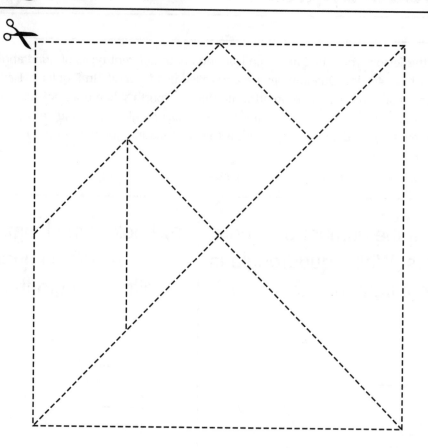

HOME LINK 5·6

3-D Shapes

On your way home, look for things that have these five shapes.

Make a list of things you see. Show your list to someone at home. Can you find any more shapes in your home? Add them to your list.

Prisms

_____

_____

_____

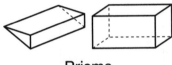

Prisms

Pyramids

_____

_____

_____

Pyramids

Cylinders

_____

_____

_____

Cylinder

Cones

_____

_____

_____

Cone

Spheres

_____

_____

_____

Sphere

Practice

1. $10 + 8 =$ _____

2. $20 + 7 =$ _____

3. $42 + 20 =$ _____

4. $66 + 30 =$ _____

143

LESSON 5·7 | **Pyramid Base Cards**

Use straws and twist-ties to build a **triangular pyramid.**

Use short straws for the base. Use long straws for the other edges.

The base of a triangular pyramid is a triangle:

Use straws and twist-ties to build a **rectangular pyramid.**

Use 2 short straws and 2 long straws for the base. Use long straws for the other edges.

The base of a rectangular pyramid is a rectangle:

Use straws and twist-ties to build a **pentagonal pyramid.**

Use short straws for the base. Use long straws for the other edges.

The base of a pentagonal pyramid is a pentagon:

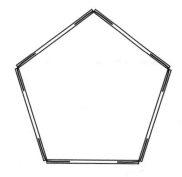

Use straws and twist-ties to build a **hexagonal pyramid.**

Use short straws for the base. Use long straws for the other edges.

The base of a hexagonal pyramid is a hexagon:

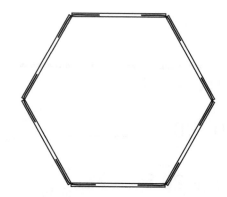

HOME LINK 5·7 Make a Triangular Pyramid

Family Note Your child has used straws and twist-ties to construct pyramids with different-shape bases. The *base* can be a triangle, a rectangle, a pentagon, or another shape. Help your child construct a triangular pyramid (a pyramid with a triangle as the base) by using the cutout pattern below. After constructing the pyramid, ask your child the following questions:

◆ What is the shape of the base? (*A triangle*)

◆ How many edges does the pyramid have? (*6*)

◆ How many faces does the pyramid have? (*4*)

◆ How many vertices does the pyramid have? (*4*)

Please return this Home Link to school tomorrow.

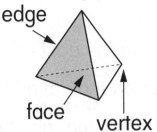

edge face vertex

Ask someone at home to help you make a triangular pyramid out of this pattern.

1. Cut on the dashed lines.

2. Fold on the dotted lines.

3. Tape or glue tabs "inside" or "outside."

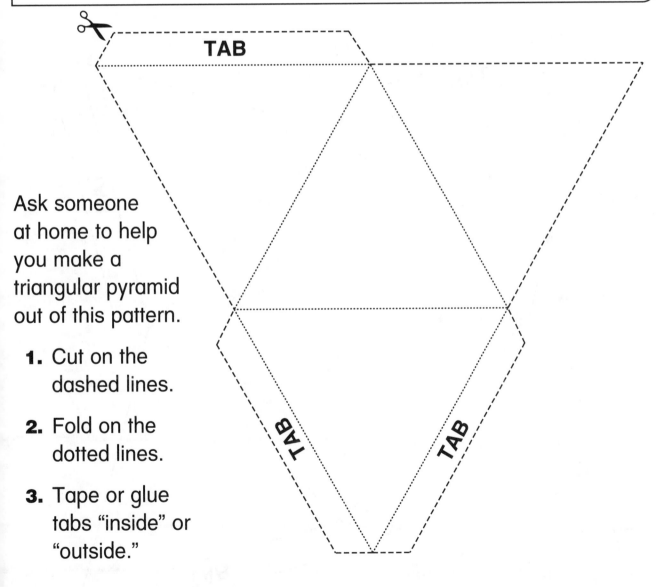

TAB

TAB TAB

LESSON 5·7 Make a Square Pyramid

Materials ☐ scissors

☐ glue or tape

Directions

1. Cut on the dashed lines.

2. Fold on the dotted lines.

3. Tape or glue tabs "inside" or "outside."

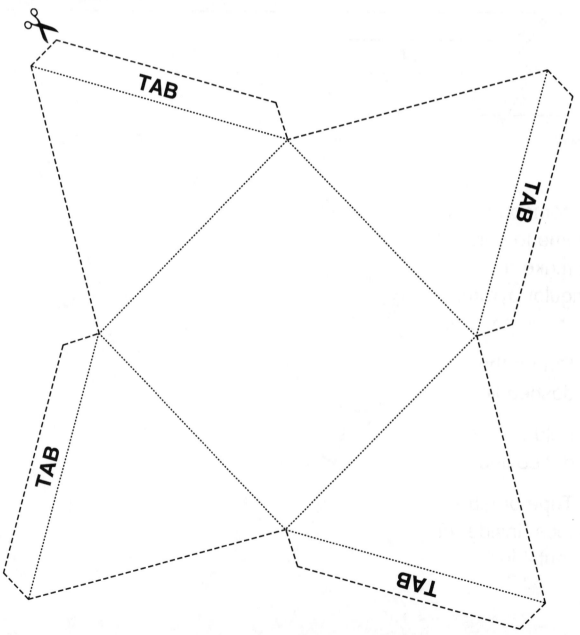

LESSON 5·7   Some Polygons

Triangles

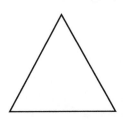 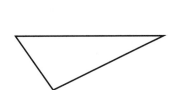 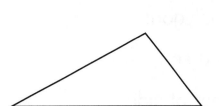

Quadrangles (Quadrilaterals)

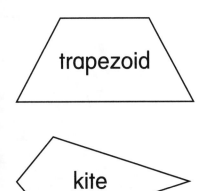

trapezoid

kite

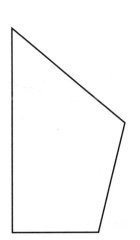

rhombus

square

rectangle

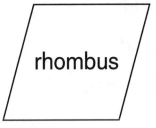

Other Polygons

hexagon

octagon

pentagon

heptagon

LESSON 5·7   **Reviewing Polygons**

Use straws and twist-ties to make the following polygons.
Draw the polygons. Record the number of sides and corners
for each polygon.

1. Make a square.

Number of sides _____

Number of corners _____

2. Make a triangle.

Number of sides _____

Number of corners _____

3. Make a hexagon.

Number of sides _____

Number of corners _____

4. Make a polygon of your choice.

Write its name. _____

Number of sides _____

Number of corners _____

5. Make another polygon.

Write its name. _____

Number of sides _____

Number of corners _____

LESSON 5·8

What's Missing?

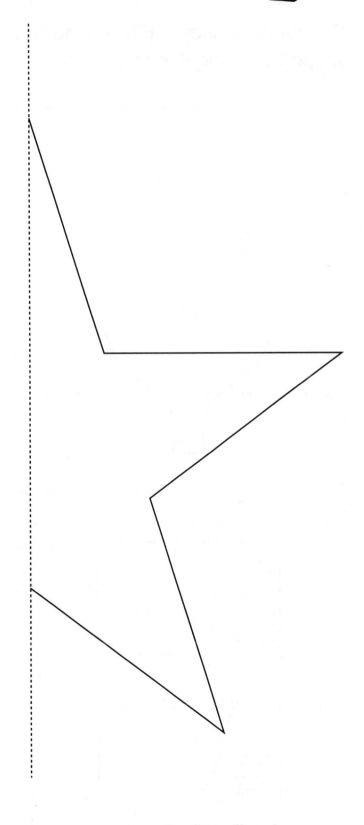

LESSON 5·8

Lines of Symmetry

Cut out each shape. Find all the lines of symmetry for each shape by folding it in half.

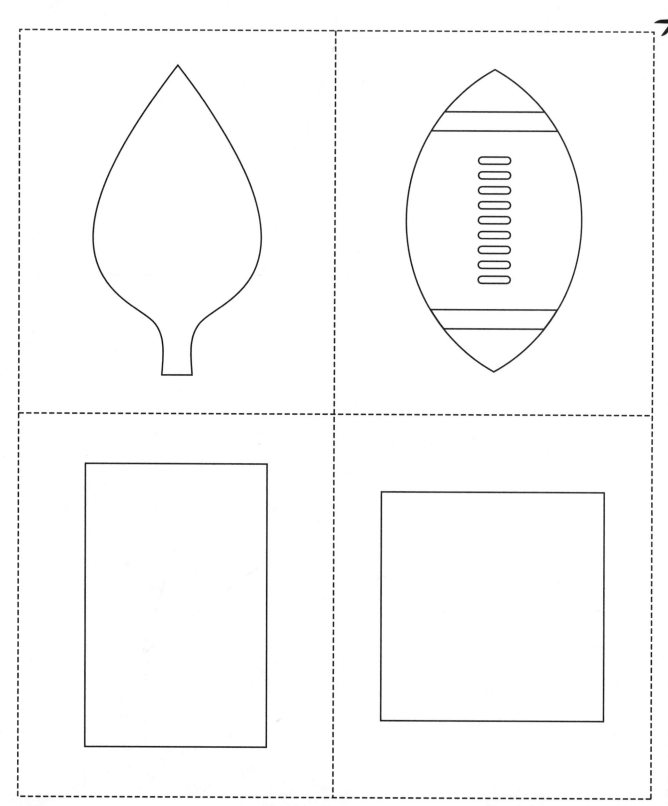

HOME LINK
5·8

Symmetry Hunt

Family Note   In this lesson, your child has been determining whether shapes are symmetrical. A shape has *symmetry* if it has two halves that look alike but face in opposite directions. A *line of symmetry* divides the shape into two matching parts. Lines of symmetry are shown in the objects below. Help your child find other objects that are symmetrical. Remember that some shapes, such as the mirror below, may be symmetrical in more than one way.

Please return this Home Link to school tomorrow.

1. Ask someone to help you make a list of things at home that have symmetry. For example, you might list a window, a sofa, or a mirror.

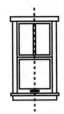 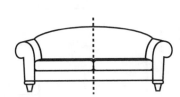 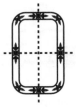

My list: _____

_____

2. Draw a picture of one thing on your list. Draw as many lines of symmetry as you can.

3. If you find pictures in books or magazines that show symmetry, bring them to school.

Practice

4. $4 + 8 =$ _____

5. $6 + 9 =$ _____

6. $8 + 8 =$ _____

7. $8 - 5 =$ _____

8. $9 - 4 =$ _____

9. $7 - 4 =$ _____

HOME LINK 5·9

Unit 6: Family Letter

Whole-Number Operations and Number Stories

In Unit 6, children will take another look at the addition and subtraction diagrams that were introduced in Unit 4.

Later in this unit, children will strengthen their understanding of multiplication and division as they act out number stories using manipulatives and arrays, complete diagrams to show the relationships in multiplication problems, and then begin to record corresponding number models.

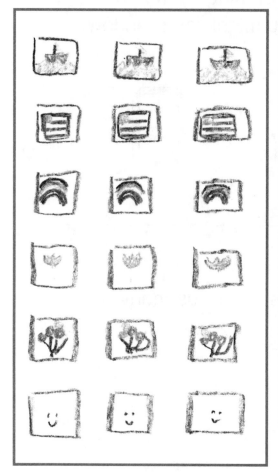

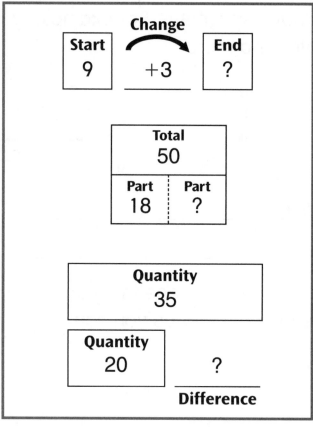

above: addition and subtraction diagrams

left: A child uses an array to solve the following problem: A sheet of stamps has 6 rows. Each row has 3 stamps. How many stamps are on a sheet?

below: multiplication diagram

boxes	marbles per box	marbles in all
3	7	?

Please keep this Family Letter for reference as your child works through Unit 6.

152

Vocabulary

Important terms in Unit 6:

comparison number story A number story that involves the difference between two quantities. For example: Ross sold 12 cookies. Anthony sold 5 cookies. How many more cookies did Ross sell?

comparison diagram A diagram used to organize the information from a comparison number story. For example, the diagram below organizes the information from Anthony's cookie story above.

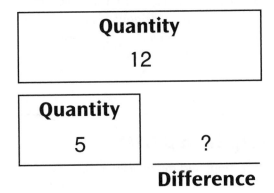

rectangular array An arrangement of objects into rows and columns. For example, 20 pencils could be arranged in 4 rows of 5 pencils each.

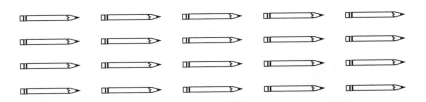

multiples of a number The product of the number and a counting number. For example, multiples of 2 are 2, 4, 6, 8, and 10 because $2 \times 1 = 2$, $2 \times 2 = 4$, $2 \times 3 = 6$, and so on.

remainder The amount left over when one number is divided by another number. For example, if 20 pencils are shared equally by 6 people, each person gets 3 pencils, and 2 are left over. The remainder is 2.

Do-Anytime Activities

To work with your child on the concepts taught in this unit and in previous units, try these interesting and rewarding activities:

1. Have your child show you how making an array or making equal groups can help solve multiplication number stories. Use common objects, such as buttons or pennies, to act out the stories.

2. Also try the opposite: Draw or make arrays and multiples of equal groups. Have your child make up and solve number stories to go with them.

3. Discuss equal-sharing (division) stories. For example, use objects (such as pennies) to portray a situation like the following: We have 7 cookies to divide equally among 3 people. How many whole cookies will each person get? (2) How many cookies will be left over? (1)

Building Skills through Games

In Unit 6, your child will practice addition, subtraction, and multiplication skills by playing the following games:

Three Addends

Players draw three cards, write addition models of the numbers they've picked, and solve the problems.

Addition Top-It

Each player turns over two cards and calls out their sum. The player with the higher sum then takes all the cards from that round.

Array Bingo

Players roll the dice and find an *Array Bingo* card with the same number of dots. Players then turn that card over. The first player to have a row, column, or diagonal of facedown cards calls out "Bingo!" and wins the game.

Number-Grid Difference Game

Players subtract 2-digit numbers using the number grid.

Fact Extension Game

Players find sums of 2-digit numbers and multiples of ten.

As You Help Your Child with Homework

As your child brings home assignments, you may want to go over the instructions together, clarifying them as necessary. The answers listed below will guide you through this unit's Home Links.

Home Link 6·1

Sample answers:

1. $13 + 6 + 7 = 26$
2. $22 + 8 + 5 = 35$
3. $15 + 9 + 25 = 49$
4. $29 + 11 + 6 = 46$
5. 69   6. 70   7. 62
8. 83   9. 148   10. 190

Home Link 6·2

1. $19; 29 − 10 = 19
2. 15 fewer laps; $20 + 15 = 35$
3. June 22; $10 + 12 = 22$

4. $\begin{array}{r} 90 \\ +11 \\ \hline 101 \end{array}$ 5. $\begin{array}{r} 40 \\ +15 \\ \hline 55 \end{array}$ 6. $\begin{array}{r} 80 \\ +\ 7 \\ \hline 87 \end{array}$

Home Link 6·3

1.
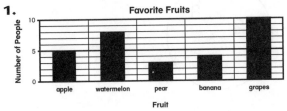

Favorite Fruits

2. grapes; pear

Home Link 6·4

1. 30
2. 28
3. 20

Home Link 6·5

1. 58; 41 cubes left; $58 − 17 = 41$
2. 26; 8 cubes left; $26 − 18 = 8$
3. 43; 18 cubes left; $43 − 25 = 18$
4. 39; 7 cubes left; $39 − 32 = 7$
5. 61; 14 cubes left; $61 − 47 = 14$

Home Link 6·6

1. 4 rows; 5 Xs in each row; 20

Home Link 6·7

1. 3; 18   2. 2; 8   3. 10; 80

Home Link 6·8

1. 24
2. 35

Home Link 6·9

1. Total = 21; $7 \times 3 = 21$
2. Total = 60; $6 \times 10 = 60$
3. 5 rows; 6 dots in each row; 30
4. 3 rows; 9 squares per row; 27
5. 6 rows; 6 squares in each row; 36

Home Link 6·10

3. by 2 people: 9¢ per person; 1¢ remaining
   by 3 people: 6¢ per person; 1¢ remaining
   by 4 people: 4¢ per person; 3¢ remaining

HOME LINK 6·1 **Adding Three Numbers**

Family Note Sometimes the order in which you add numbers can make it easier to find the sum. For example, when adding 17, 19, and 23, some people may first calculate 17 + 23, which equals 40, and then add 19 *(40 + 19 = 59)*. For Problems 1–4, help your child look for easy combinations. Before working on Problems 5–10, you might go over the example with your child.

Please return this Home Link to school tomorrow.

For each problem:

◆ Think about an easy way to add the numbers.

◆ Write a number model to show the order in which you are adding the numbers.

◆ Find each sum. Tell someone at home why you added the numbers in that order.

1.

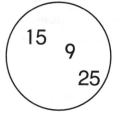

Number model:

_____ + _____ + _____ = _____

2.

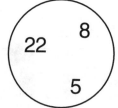

Number model:

_____ + _____ + _____ = _____

3.

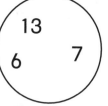

Number model:

_____ + _____ + _____ = _____

4.

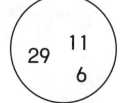

Number model:

_____ + _____ + _____ = _____

HOME LINK
6·1

Adding Three Numbers *continued*

Add. Use the partial-sums method.

Example:

$$
\begin{array}{r}
33 \\
42 \\
+\ 11 \\
\end{array}
$$

Add the tens.	→ (30 + 40 + 10)	→	80
Add the ones.	→ (3 + 2 + 1)	→	6
Add the partial sums.	→ (80 + 6)	→	86

Practice

5.
$$
\begin{array}{r}
23 \\
32 \\
+\ 14 \\
\hline
\end{array}
$$

6.
$$
\begin{array}{r}
14 \\
29 \\
+\ 27 \\
\hline
\end{array}
$$

7.
$$
\begin{array}{r}
8 \\
19 \\
+\ 35 \\
\hline
\end{array}
$$

8.
$$
\begin{array}{r}
46 \\
25 \\
+\ 12 \\
\hline
\end{array}
$$

9.
$$
\begin{array}{r}
40 \\
45 \\
+\ 63 \\
\hline
\end{array}
$$

10.
$$
\begin{array}{r}
9 \\
85 \\
+\ 96 \\
\hline
\end{array}
$$

LESSON 6·1 Addition with Several Addends

For each sum, write a number sentence using four or more addends. Each number sentence must include a double and at least one pair of addends that equal ten.

43	**62**
79	**112**

HOME LINK 6·2 Comparison Number Stories

Family Note

Today your child learned about a device that is useful when solving number stories. We call it a comparison diagram. Diagrams like these can help your child organize the information in a problem. When the information is organized, it is easier to decide which operation (+, −, ×, or ÷) to use to solve the problem.

Comparison diagrams are used to represent problems in which two quantities are given and the question is how much more or less one quantity is than the other (the difference).

Example 1: There are 49 fourth graders and 38 third graders. How many more fourth graders are there than third graders?

Note that the number of fourth graders is being compared with the number of third graders.

- *Answer:* There are 11 more fourth graders than third graders.

- *Possible number models:* Children who think of the problem in terms of subtraction will write $49 - 38 = 11$. Other children may think of the problem in terms of addition: "Which number added to 38 will give me 49?" They will write the number model as $38 + 11 = 49$.

Quantity
49 fourth graders

Quantity	
38 third graders	?
	Difference

Your child may write words in the diagram as a reminder of what the numbers mean.

Example 2: There are 53 second graders. There are 10 more second graders than first graders. How many first graders are there?

Note that sometimes the difference is known and that one of the two quantities is unknown.

- *Answer:* There are 43 first graders.

- *Possible number models:*
  $53 - 10 = 43$ or $10 + 43 = 53$

Quantity
53

Quantity	
?	10
	Difference

For Problems 1 and 2, ask your child to explain the number model that he or she wrote. Also ask your child to explain the steps needed to solve Problems 4–6.

*Please return the **second page** of this Home Link to school tomorrow.*

MRB
110 111

159

HOME LINK 6·2 Comparison Stories *continued*

In each number story:

◆ Write the numbers you know in the comparison diagram.

◆ Write ? for the number you want to find.

◆ Solve the problem. Then write a number model.

---

1. Ross has $29. Omeida has $10.

Ross has $_____ more than Omeida.

Number model: _____

Quantity

Quantity
Difference

---

2. Omar swam 35 laps in the pool. Anthony swam 20 laps.

Anthony swam _____ fewer laps than Omar.

Number model: _____

Quantity

Quantity
Difference

---

3. Claudia's birthday is June 10. Tisha's birthday is 12 days later.

Tisha's birthday is June _____.

Number model: _____

Quantity

Quantity
Difference

Practice

Add. Use the partial-sums method.

Unit

4.   39
      + 62
      ____

5.   48
      + 7
      ____

6.   33
      + 54
      ____

LESSON 6·2 | Comparing Number Stories

Solve each number story. Be sure to write a number model.
Then answer the questions at the bottom of the page.

1. There were 23 children in the classroom. 17 went to the computer lab. How many were left in the classroom?

Number Model: _____

2. There were 6 children in the classroom. 17 came back from the computer lab. How many children are in the classroom now?

Number Model: _____

How are the problems alike?

_____

_____

_____

_____

How might solving Problem 1 help you solve Problem 2?
Explain your thinking.

_____

_____

_____

_____

_____

161

LESSON 6·3 | **Dietary Guidelines for Second Graders**

Grains		Eat 6 servings a day. Choose whole grain cereals, breads, crackers, or pasta.
Fruits		Eat 4 servings a day.
Vegetables		Eat 3–4 servings a day.
Low-fat Dairy		Eat 2 servings a day. Choose low-fat or fat-free milk, cheese, and/or yogurt.
Meat and Beans		Eat 1–2 servings a day. Choose lean meats. Eat more fish.
Fats and Oils		Use sparingly.
Sweets		If you are eating lots of healthy foods, then you may have sweets a few times a week.

The 4 Basic Food Groups (Samples)

fruit/ vegetables	bread/cereal/ rice/pasta	dairy products	meat/poultry/ fish/beans/ eggs/nuts
watermelon	pancakes	ice cream	hamburgers
bananas	fried rice	Swiss cheese	omelets
grapes	French toast	yogurt	almonds
pears	cornflakes	chocolate milk	peanut butter
apples	muffins	cream cheese	chicken
broccoli	crackers	milk shakes	fish
corn	spaghetti	frozen yogurt	pork chops
potatoes	bagels		black beans
carrots	English muffins		refried beans
squash	waffles		scrambled eggs
raisins			turkey
strawberries			bacon

LESSON 6·3   **What Is Your Favorite Food?**

1. Make tally marks to show the number of children who chose a favorite food in each group.

fruit/ vegetables	bread/cereal/ rice/pasta	dairy products	meat/poultry/ fish/beans/ eggs/nuts

2. Make a graph that shows how many children chose a favorite food in each group.

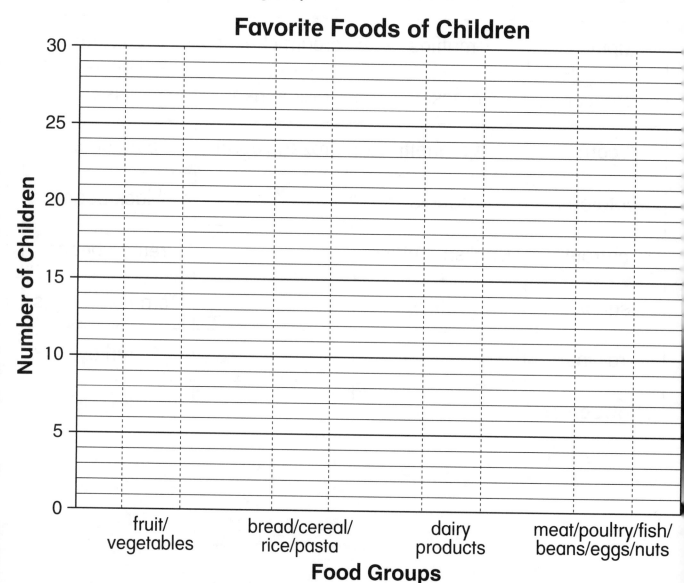

Favorite Foods of Children

HOME LINK 6·3

Graphing Data

In a survey, people were asked to name their favorite fruit. The table below shows the results.

apple	watermelon	pear	banana	grapes
﹨卌	卌 ///	///	////	卌 卌

1. Make a bar graph that shows how many people chose each fruit. The first bar has been colored for you.

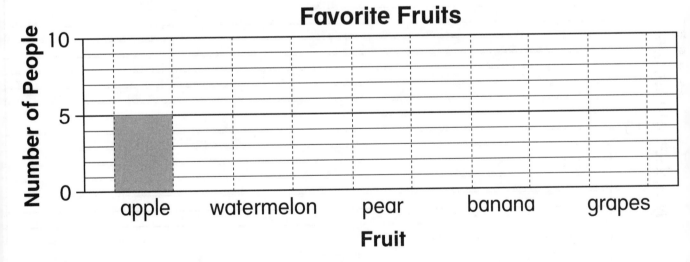

2. Which fruit is the most popular? _____

   Which fruit is the least popular? _____

   What is your favorite kind of fruit? _____

165

LESSON 6·3 **Adults: What's Your Favorite Food?**

1. Make tally marks to show the number of adults who chose a favorite food in each group.

fruit/ vegetables	bread/cereal/ rice/pasta	dairy products	meat/poultry/ fish/beans/ eggs/nuts

2. Make a graph that shows how many adults chose a favorite food in each group.

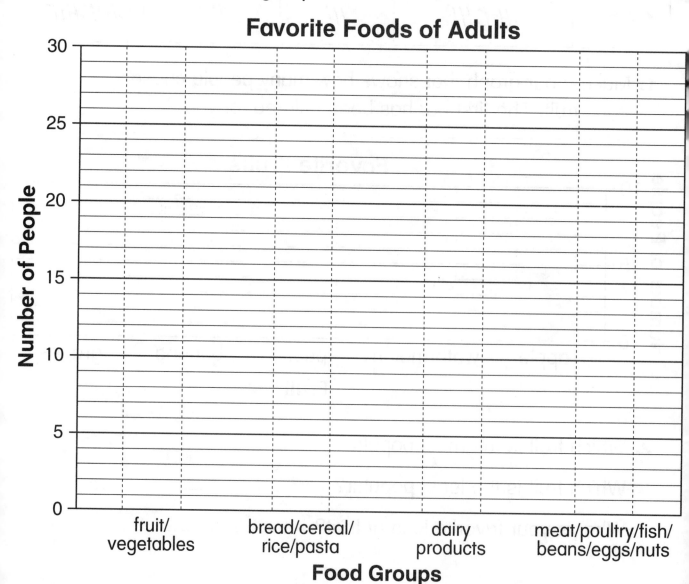

Favorite Foods of Adults

Number of People

30
25
20
15
10
5
0

fruit/ vegetables   bread/cereal/ rice/pasta   dairy products   meat/poultry/fish/ beans/eggs/nuts

Food Groups

HOME LINK 6·4

Number Stories and Diagrams

Family Note In today's lesson, your child used diagrams to solve number stories. Listen to your child's stories. Ask your child to explain how each story relates to both the diagram and the number model. (See Home Link 5.10: *Unit 6 Family Letter* for information about number stories and diagrams.)

Please return this Home Link to school tomorrow.

MRB
109–118

Write number stories to match each diagram. Then finish the number model. Tell your stories to someone at home.

1.

Unit
building blocks

Change

Start		End
24	+6	?

_____

_____

_____

Finish the number model: 24 + 6 = _____

2.

Unit
books

Total	
Part	**Part**

_____

_____

_____

Finish the number model: 15 + 13 = _____

HOME LINK 6·4

Number Stories and Diagrams *cont.*

3.

Unit
bananas

Quantity

Quantity

_____
Difference

_____

_____

Finish the number model: 28 − 8 = _____

4.

Unit
baseball cards

Total	
Part	**Part**

_____

_____

Write a number model for your story.

Number model: _____

HOME LINK 6·5

Subtracting with Base-10 Blocks

Family Note

In this lesson, your child found the answers to subtraction problems by using longs and cubes to represent tens and ones, respectively.

This will help your child understand the concept of subtraction before he or she learns to subtract using a step-by-step procedure, or algorithm, with paper and pencil. When you see the problems on this Home Link, you may be eager to teach your child to subtract the way you were taught. Please wait—the introduction of a formal algorithm for subtraction will be taught later in second grade.

Please return this Home Link to school tomorrow.

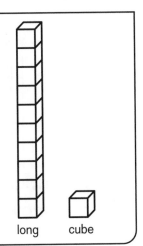

MRB
31

long   cube

Show subtraction by crossing out cubes.

Example:

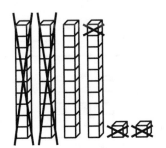

How many cubes
are shown as
separate cubes and
as part of the longs? **42**

Cross out (subtract)
23 cubes. How
many cubes are left? **19**

Number model:

42 − 23 = 19

1.

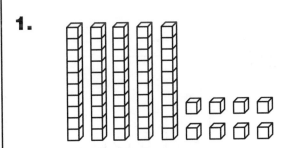

How many cubes
are shown in all? _____

Cross out (subtract)
17 cubes. How
many cubes are left? _____

Number model:

_____ − _____ = _____

169

HOME LINK 6·5

Subtracting with Blocks *continued*

2.

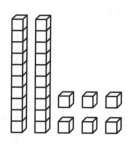

How many cubes
are shown in all? _____

Cross out (subtract)
18 cubes. How
many cubes are left? _____

Number model:

_____ − _____ = _____

3.

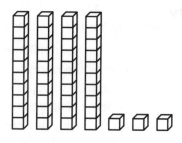

How many cubes
are shown in all? _____

Cross out (subtract)
25 cubes. How
many cubes are left? _____

Number model:

_____ − _____ = _____

4.

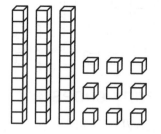

How many cubes
are shown in all? _____

Cross out (subtract)
32 cubes. How
many cubes are left? _____

Number model:

_____ − _____ = _____

5.

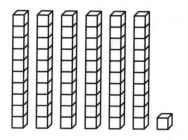

How many cubes
are shown in all? _____

Cross out (subtract)
47 cubes. How
many cubes are left? _____

Number model:

_____ − _____ = _____

LESSON 6·5 | A Subtraction Strategy

Meredith uses an interesting strategy for solving subtraction problems when you have to trade. Try to figure out how it works.

42 − 27

On my first step, I get 12.

On my second step I get 15.

15 is my final answer.

34 − 19

On my first step, I get 14.

On my second step I get 15.

15 is my final answer.

71 − 36

First Step: _____

Second Step: _____

Final Answer: _____

Try This

93 − 48

First Step: _____

Second Step: _____

Final Step: _____

LESSON 6·6 — Geoboard Arrays

Materials
- ☐ geoboard dot paper for each person
- ☐ geoboard for each person
- ☐ rubber band for each person
- ☐ scissors for the group
- ☐ glue or paste for the group (optional)
- ☐ large sheet of paper for the group (optional)

Work by yourself to complete Steps 1–5.

1. Use one rubber band to make a rectangle on your geoboard. The pegs inside and the pegs that touch the rubber band make an array.

2. Draw your array on the geoboard dot paper.

3. Write about your array at the bottom of the geoboard dot paper. Tell how many rows are in your rectangle, how many dots are in each row, and how many dots in all are in your rectangle.

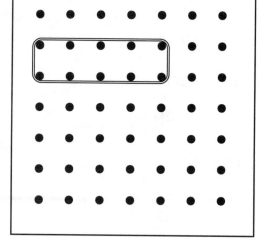

There are 2 rows of 5 pegs.
10 pegs are in the array.

4. Make 3 more arrays—all different. Follow steps two and three.

5. Cut apart the dot-paper records of your 4 arrays.

Work with your group to complete Step 6.

6. Sort your group's arrays into piles that have the same number of dots. You might want to use the arrays in each pile to make a display about that number.

LESSON 6·6   **Geoboard Arrays (5 × 5)**

1.

2.

3.

4.

	How many rows?	How many dots in each row?	How many dots in all?
1.			
2.			
3.			
4.			

LESSON 6·6   **Geoboard Arrays (7 × 7)**

1.

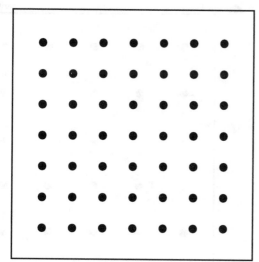

2.

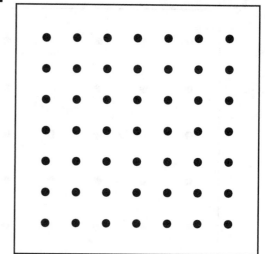

3.

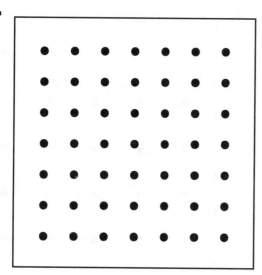

4.

	How many rows?	How many dots in each row?	How many dots in all?
1.			
2.			
3.			
4.			

174

LESSON 6·6 | **Making a Dollar**

Work together in a small group.

Materials ☐ 20 nickels

☐ 10 dimes

☐ 4 quarters

☐ paper and pencil

Directions

1. Use the coins to find as many different ways as you can to make $1.00.

2. Before you begin, THINK about how to do this. *Hint:* First, make a dollar using 3 quarters and some other coins.

3. Plan how you will record the different ways to make $1.00.

4. On a sheet of paper, record the different ways you find to make $1.00. Use Ⓝ, Ⓓ, and Ⓠ to show the coins.

Follow-Up

◆ How many ways did you find to make $1.00? Check with other groups to see if they thought of any ways that your group didn't find.

◆ Did you have a plan to find all the combinations? Compare your plan with the plan used by another group.

LESSON 6·6

How Many Children Get *n* Things?

Materials
- ☐ *Math Journal 1*, p. 146 (per person)
- ☐ one container with about 50 pennies or other counters (per group)
- ☐ 1 six-sided die (per group)

Use counters to make up and solve problems like this one:
Your group has been given 32 crayons.
Each person is to get 8 crayons.
How many of you will get 8 crayons?
Are there any crayons left over?

Now make up your own problems. Follow these steps:

1. Each person takes a handful of counters. Put all the counters together in a pile.

   How many counters are in the pile? Count them and record the number on the journal page.

2. Make equal-size groups of counters. One person rolls the die. The number that lands faceup tells how many counters to put in each group.

   Record this number on the journal page.

3. Make as many groups as you can with the counters in the pile.

4. Record on the journal page how many groups you made. If any counters are left over, record that number, too.

5. Put the counters back in the container. Repeat Steps 1–4.

HOME LINK 6·6   How Many?

Family Note Your child has been working with arrays—rectangular arrangements of objects having the same number of objects in each row—to develop readiness for multiplication. Because this is a readiness activity, children have not yet written number models for multiplication, such as 4 × 5 = 20. Your child will do this in later lessons in this unit.

Please return this Home Link to school tomorrow.

1. Show someone at home this array.

```
X X X X X
X X X X X
X X X X X
X X X X X
```

How many rows? _____

How many **X**s in each row? _____

How many **X**s in all? _____

2. Draw an array of 16 **X**s.

How many rows? _____

How many **X**s in each row? _____

3. Draw an array of 24 **X**s.

How many rows? _____

How many **X**s in each row? _____

4. Draw a different array of 24 **X**s.

How many rows? _____

How many **X**s in each row? _____

177

LESSON 6·6 | **Solving Dollar Riddles**

1. To make a dollar, use all four types of coins and create a coin combination where there are two times as many of one type of coin as another.

_____

_____

2. To make a dollar, use all four types of coins. Use half as many of one type of coin.

_____

_____

3. To make a dollar, use only nickels and dimes and create a coin combination where one type of coin is used twice as much as the other type. _____

_____

4. Using only three types of coins, make a dollar with the least number of coins you could use. _____

Using only three types of coins, make a dollar with the greatest number of coins you could use. _____

_____

Try This

Use pennies, nickels, dimes, and quarters. Make a combination that is worth one dollar where you have one of some kind of coin, double of another, double that of another, and some number of the last coin.

_____

_____

HOME LINK 6·7

How Many?

Family Note In today's lesson, your child learned that multiplication is an operation used to find the total number of things in several equal groups. As you help your child solve the following problems, emphasize that each group has the same number of things. Your child can use objects, draw pictures, count, or use any other helpful devices to find the answers.

Please return this Home Link to school tomorrow.

Example:

How many apples in 4 packages?

HHT   HHT   HHT   HHT

$5 + 5 + 5 + 5 = 20$

There are 20 apples in 4 packages.

1. △ △ △ △ △ △

How many sides on each triangle? _____ sides

How many sides in all? _____ sides

2.

How many wheels on each bike? _____ wheels

How many wheels in all? _____ wheels

3.

How many fingers for each person?

_____ fingers

How many fingers in all?

_____ fingers

179

LESSON 6·7 | Finding Totals for Equal Groups

You may use your calculator to help you solve the problems.

1. How many people are in my group? _____

How many hands do the people in my group have all together? _____

How many fingers do the people in my group have all together? _____

2. How many tables are in the classroom? _____

How many legs do the tables have? _____

3. One flower has 5 petals.

How many petals do 6 flowers have? _____

4. Make up your own problem like the ones above. Draw a picture to help someone solve your problem.

_____

_____

_____

LESSON 6·7 | Equal-Groups Riddles

What Number Am I?

1. If you put me into 7 equal groups with 3 in each group and 5 are left over, what number am I?

_____

Draw a picture of what you did.

2. I am a number between 20 and 30. When you put me into 6 equal groups, there is an even number in each group and 1 is left over.

What number am I? _____

Draw a picture of what you did.

3. Try writing your own equal-groups riddle.

_____

_____

_____

LESSON 6·8 | Array Number Stories

Array

o o o o o o o o o o
o o o o o o o o o o
o o o o o o o o o o
o o o o o o o o o o
o o o o o o o o o o
o o o o o o o o o o

Multiplication Diagram

rows	___ per row	___ in all

Number model: ____ × ____ = ____

Array

o o o o o o o o o o
o o o o o o o o o o
o o o o o o o o o o
o o o o o o o o o o
o o o o o o o o o o
o o o o o o o o o o

Multiplication Diagram

rows	___ per row	___ in all

Number model: ____ × ____ = ____

Array

o o o o o o o o o o
o o o o o o o o o o
o o o o o o o o o o
o o o o o o o o o o
o o o o o o o o o o
o o o o o o o o o o

Multiplication Diagram

rows	___ per row	___ in all

Number model: ____ × ____ = ____

Array

o o o o o o o o o o
o o o o o o o o o o
o o o o o o o o o o
o o o o o o o o o o
o o o o o o o o o o
o o o o o o o o o o

Multiplication Diagram

rows	___ per row	___ in all

Number model: ____ × ____ = ____

Arrays

Family Note In this lesson, your child solved multiplication problems about arrays, which are rectangular arrangements of objects in rows and columns. Encourage your child to use counters, such as pennies or buttons, while working on the following exercises.

Please return this Home Link to school tomorrow.

Tell someone at home what you know about arrays.

1. Look at the array and fill in the blank.

• • • • • •
• • • • • •
• • • • • •
• • • • • •

4 rows of dots

6 dots in each row

_____ dots in all.

2. Draw an array of dots. Your array should have

5 rows of dots

7 dots in each row

That's _____ dots in all.

3. Draw an array of 12 dots.

Telephone:
a 4-by-3 array

Muffins:
a 3-by-2 array

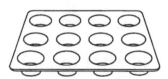

Muffins:
a 3-by-4 array

Tic-tac-toe Grid:
a 3-by-3 array

Checkerboard:
an 8-by-8 array

Eggs:
a 2-by-6 array

183

HOME LINK 6·9 | Arrays

> **Family Note** In this lesson, your child continued to work with arrays to develop multiplication concepts. Your child described each array by naming the number of rows, the number of items in each row, and the total number of items in the array. Your child wrote number models to describe arrays. In the example, an array with 2 rows of 4 dots can be described using the number model $2 \times 4 = 8$.
>
> *Please return this Home Link to school tomorrow.*

Show an array for the numbers that are given. Find the total number of dots in the array. Complete the number model.

Example:

Numbers: 2, 4

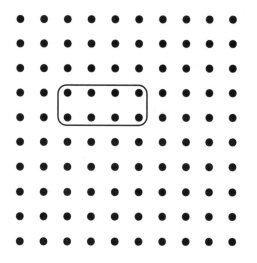

Total: __8__

Number model:

__2__ × __4__ = __8__

1. Numbers: 7, 3

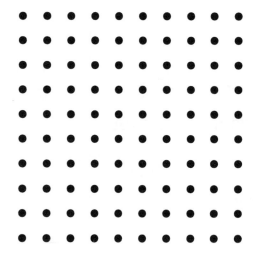

Total: _____

Number model:

_____ × _____ = _____

HOME LINK 6·9

Arrays *continued*

2. Numbers: 6, 10

Total: _____

Number model:

_____ × _____ = _____

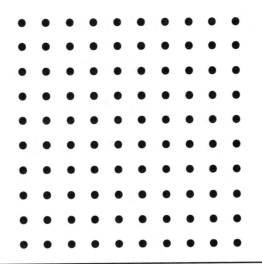

Answer the questions about each array.

3.

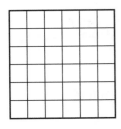

How many rows? _____

How many
dots in each row? _____

How many
dots in the array? _____

4.

How many rows? _____

How many
squares per row? _____

How many
squares in the array? _____

5.

(grid)

How many rows? _____

How many squares in each row? _____

How many squares in the array? _____

Building Arrays

Materials ☐ pattern blocks ☐ Pattern-Block Template

☐ 1 six-sided die or number cube

☐ *Math Masters,* p. 187

1. Choose one of these blocks.

 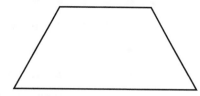 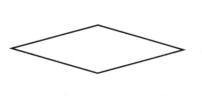 

2. Roll the die 2 times.

The first number you roll tells how many rows to make in your array.

The second number you roll tells how many blocks to put in each row of your array.

Example:

If you roll a 1 first and then a 5, you might make this:

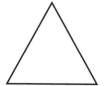 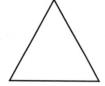 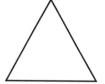 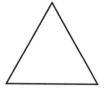 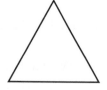

3. Record the arrays you make on *Math Masters,* page 187.

Use the Pattern-Block Template. At the top of the page, draw the first array you made.

Fill in the table for Number 1 at the bottom of the page.

4. Make 4 more arrays. Follow the same steps. If you have room, draw the arrays you make. After you run out of room, fill in the table only.

186

Building Arrays *continued*

Use your Pattern-Block Template. Show one or more of your arrays.

Record the arrays you made.

	How many rows?	How many shapes in each row?	How many shapes in all?
1.			
2.			
3.			
4.			
5.			

HOME LINK 6·10 | Division

Family Note In this lesson, your child worked on the concept of division by putting objects into equal groups and sharing objects equally among several people. Objects that are left over are called the *remainder*. If 9 books are shared equally among 4 people, each person gets 2 books, and the 1 book that is left over is the remainder.

Watch as your child divides things equally among family members. Try to use groups of objects that can be divided with no remainder as well as groups that have remainders.

Please return this Home Link to school tomorrow.

MRB
36 37

1. Have someone at home give you a group or handful of small items, such as raisins, buttons, or popcorn. Show how you can divide the items equally among your family members. Are any items left over?

   Make a record of what you did. Be ready to tell about it in class.

   I shared _____ (how many?) items equally among _____ people.

   Each person got _____. There were _____ left over.

2. Do this again with some other kind of item.

   I shared _____ items equally among _____ people.

   Each person got _____. There were _____ left over.

3. 19 cents shared equally

   by 2 people   by 3 people   by 4 people

   _____¢ per person   _____¢ per person   _____¢ per person

   _____¢ remaining   _____¢ remaining   _____¢ remaining

LESSON 6·10 | **Sharing Cookies Equally**

Use counters to help you solve the problems.

1. Ruth's grandma had just baked a fresh tray of 12 cookies.

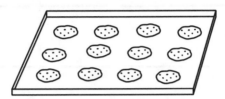

When Ruth came into the kitchen, her grandma gave her 3 warm cookies.

Write a number model to show how many cookies were still on the tray. _____

When Ruth's sister came into the kitchen, Grandma gave her 3 cookies.

Write a number model to show how many cookies were still on the tray. _____

How many more people can Grandma give cookies to if she gives each person three cookies?

Show your work.

2. The next time grandma baked cookies, she used a larger tray. She made 15 cookies.

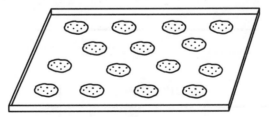

How many people can have cookies this time if everyone gets 3?

Show your work.

LESSON 6·10 | Multiplication Diagrams

rows	_____ per row	_____ in all

rows	_____ per row	_____ in all

rows	_____ per row	_____ in all

rows	_____ per row	_____ in all

HOME LINK 6·11

Unit 7: Family Letter

Patterns and Rules

In Unit 7, children will concentrate on number patterns, computational skills, and the application of mathematics through the use of data. They will continue to use the 100-grid to support their numeration skills. Children will also explore the patterns of doubling and halving numbers, which will help prepare them for multiplication and division.

Computational work will be extended to several 2-digit numbers and to the subtraction of 1- and 2-digit numbers from multiples of 10.

Children will learn to find complements of tens; that is, they will answer such questions as "What must I add to 4 to get to 10? What must I add to 47 to get to 50?" or "How many tens are needed to get from 320 to 400?"

Children will also collect and work with real-life data about animals, adults, and themselves. For example, they will collect data by measuring the lengths of their standing long jumps and then find the median jump length for the class.

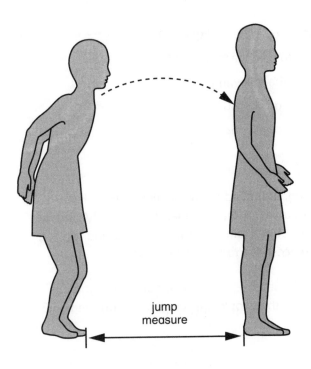

jump measure

Please keep this Family Letter for reference as your child works through Unit 7.

Vocabulary

Important terms in Unit 7:

median (middle number) The number in the middle of a list of data ordered from least to greatest or vice versa. For example, 35 is the middle number in the following ordered list.

30, 32, 32, 35, 36, 38, 40

frequency The number of times an event or value occurs in a set of data. For example, in the set of data above, 32 has a frequency of 2.

Do-Anytime Activities

To work with your child on the concepts taught in this unit and in previous units, try these interesting and rewarding activities:

1. If you have a calculator at home, practice making (and breaking) tens.

   For example:

   Making tens: Enter 33. What needs to be done to display 50? $33 + \underline{\hspace{2cm}} = 50$

   Breaking tens: Enter 60. What needs to be done to display 52? $60 - \underline{\hspace{2cm}} = 52$

   Or, for more challenging practice, try the following:

   Enter 27. What needs to be done to display 40?

   Enter 90. What needs to be done to display 66?

   Try other similar numbers.

2. Make a game out of doubling, tripling, and quadrupling small numbers. For example, using the number 2, first double it. What number do you get? Continue the doubling process five more times. Start again with the number 2 and triple it; then quadruple it. Discuss the differences among the final numbers.

3. Collect a simple set of data from family and friends. For example, how high can different people's fingertips reach while the people are standing flat on the floor? Order the data to find the median.

Building Skills through Games

In Unit 7, your child will practice skills related to addition and subtraction as well as chance and probability by playing the following games:

Array Bingo

Players roll the dice and find an *Array Bingo* card with the same number of dots. Players then turn that card over. The first player to have a row, column, or diagonal of facedown cards calls out "Bingo!" and wins the game.

Soccer Spin

Players choose a spinner to use during the game. They choose a team to cheer for, Checks or Stripes. They then predict which team will win based on their spinner. They spin the spinner to check their prediction.

Basketball Addition

The basketball game is played by two teams, each consisting of 3–5 players. The number of points scored by each player in each half is determined by rolling a twenty-sided polyhedral die or 3 regular dice and using their sum. The team that scores the greater number of points wins the game.

Hit the Target

Players choose a 2-digit multiple of ten (10, 20, 30, and so on) as a target number. One player enters a starting number on a calculator and tries to change the starting number to the target number by adding a number to it on the calculator. Children practice finding differences between 2-digit numbers and higher multiples of tens.

As You Help Your Child with Homework

As your child brings home assignments, you might want to go over the instructions together, clarifying them as necessary. The answers listed below will guide you through this unit's Home Links.

Home Link 7·1

1. 202, 204, 206, 208, 210, 212, 214, 216, 218

2. 500, 505, 510, 515, 520, 525, 530, 535, 540, 545

3. 550, 560, 570, 580, 590, 600, 610, 620, 630, 640

Home Link 7·2

1. 6; 7; 5; 9; 2   **2.** 6; 7; 5; 9; 8

3. 32 + 38; 65 + 5; 10 + 60; 43 + 27; 19 + 51; 51 + 19; 27 + 43

Home Link 7·3

1. Team A: 35; Team B: 25; A

2. Team A: 30; Team B: 35; B

3. Team A: 29; Team B: 40; B

4. Team A: 45; Team B: 59; B

Home Link 7·4

1.

in	out
12	6
50	25
40	20
30	15
16	8
18	9

Rule: Halve

2. 1, 2, 4, 8, 16, 32, 64

3. 3, 6, 12, 24, 48, 96, 192

4. 127 pennies, or $1.27

5. 9   **6.** 32   **7.** 38

Home Link 7·5

1. 8 pounds   **2.** 20 pounds   **3.** 5 pounds

4. 11,000 pounds   **5.** 199   **6.** 49

7. 107   **8.** 90

Home Link 7·6

5. 42   **6.** 103   **7.** 25   **8.** 29

Home Link 7·7

1. $\frac{3}{\text{points}}$ $\frac{7}{\text{points}}$ $\frac{9}{\text{points}}$ $\frac{\boxed{12}}{\text{points}}$ $\frac{15}{\text{points}}$ $\frac{20}{\text{points}}$ $\frac{21}{\text{points}}$

2. 56 in. 66 in. (68 in.) 70 in. 73 in.

3. 142 cm 168 cm (173 cm) 178 cm 185 cm

Home Link 7·8

1. 2   **2.** 0   **3.** 46   **4.** 52

5. 9   **6.** 48   **7.** 49

Using a Calculator to Find Patterns

LESSON 7·1

1. Use a calculator to count by 5s starting with the number 102.
   Color the counts on the grid with a crayon. Look for a pattern.

									100
101	102	103	104	105	106	107	108	109	110
111	112	113	114	115	116	117	118	119	120
121	122	123	124	125	126	127	128	129	130

2. Pick a number to count by. Start with a number less than 310.
   Use your calculator to count. Record your counts on the grid with
   a crayon.

									300
301	302	303	304	305	306	307	308	309	310
311	312	313	314	315	316	317	318	319	320
321	322	323	324	325	326	327	328	329	330
331	332	333	334	335	336	337	338	339	340
341	342	343	344	345	346	347	348	349	350
351	352	353	354	355	356	357	358	359	360
361	362	363	364	365	366	367	368	369	370

I counted by _____ starting with the number _____.

Here is a pattern that I found: _____

_____

HOME LINK 7·1 | Count by 2s, 5s, and 10s

Family Note In this lesson, your child has been counting by 2s, 5s, and 10s. After your child has completed these problems, help him or her look for patterns in the ones digits of the answers. In the example, the ones digits repeat: 0, 2, 4, 6, 8, 0, 2, 4, and so on. If your child is successful with these problems, ask him or her to count backward by 2s, 5s, or 10s. Start from a number that is a multiple of 10, such as 200.

Please return this Home Link to school tomorrow.

MRB 96

Example:

Count by 2s. Begin at 100. Write your first 10 counts below.

_100_, _102_, _104_, _106_, _108_, _110_, _112_, _114_, _116_, _118_

1. Count by 2s. Begin at 200. Write your first 10 counts below.

_200_, ____, ____, ____, ____, ____, ____, ____, ____, ____

2. Count by 5s. Begin at 500. Write your first 10 counts below.

____, ____, ____, ____, ____, ____, ____, ____, ____, ____

3. Count by 10s. Begin at 550. Write your first 10 counts below.

____, ____, ____, ____, ____, ____, ____, ____, ____, ____

Look at your counts. Write about any patterns you find in the counts.

_____

_____

_____

196

Patterns on a Number Chart

−9	−8	−7	−6	−5
−4	−3	−2	−1	0
1	2	3	4	5
6	7	8	9	10
11	12	13	14	15
16	17	18	19	20
21	22	23	24	25
26	27	28	29	30
31	32	33	34	35
36	37	38	39	40

HOME LINK 7·2 Missing Addends

Family Note In this lesson, your child found the difference between a number and a multiple of 10. In Problems 1 and 2, your child will find the difference between a number and the next-higher multiple of 10. For example, your child will determine which number added to 62 equals 70 (8). In Problem 3, your child will find different combinations of numbers that add to 70. If your child has difficulty with this problem, suggest changing the first number in each combination to the next-higher multiple of 10. For example, add 2 to 48 to make 50 and then add 20 to 50 to make 70. 2 + 20 = 22, so 48 + 22 = 70.

Please return this Home Link to school tomorrow.

1. 4 + _____ = 10

10 = 3 + _____

_____ + 5 = 10

10 = _____ + 1

8 + _____ = 10

2. 54 + _____ = 60

90 = 83 + _____

75 + _____ = 80

40 = 31 + _____

_____ + 62 = 70

Unit

3. Make 70s. Show someone at home how you did it.

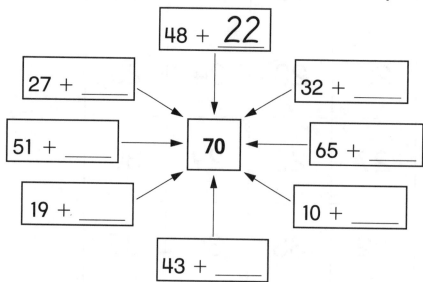

48 + _22_

27 + ____   32 + ____

51 + ____   70   65 + ____

19 + ____   10 + ____

43 + ____

LESSON 7·2 | Making Multiples of 10

For each problem, tell how many dots must be added to fill the ten frames. Write a number model to show what you did.

1.

Number model:

_____

2.

Number model:

_____

3.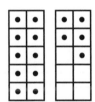

Number model:

_____

4.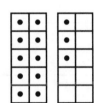

Number model:

_____

5.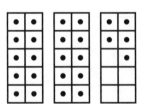

Number model: _____

6.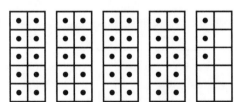

Number model: _____

LESSON 7·3 — Basketball Addition

	Points Scored			
	Team 1		Team 2	
	1st Half	2nd Half	1st Half	2nd Half
Player 1				
Player 2				
Player 3				
Player 4				
Player 5				
Team Score				

Point Totals	1st Half	2nd Half	Final
Team 1	_____	_____	_____
Team 2	_____	_____	_____

1. Which team won the first half? _____

By how much? _____ points

2. Which team won the second half? _____

By how much? _____ points

3. Which team won the game? _____

By how much? _____ points

HOME LINK 7·3

Who Scored More Points?

Family Note
In this lesson, your child added three or more 1-digit and 2-digit numbers. As your child completes the problems below, encourage him or her to share the different ways in which the points can be added. Your child might add all the tens first and then add all the ones. For example, 20 + 5 + 4 + 6 = 20 + 15 = 35. Your child may also look for combinations of numbers that are easier to add. In Game 1, for example, first add 14 and 6 to get 20 and then add 15 to get 35.

Please return this Home Link to school tomorrow.

Do the following for each problem:

Unit
points

◆ Add the points for each team.

◆ Decide which team scored more points. The team with the greater number of points wins the game.

◆ Circle your answer.

1. Game 1

Team A:
15 + 14 + 6 = _____

Team B:
5 + 13 + 7 = _____

Who won? A or B

2. Game 2

Team A:
12 + 6 + 4 + 8 = _____

Team B:
5 + 10 + 19 + 1 = _____

Who won? A or B

3. Game 3

Team A:
17 + 4 + 5 + 3 = _____

Team B:
2 + 11 + 9 + 18 = _____

Who won? A or B

4. Game 4

Team A:
7 + 4 + 16 + 13 + 5 = ___

Team B:
22 + 9 + 8 + 3 + 17 = ___

Who won? A or B

LESSON 7·3

Addition and Subtraction Puzzles

Solve these addition and subtraction puzzles.

Example:

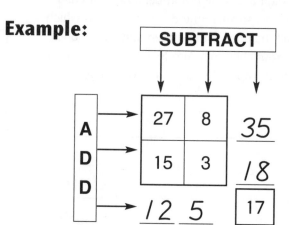

1.

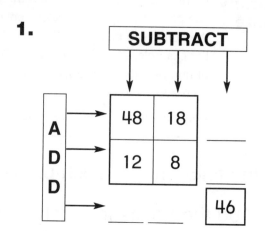

2.

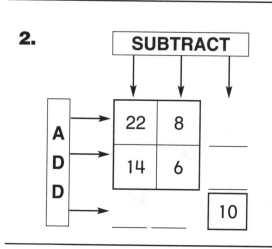

3.

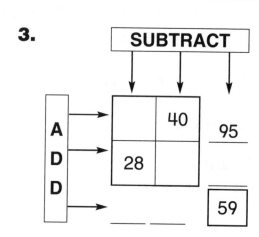

Make up addition and subtraction puzzles of your own.

4.

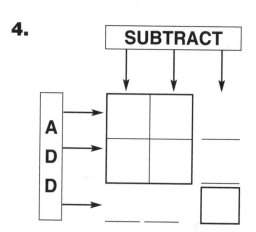

5.

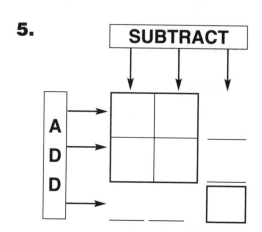

HOME LINK 7·4

Doubles and Halves

1. Write a rule in the rule box. Then complete the table.

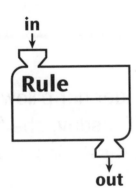

in	out
12	6
50	25
40	
30	
	8
	9

2. Fill in the frames using the rule in the rule box.

Rule
Double

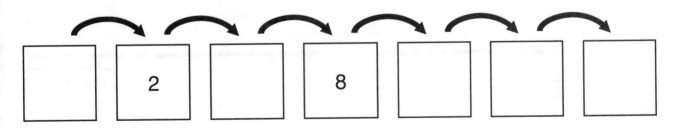

| | 2 | | 8 | | | |

HOME LINK
7·4

Doubles and Halves *continued*

3. Fill in the frames using the rule in the rule box.

Rule

Double

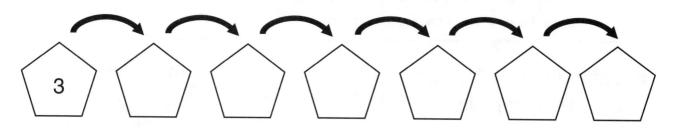

3

Try This

4. Maria finds 1 penny under her pillow when she wakes up on Monday morning. On Tuesday, she finds 2 pennies. On Wednesday, she finds 4 pennies. So, on Wednesday, she has a total of 7 cents.

On Thursday, Friday, Saturday, and Sunday, Maria finds double the amount of money she found under her pillow the day before. How much money does Maria have on Sunday?

_____

Practice

Unit

5. $28 - 19 =$ _____

6. $74 - 42 =$ _____

7. $67 - 29 =$ _____

204

LESSON 7·4 Halves and Doubles

For each rectangle with dots:

Circle "yes" if half of the dots are shaded.

Circle "no" if more or less than half of the dots are shaded.

1.

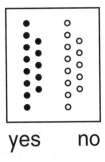

yes   no

2.

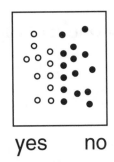

yes   no

3.

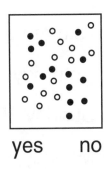

yes   no

4. Which problem was hardest to solve? Explain your answer.

_____

_____

For each problem, circle the answer that is "double."

Example:	**Answer Choices:**		
_____			
5.			
Try This			
6.			

LESSON 7·4 | **The Budruples**

Remember what you learned about the Wubbles and how they double. There is a different kind of Wubble called a Budruple. It quadruples every night. Use your calculator.

1. On each line, write the number of Budruples after quadrupling.

You started on Friday with one Budruple.

On Saturday, there were _____ Budruples.

On Sunday, there were _____ Budruples.

On Monday, there were _____ Budruples.

On Tuesday, there were _____ Budruples.

On Wednesday, there were _____ Budruples.

On Thursday, there were _____ Budruples.

On Friday, there were _____ Budruples.

A Budruple

2. On each line, write the number of Budruples after quartering. Remember that "$\frac{1}{4}$ of" means "divide by 4."

There were _____ Budruples.

After Wink 1, there were _____ Budruples.

After Wink 2, there were _____ Budruples.

After Wink 3, there were _____ Budruples.

After Wink 4, there were _____ Budruples.

After Wink 5, there were _____ Budruples.

After Wink 6, there were _____ Budruples.

After Wink 7, there was _____ Budruple.

Adapted with permission from *Calculator Mathematics Book 2* by Sheila Sconiers, pp. 10 and 11 (Everyday Learning Corporation, © 1990 by the University of Chicago).

LESSON 7·5 Measuring Weight with a Bath Scale

1. Place books on a bath scale. Try to make a stack of books that weighs about 5 pounds. Lift the stack of books and feel the weight of that stack.

2. Start again. Make a stack of books that weighs about 10 pounds. Then lift the stack and feel the weight.

3. Start again. Make a stack of books that weighs about 15 pounds. Then lift the stack and feel the weight.

Make a 5-pound stack of books.

Make a 10-pound stack of books.

Make a 15-pound stack of books.

4. Make a stack of books on the floor. Estimate how much your stack weighs. Weigh the stack and see how close your estimate was.

5. Repeat with other stacks of books that are different sizes.

Are you getting better at estimating weight?

LESSON 7·5 | Sharing Money

Work in a small group.

Materials   ☐ $5 bill, $1 bills, quarters, dimes, nickels, pennies

☐ half-sheets of paper

At school, 4 children found an envelope. Inside was a $5 bill. They took the envelope to the principal. A week went by and nobody claimed it. The principal returned the money to the children and said that it now belonged to them.

How would you divide $5 so each of the children gets the same amount of money?

1. First, think about what you could do.

   ◆ How could you begin?

   ◆ What could you do next?

2. After you have divided the money, count each person's share. Did each one get the same amount?

3. Write a group report or make a drawing. Tell how you divided the $5 equally among the 4 children.

Follow-Up

◆ Make up your own problems for dividing an amount of money equally among 4 or 5 children.

◆ Write some of your problems on half-sheets of paper for others to solve.

208

LESSON 7·5 Two-Block Patterns

Work with a partner.

Materials   ☐ Pattern-Block Template

☐ pattern blocks

1. Choose two different pattern-block shapes.

2. Explore. Try to make a pattern using just these
two shapes.

♦ Do not leave any open spaces in your pattern.

♦ Make the pattern so it covers about a quarter of a sheet
of paper.

♦ Make the pattern so you could continue it forever if you
had enough blocks.

3. Use your Pattern-Block Template and crayons to record
your pattern on a quarter-sheet of paper.

Example:

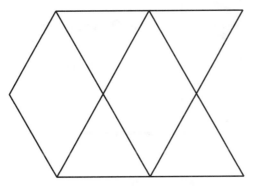

4. If there is time, explore with two other different pattern blocks.

Estimating Weights

HOME LINK 7·5

Family Note In today's lesson, your child practiced reading weights, in pounds, on a bath scale. One purpose of this activity is to improve your child's perception of weight so he or she can make more realistic estimates of weights. To help develop your child's ability to read a bath scale, take every opportunity at home to use your bath scale to determine the weights of objects.

Please return this Home Link to school tomorrow.

Circle the best estimate for the weight of each object.

1. newborn baby

8 pounds

20 pounds

70 pounds

2. Thanksgiving turkey

$\frac{1}{2}$ pound

20 pounds

70 pounds

3. bag of apples

5 pounds

35 pounds

65 pounds

4. An adult bull African elephant (the largest animal on land)

100 pounds

500 pounds

11,000 pounds

Practice

5.   236
       − 37

6.   199
     − 150

7.   78
     + 29

8.   45
     + 45

LESSON 7·5 Estimating Weight

Find objects in the room that you think might weigh about 1 pound.
Then find objects that you think might weigh about 10 pounds.
Record the objects in the boxes below. Weigh the objects and
record their approximate weight.

Objects Weighing About 1 Pound	
Object	**Weight**

Objects Weighing About 10 Pounds	
Object	**Weight**

Imagine you found a dog and are writing a lost-and-found notice. To
describe the dog, you want to tell its weight. The dog will not get
on the scale and stay. How can you find his weight? Explain.

_____

_____

_____

HOME LINK 7·6 | Comparing Arm Spans

Family Note In today's lesson, your child measured his or her standing long jump in centimeters and his or her arm span in inches. Help your child compare his or her arm span to someone else's arm span at home. Also, help your child find objects in the house that are about the same length as his or her arm span.

Please return this Home Link to school tomorrow.

MRB
62

My arm span is about _____ inches long.

1. Tell someone at home about how long your arm span is in inches.

2. Compare your arm span to someone at home. Can you find someone who has a longer arm span than you do? Is there someone at home who has a shorter arm span?

   _____ has a longer arm span than I do.

   _____ has a shorter arm span than I do.

3. List some objects below that are about the same length as your arm span.

   _____   _____

   _____   _____

4. Explain how you know the objects you listed in Problem 3 are about the same length as your arm span.

   _____

   _____

   _____

Practice

5.   23
   + 19

6.   45
   + 58

7.   64
   − 39

8.   86
   − 57

LESSON 7·6

Measuring Objects

Use a centimeter cube to find objects that measure about **1 centimeter** in length. List your objects below.

Use a 1-inch square pattern block to find objects that measure about **1 inch** in length. List your objects below.

Use a base-10 long to find objects that measure about **10 centimeters** in length. List your objects below.

Use 1-inch square pattern blocks to find objects that measure about **10 inches** in length. List your objects below.

213

LESSON 7·6   Amazing Leaps

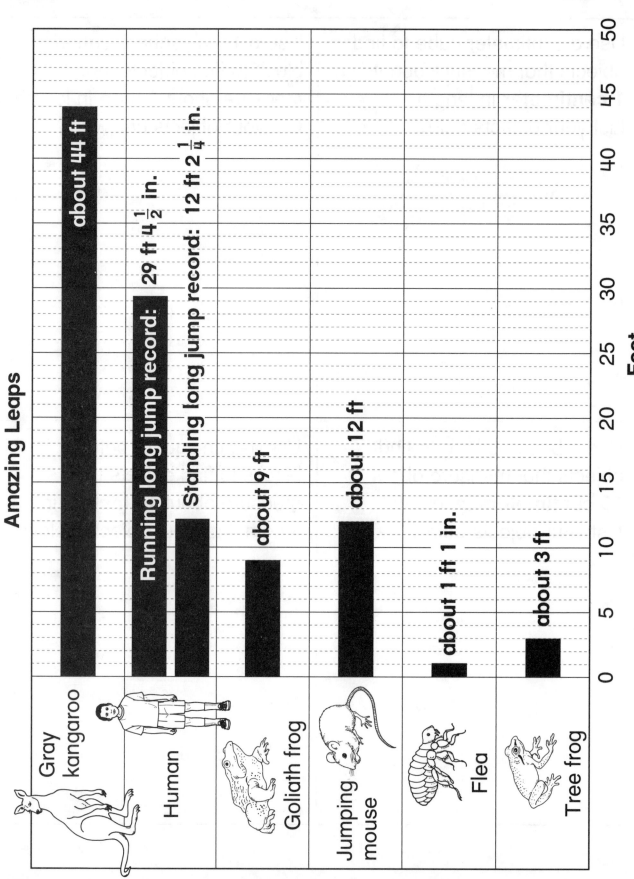

Amazing Leaps

- Gray kangaroo: about 44 ft
- Human: Running long jump record: 29 ft 4 $\frac{1}{2}$ in.
- Human: Standing long jump record: 12 ft 2 $\frac{1}{4}$ in.
- Goliath frog: about 9 ft
- Jumping mouse: about 12 ft
- Flea: about 1 ft 1 in.
- Tree frog: about 3 ft

Feet (0, 5, 10, 15, 20, 25, 30, 35, 40, 45, 50)

HOME LINK 7·7 Find the Middle Value

Family Note

In this lesson, your child sorted data to find the median. *Median* is a term used for the middle value. To find the median of a set of data, arrange the data in order from smallest to largest. Count from either end to the number in the middle. The middle value is the median. As your child finds the median in Problems 2 and 3, remind him or her that "in." is the abbreviation for inches and "cm" is the abbreviation for centimeters.

Please return this Home Link to school tomorrow.

MRB
46

List the data in order from smallest to largest.

Draw a circle around the median in your list.

1.

12 points	3 points	21 points	15 points	20 points	7 points	9 points

_____ _____ _____ _____ _____ _____ _____

points · · · · · · · points · · · · · · · points · · · · · · · points · · · · · · · points · · · · · · · points · · · · · · · points

smallest · **largest**

Find the Middle Value *continued*

2.

Jarel: 66 in. tall	Suki: 70 in. tall	Peter: 56 in. tall	Keisha: 73 in. tall	Cesar: 68 in. tall

_____ in.   _____ in.   _____ in.   _____ in.   _____ in.

smallest   **largest**

3.

Jarel: 168 cm tall	Suki: 178 cm tall	Peter: 142 cm tall	Keisha: 185 cm tall	Cesar: 173 cm tall

_____ cm   _____ cm   _____ cm   _____ cm   _____ cm

smallest   **largest**

LESSON 7·7 | Ordering Numbers

Choose from the number cards pictured below.

Match a number card to each of the sets of pictured dots.

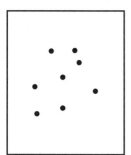 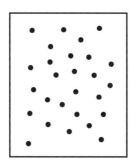 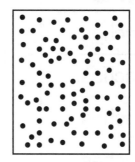 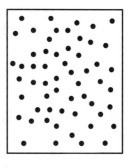

_____   _____   _____   _____

Match a number card to each of the number lines below.

Draw a small mark on the number line about where you think the number would be. Label your mark with the number.

1.

0   100

2.

0   10

3.

0   40

4.

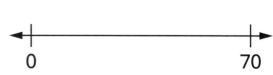

0   70

LESSON 7·7   Find the Median

Solve.

The track team collected standing long jump data.

They are as follows:

Our Jumps
93 inches
97 inches
82 inches
96 inches
85 inches
91 inches
89 inches
87 inches

Find the median. _____

Explain your work.

_____

_____

_____

_____

_____

LESSON 7·8 | Table of Our Arm Spans

Make a table of the arm spans of your classmates.

Our Arm Spans		
Arm Span (inches)	**Frequency**	
	Tallies	**Number**
	Total =	

LESSON 7·8 | **Bar Graph of Our Arm Spans**

Make a bar graph of the arm spans of your classmates.

Our Arm Spans

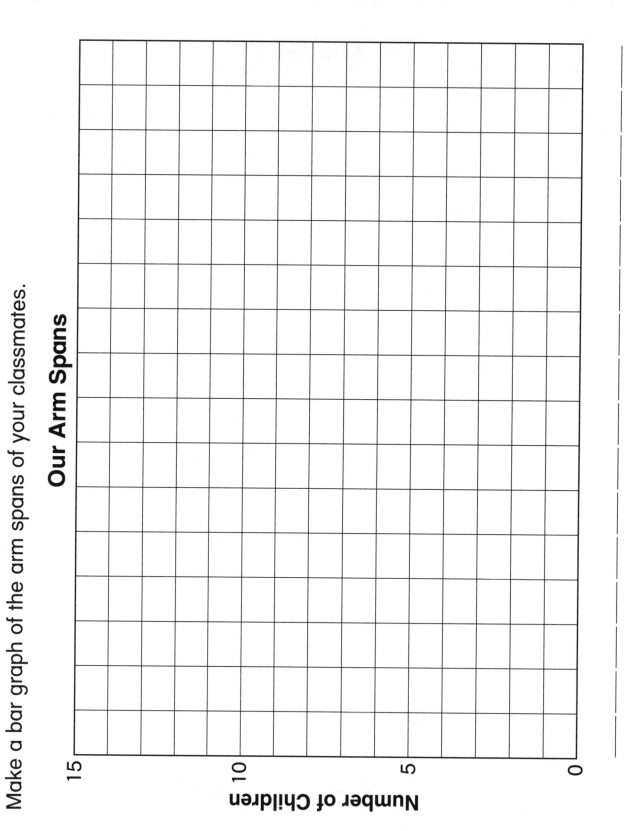

Number of Children

Arm Span (inches)

HOME LINK 7·8 Interpreting Data

Family Note

Today your child represented data using a bar graph and a frequency table. The table below is called a *frequency table* because it shows how often different heights occurred. Help your child use the data to answer the questions. Remind your child that to find the median of a set of data, he or she should arrange the data in order from smallest to largest and then count from either end to the number in the middle. The middle value is the median.

Please return this Home Link to school tomorrow.

MRB
46

Ms. Ortiz is a basketball coach. She measured the height of each player. Then she made the data table shown below.

Players' Heights	
Height (inches)	**Number of Players**
46	1
47	0
48	3
49	1
50	2
51	1
52	1

1. How many players are 50 inches tall? _____ players

2. How many players are 47 inches tall? _____ players

3. The shortest player is _____ inches tall.

4. The tallest player is _____ inches tall.

5. How many players did Ms. Ortiz measure? _____ players

6. Which height occurs most often? _____ inches

7. Find the middle (median) height. _____ inches

LESSON 7·8 Median Arm Spans Bar Graph

Median Arm Spans
for Boys and Girls in Room _____

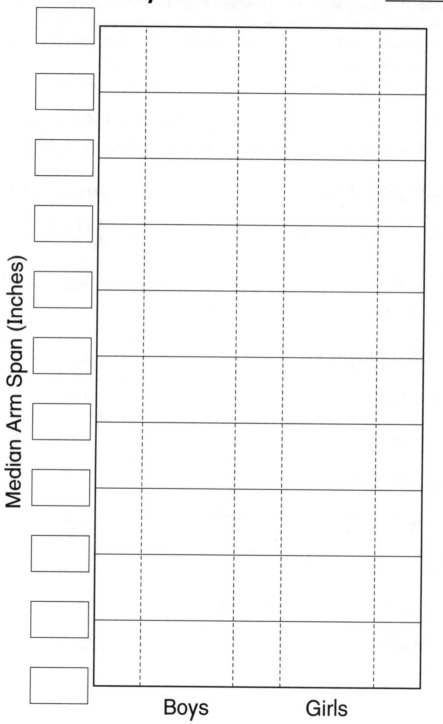

Median Arm Span (Inches)

Boys   Girls

HOME LINK
7·9

Unit 8: Family Letter

Fractions

In Unit 8, children will review and extend concepts of fractions. Specifically, they will recognize fractions as names for parts of a whole, or ONE.

Children will see that, as with whole numbers, many different fractions can name the same quantity. For example, $\frac{2}{4}$ and $\frac{6}{12}$ are names for $\frac{1}{2}$.

Children will also explore relationships among fractions as they work with pattern-block shapes and Fraction Cards that show shaded regions.

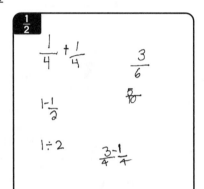

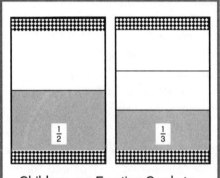

Children use Fraction Cards to compare fractions by looking at the shaded areas.

Please keep this Family Letter for reference as your child works through Unit 8.

223

Vocabulary

Important terms in Unit 8:

fraction A number that names equal parts of a whole, or ONE.

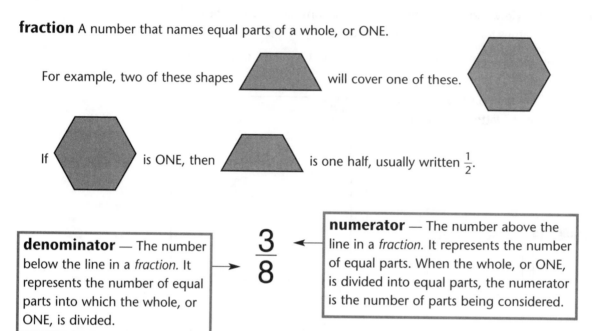

For example, two of these shapes will cover one of these.

If is ONE, then is one half, usually written $\frac{1}{2}$.

denominator — The number below the line in a *fraction*. It represents the number of equal parts into which the whole, or ONE, is divided.

$$\frac{3}{8}$$

numerator — The number above the line in a *fraction*. It represents the number of equal parts. When the whole, or ONE, is divided into equal parts, the numerator is the number of parts being considered.

It is not necessary for children to use the words numerator and denominator now. They will learn them over time with repeated exposure. Do, however, use these words, as well as the informal "number on the top" and "number on the bottom," when you discuss fractions with your child.

equivalent fractions *Fractions* with different denominators that name the same number. For example, $\frac{1}{2}$ and $\frac{2}{4}$ are equivalent fractions.

Do-Anytime Activities

To work with your child on the concepts taught in this unit and in previous units, try these interesting and rewarding activities:

1. Review fraction notation. For example, ask: "In a fraction, what does the number on the bottom (the denominator) tell you?" "What does the number on the top (the numerator) tell you?"

2. Draw a picture of a rectangular cake, a circular pizza, or a similar food (better yet, have the real thing). Discuss ways to cut the food to feed various numbers of people so each person gets an equal portion.

3. Read a recipe and discuss the fractions in it. For example, ask: "How many $\frac{1}{4}$ cups of sugar would we need to get 1 cup of sugar?"

4. Compare two fractions and tell which is larger. For example, ask: "Which would give you more of a pizza: $\frac{1}{8}$ of it, or $\frac{1}{4}$?"

As You Help Your Child with Homework

As your child brings home assignments, you might want to go over the instructions together, clarifying them as necessary. The answers listed below will guide you through this unit's Home Links.

Home Link 8·1

1. $\frac{1}{2}$; $\frac{1}{2}$ 2. $\frac{3}{4}$; $\frac{1}{4}$

Home Link 8·2

1. $\frac{1}{2}$ 2. $\frac{1}{6}$ 3. $\frac{2}{3}$ 4. 101

5. 101   6. 132   7. 158

Home Link 8·3

1. 4; 4; 8   2. 44   3. 98

4. 38   5. 90

Home Link 8·4

1. $\frac{1}{2} = \frac{2}{4}$ 2. $\frac{1}{2} = \frac{4}{8}$ 3. $\frac{1}{4} = \frac{4}{16}$

4. $\frac{1}{4} = \frac{2}{8}$ 5. $\frac{1}{5} = \frac{4}{20}$ 6. 100

7. 82

Home Link 8·5

1. 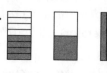   2.

3.   4. 84   5. 133

Home Link 8·6

1. Answers vary.   2. Answers vary.

3. 77   4. 37   5. 94   6. 15

Home Link 8·7

1. $\frac{4}{7}$ 2. $\frac{2}{12}$, or $\frac{1}{6}$ 3. $\frac{1}{3}$ 4. 4 tulips

5. 104   6. 53   7. 21   8. 39

Building Skills through Games

In Unit 8, your child will practice multiplication and fraction skills by playing the following games:

Array Bingo

Players roll the dice and find an *Array Bingo* card with the same number of dots. Players then turn that card over. The first player to have a row, column, or diagonal of facedown cards calls "Bingo!" and wins the game.

Equivalent Fractions Game

Players take turns turning over Fraction Cards and finding matching cards that show equivalent fractions.

Fraction Top-It

Players turn over two Fraction Cards and compare the shaded parts of the cards. The player with the larger fraction keeps both of the cards. The player with more cards at the end wins.

Name That Number

Each player turns over a card to find a number that must be renamed using any combination of five faceup cards.

HOME LINK 8·1 — Equal Parts

Family Note

Help your child collect things that can be easily folded into equal parts. As your child works with fractions, remind him or her that the number under the fraction bar, the *denominator*, gives the total number of equal parts into which the whole is divided. The number over the fraction bar, the *numerator*, tells the number of equal parts that are being considered. Don't expect your child to use these words. They will be learned over time with repeated exposure.

Please return this Home Link to school tomorrow.

Use a straightedge.

1. Divide the shape into 2 equal parts. Color 1 part.

Part colored = □/□ Part not colored = □/□

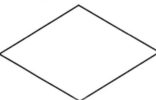

2. Divide the shape into 4 equal parts. Color 3 parts.

Part colored = □/□ Part not colored = □/□

3. Fold some things into equal parts.

Examples: paper napkin, paper plate, magazine picture

Label each part with a fraction. Show your folded things to someone at home. Talk about what the fractions mean.

Bring the things you folded to school for the Fractions Museum.

I folded a _____ into _____ equal parts.

Each part shows _____.

LESSON 8·1 | **Pattern-Block Equal Parts**

Cover the larger block with smaller blocks. Use your template to show what you did.

1.

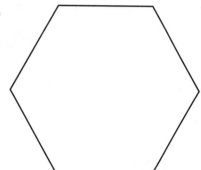 = _____

2.

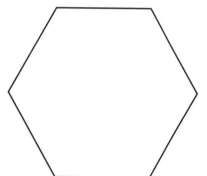 = _____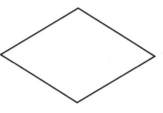

3.

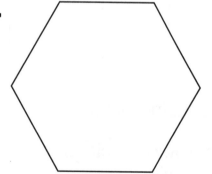 = _____

4.

 = _____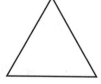

5.

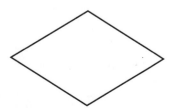 = _____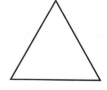

LESSON 8·1 | Equal Parts

Do the following for each problem:

◆ Use 1 rubber band to make the shape on a geoboard.

◆ Use rubber bands to divide the shape into 6 equal parts.

◆ Record how you divided the shape.

◆ Repeat for the same shape. Divide it a different way into 6 equal parts.

◆ Record how you divided the shape the second way.

1.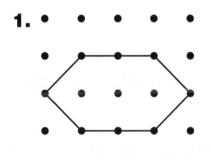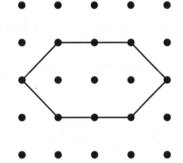

2.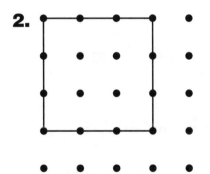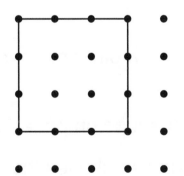

LESSON 8·2 | **Pattern-Block Fractions**

Work with a partner.

Materials ☐ *Math Journal 2*, pp. 187 and 188

☐ pattern blocks

☐ Pattern-Block Template

Study the example at the top of journal page 187. Cover the ⬜ with △s.

You need 3 triangles, so a △ is $\frac{1}{3}$ of a ⬜.

1. Do Problem 1 on journal page 187.

   Cover the larger shape with hexagon blocks.

   The number of hexagons helps you find the fraction to write as the answer.

   Use your Pattern-Block Template to divide the larger shape into hexagons.

2. Do the rest of the problems on journal pages 187 and 188 in the same way.

3. Get together with other partners in the class. Check one another's work.

   Each smaller shape on page 187 is $\frac{1}{3}$ of the larger shape.

   Are all the smaller shapes the same size? _____

   Each smaller shape on page 188 is $\frac{1}{4}$ of the larger shape.

   Are all the smaller shapes the same size? _____

LESSON 8·2 | Geoboard Fences

Work in a small group.

Materials ☐ *Math Journal 2*, p. 189 ☐ geoboard

☐ 4 rubber bands ☐ straightedge

Each group member does Steps 1–6:

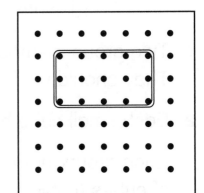

1. Make a rectangle on a geoboard. Use 1 rubber band. Think of the rubber band as a fence.

2. Draw your rectangle (fence) on the first geoboard on journal page 189.

3. Count the number of pegs inside your rectangle (fence). Include the pegs that touch the rubber band.

4. Fill in the table at the bottom of the journal page. Include

   ◆ the number of pegs inside the fence.

   ◆ the number of rows of pegs inside the fence.

   ◆ the number of pegs in each row.

5. Make 3 more rectangles (fences) on your geoboard. Draw each rectangle (fence) on the journal page.

6. Fill in the table for your other three fences.

Follow-Up

Compare your table to those of the other members of your group.

Do any members of your group have the same total number of pegs inside a fence (but with a different number of rows)? What else is different? Can you tell why this happened?

231

LESSON 8·2   Volumes of Base-10 Structures

Work in a group.

Materials   ☐ base-10 blocks: cubes, longs, flats; a big cube (thousands), if available

           ☐ slate for each person

1. Two group members use the blocks to build a structure. They should work quickly so others can have a turn later.

2. Each small cube has a volume of 1 cubic centimeter.

Each group member writes an estimate of the total number of cubes (cubic centimeters) in the structure on her or his slate.

3. Together, count the cubes as the builders take the structure apart.

The total number of cubes equals the **volume** of the structure in **cubic centimeters.**

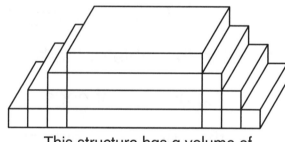

This structure has a volume of 520 cubic centimeters.

Record the result like this:

"This structure has a volume of _____ cubic centimeters."

4. Compare the actual number of cubes to the estimates of the group members.

5. Change builders. Repeat Steps 1–4. Continue until everyone has had a turn. As you build the structures, think of ways to improve your estimates.

6. Write a group report about your estimates and the actual volumes of the structures.

HOME LINK 8·2 Fractions of Shapes

Family Note In today's lesson, your child compared pattern blocks, one of which represents ONE whole. As you work on this activity with your child, keep in mind that the shape below the ONE is a fractional part of the whole shape. Remind your child that the size of a fractional part of a whole depends on the size of the whole.

Please return this Home Link to school tomorrow.

1. If this shape is ONE,

then ◺ is what fraction of the shape? ____

2. If this shape is ONE,

then ▽ is what fraction of the shape? ____

Try This

3. If this shape is ONE, ⏢

then ▱ is what fraction of the whole shape? ____

Practice

Solve.

Unit

4. 75	**5.** 56	**6.** 84	**7.** 91
+ 26	+ 45	+ 48	+ 67

LESSON 8·2 | **Fraction Puzzles**

1. The first figure is $\frac{1}{2}$ of the whole. What fraction of the *same* whole is each of the other figures? Write the fraction inside the figure.

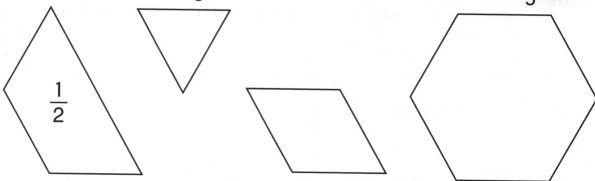

2. The first figure is $\frac{1}{3}$ of the whole. What fraction of the *same* whole is each of the other figures? Write the fraction inside the figure.

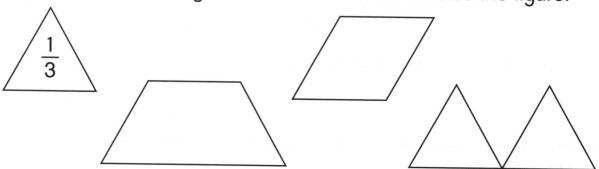

Try This

3. The first figure is $\frac{1}{3}$ of the whole. What fraction of the *same* whole is each of the other figures? Write the fraction inside the figure.

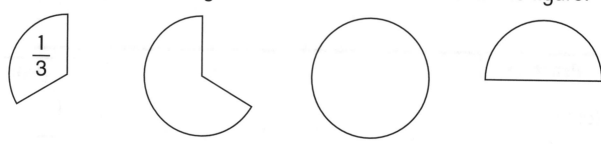

4. Create your own fraction puzzle.

HOME LINK 8·3 Fractions of Collections

Family Note In this lesson, your child learned to use fractions to name part of a collection of objects. For example, your child could identify 2 out of 4 objects as $\frac{2}{4}$ or $\frac{1}{2}$. Show your child how to use pennies to act out Problem 1. Help your child collect household items that can be separated into fractional parts—or any other items that have fractions written on them. Encourage your child to bring these items to school for the class's Fractions Museum.

Please return this Home Link to school tomorrow.

1.

Three people share 12 pennies. Circle each person's share.

How many pennies does each person get? _____ pennies

$\frac{1}{3}$ of 12 pennies = _____ pennies.

$\frac{2}{3}$ of 12 pennies = _____ pennies.

Practice

Solve.

2. 68 − 24 = _____

3. 53 + 45 = _____

4. 65
      − 27

5. 64
      + 26

> **Unit**
> Cars

Ask someone at home to help you find more things to bring to school for the Fractions Museum.

235

LESSON 8·3

Exploring Fractions

These show $\frac{1}{4}$.	These do **NOT** show $\frac{1}{4}$.

1. Explain how you can tell if something shows $\frac{1}{4}$.

_____

_____

For each problem—

◆ Take the number of counters.

◆ Figure out how to show $\frac{1}{4}$ of the counters.

◆ Use the rectangles to the right to make four equal piles of counters.

◆ Record your answer in the rectangles below each problem.

2. Take 4 counters.

Show $\frac{1}{4}$ of 4 counters.

3. Take 8 counters.

Show $\frac{1}{4}$ of 8 counters.

4. Take 12 counters.

Show $\frac{1}{4}$ of 12 counters.

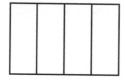

5. Take _____ counters.

Show $\frac{1}{4}$ of _____ counters.

LESSON 8·3   **A Fraction Puzzle**

Use counters or draw pictures to solve the fraction puzzle.
Show all of your work. If you have time, write a fraction puzzle
of your own on the back of this page.

José was playing a game with marbles.

In the first round of the game, he lost $\frac{1}{4}$ of his marbles.

In the second round of the game, he lost $\frac{1}{3}$ of his remaining marbles.

In the third round of the game, he lost $\frac{1}{2}$ of his remaining marbles.

He gave 1 marble to his friend Shavana.

He had 1 marble left.

How many marbles did José start with? _____

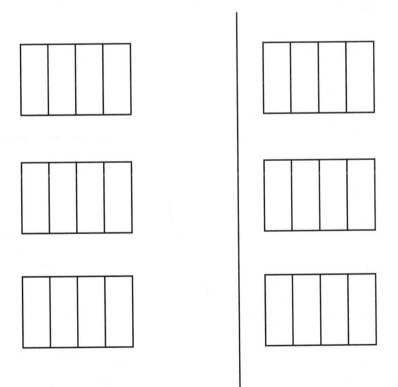

LESSON 8·3 — Fractions of Sets

Use 25 pennies or other counters to help you solve these problems. Share solution strategies with others in your group.

Make a set of 8 pennies to use with Problems 1–3.

Unit
pennies

1. Show $\frac{1}{4}$ of a set of 8 pennies.

How many pennies is that? _____

2. Put the pennies back.

Show $\frac{2}{4}$ of the set.

How many pennies is that? _____

3. Put the pennies back.

Show $\frac{3}{4}$ of the set.

How many pennies is that? _____

4. Show $\frac{4}{5}$ of a set of 15 pennies.

How many pennies is that? _____

5. Show $\frac{3}{4}$ of a set of 20 pennies.

How many pennies is that? _____

Try This

6. Five pennies is $\frac{1}{5}$ of a set.

How many are in the whole set? _____

Make up your own problem.

_____

_____

_____

LESSON 8·4 | **Fraction Circles**

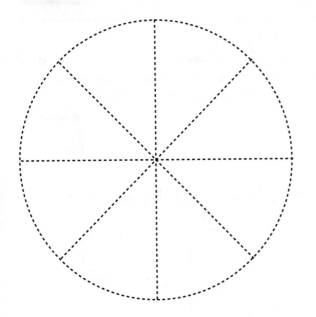
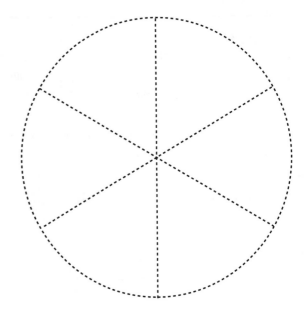

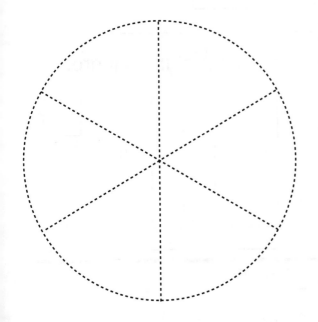
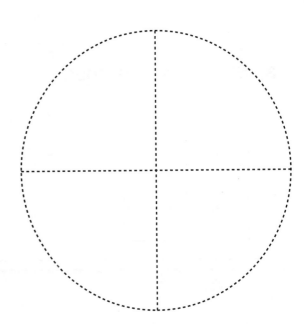

HOME LINK 8·4

Shading Fractional Parts

Family Note In this lesson, your child learned that a fractional part of a whole can be named in many different ways with *equivalent* fractions. For example, $\frac{2}{4}$, $\frac{4}{8}$, and $\frac{3}{6}$ are names for $\frac{1}{2}$, while $\frac{2}{8}$ and $\frac{4}{16}$ are names for $\frac{1}{4}$. Help your child shade each of the shapes below to show the appropriate fraction. Make sure your child understands that the fractions are equivalent because they name the same part of the shape.

Please return this Home Link to school tomorrow.

1. Shade $\frac{1}{2}$ of the rectangle.

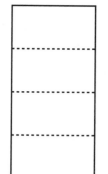

$$\frac{1}{2} = \frac{\square}{4}$$

2. Shade $\frac{1}{2}$ of the rectangle.

$$\frac{1}{2} = \frac{\square}{8}$$

3. Shade $\frac{1}{4}$ of the square.

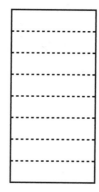

$$\frac{1}{4} = \frac{\square}{16}$$

4. Shade $\frac{1}{4}$ of the square.

$$\frac{1}{4} = \frac{\square}{8}$$

Try This

5. Shade $\frac{1}{5}$ of the rectangle.

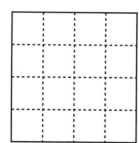
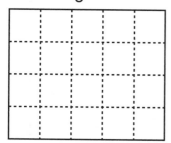

$$\frac{1}{5} = \frac{\square}{20}$$

Practice

Solve.

6. $130 - 30 =$ _____

7. $37 + 45 =$ _____

**LESSON
8·4**

Circle Parts

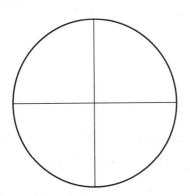

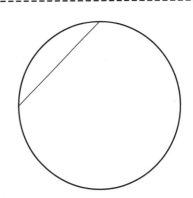

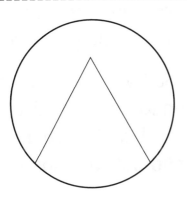

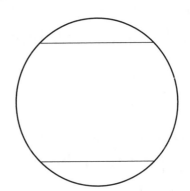

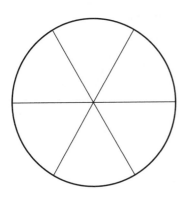

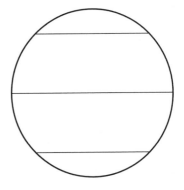

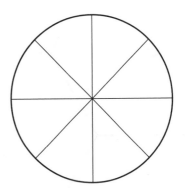

241

LESSON 8·4 — Covering Hexagons

Materials: ☐ pattern blocks   ☐ *Math Masters*, p. 242

☐ 1 crayon per child (different colors)

Directions Take turns doing the following:

1. Choose pattern blocks that are worth exactly one trapezoid. Decide where to place your block(s) on the board below. (If you are using more than 1 block, you can place them in different hexagons.) Your blocks must fit in the outlines. You can place your blocks in any hexagon that is not completely covered.

2. When you finish covering a hexagon, you "win" the hexagon. Remove the blocks and use your crayon to put your initials on the hexagon. This hexagon cannot be covered again. When all hexagons have been "won," count to find out who has won the most.

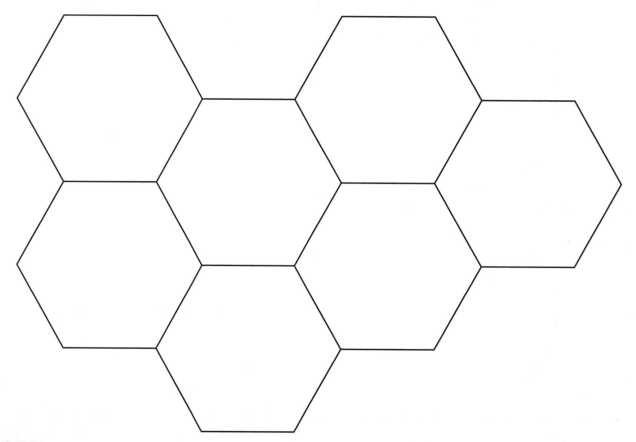

HOME LINK 8·5 | Fractions of Regions

Family Note In today's lesson, your child played a game in which he or she matched pictures of equivalent fractions. Stress the idea to your child that equivalent fractions show different ways to name a fractional part of a whole.

Please return this Home Link to school tomorrow.

1. Circle the pictures that show $\frac{1}{2}$ of the rectangle shaded.

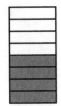 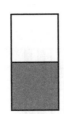  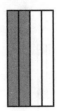

2. Circle the pictures that show $\frac{3}{4}$ of the rectangle shaded.

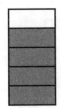 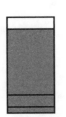 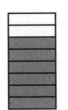 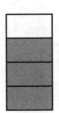

3. Circle the pictures that show $\frac{2}{3}$ of the rectangle shaded.

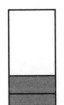 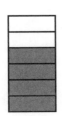 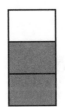 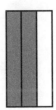

Practice

Add.

4. $\begin{array}{r} 36 \\ + \ 48 \\ \hline \end{array}$

5. $\begin{array}{r} 76 \\ + \ 57 \\ \hline \end{array}$

Unit

243

LESSON 8·5 | **Fractions Worth One-Half**

1. Circle the pictures below that have $\frac{1}{2}$ shaded.

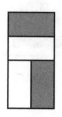 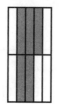 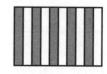

 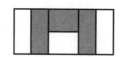

2. Shade $\frac{1}{2}$ of the figure.

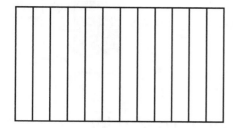

3. Draw a figure and shade $\frac{1}{2}$.

244

HOME LINK 8·6 More or Less Than $\frac{1}{2}$?

Cut out the number tiles.

1. Use the tiles to make fractions that are less than $\frac{1}{2}$.

Make as many fractions as you can. Record the fractions you make.

Example: $\dfrac{1}{3}$

_____

2. Use the tiles to make fractions that are more than $\frac{1}{2}$.

Make as many fractions as you can. Record the fractions you make.

Example: $\dfrac{2}{3}$

_____

_____

Number tiles
0
1
2
3
4
5
6
7
8
9

Practice

Unit

Solve.

3. $23 + 54 =$ _____

4. $73 - 36 =$ _____

5. $\begin{array}{r} 56 \\ +\ 38 \\ \hline \end{array}$

6. $\begin{array}{r} 42 \\ -\ 27 \\ \hline \end{array}$

245

LESSON 8·6 | **Who Has More?**

Nick and Kyoko had the following set of coins—7 quarters, 5 dimes, 5 nickels, and 4 pennies. Their parents told them to share the money equally.

Kyoko said, "I will give you $\frac{1}{2}$ of the total amount, but you will have $\frac{1}{3}$ of the coins."

Nick said, "I must have $\frac{1}{2}$ of the coins to have $\frac{1}{2}$ of the total amount."

Use pictures and coins to help you figure out who is correct. Show your work.

Who do you agree with? Explain.

Use ⓠ ⓓ ⓝ ⓟ to show the coins you think each child will have:

Kyoko will have: Nick will have:

HOME LINK 8·7 | Fractions

Family Note In this lesson, your child has been completing number stories about fractions. Encourage your child to draw pictures or use small objects, such as pennies, to help him or her complete fraction number stories.

Please return this Home Link to school tomorrow.

1. 7 children are waiting for the school bus.

4 of them are girls.

What fraction of the children are girls? _____

2. 12 dogs were in the park.

2 of them were dalmatians.

What fraction of the dogs were dalmatians? _____

3. There are 15 cupcakes.

5 of the cupcakes are chocolate.

What fraction of the cupcakes are chocolate? _____

4. There are 16 tulips in the garden.

$\frac{1}{4}$ of the tulips are red.

How many tulips are red? _____ tulips

Practice

Unit

Solve.

5. 23
+ 81

6. 17
+ 36

7. 42
− 21

8. 78
− 39

HOME LINK 8·8 | Unit 9: Family Letter

Measurement

In Unit 9, children will explore measurements of various types. Your child will be asked to look for examples of measurements and measuring tools to bring to school for the Measures All Around Museum. The examples will help children appreciate the important role that measurement plays in everyday life.

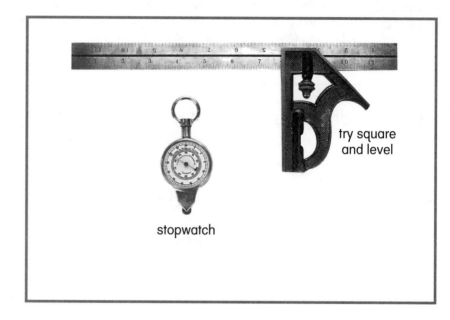

stopwatch

try square and level

Children will estimate and measure distances by inch, foot, and yard, as well as centimeter, decimeter, and meter. Children will learn that measurements are not always exact; they will use terms such as *close to, between,* and *about* when describing measurements. For closer or more exact measurements, children will measure to the nearest half-inch and half-centimeter.

In addition to measures of length, children will explore the areas of shapes using square inches and square centimeters. Children will also begin to develop a sense of the size of units of capacity and weight, such as cups and liters and pounds and kilograms.

Everyday Mathematics uses U.S. customary and metric units of measure. Although children make conversions within each system (length, capacity, or weight), they will not make conversions from one system to the other at this time.

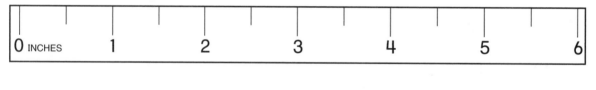

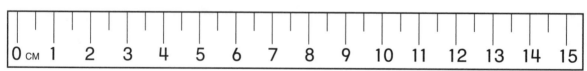

Please keep this Family Letter for reference as your child works through Unit 9.

Vocabulary

Important terms in Unit 9:

capacity The amount a container can hold. The volume of a container. Capacity is usually measured in units such as gallons, pints, cups, fluid ounces, liters, and milliliters.

perimeter The distance around a 2-dimensional shape, along the boundary of the shape. (The perimeter measures the length of a shape's "rim.")

area The amount of surface inside a 2-dimensional figure. Area is measured in square units, such as square inches or square centimeters.

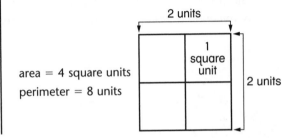

area = 4 square units
perimeter = 8 units

Metric System

Units of Length

1 meter (m)	= 10 decimeters (dm)
	= 100 centimeters (cm)
1 decimeter	= 10 centimeters
1 kilometer (km)	= 1,000 meters

Units of Weight

1 kilogram (kg)	= 1,000 grams (g)

Units of Capacity

1 liter (L)	= 1,000 milliliters (mL)
$\frac{1}{2}$ liter	= 500 milliliters

U.S. Customary System

Units of Length

1 yard (yd)	= 3 feet (ft)
	= 36 inches (in.)
1 foot	= 12 inches
1 mile (mi)	= 1,760 yards
	= 5,280 feet

Units of Weight

1 pound (lb)	= 16 ounces (oz)
2,000 pounds	= 1 ton (T)

Units of Capacity

1 cup (c)	= $\frac{1}{2}$ pint (pt)
1 pint	= 2 cups
1 quart (qt)	= 2 pints
1 half-gallon $\left(\frac{1}{2}\text{ gal}\right)$	= 2 quarts
1 gallon (gal)	= 4 quarts

Do-Anytime Activities

To work with your child on the concepts taught in this unit and in previous units, try these interesting and rewarding activities:

1. Gather a tape measure, a yardstick, a ruler, a cup, a gallon container, and a scale. Discuss the various things you and your child can measure—for example, the length of a room, how many cups are needed to fill a gallon container, and your child's weight alone and when he or she is holding objects such as books. Record the data and continue to measure and weigh different items periodically.

2. Mark certain routes on a road map and together figure the distance between two points in miles and kilometers.

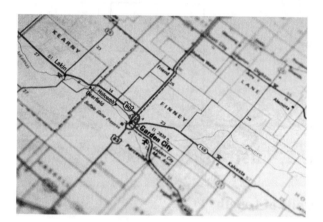

Building Skills through Games

In Unit 9, your child will practice mathematical skills by playing the following games:

Equivalent Fractions Game

Players take turns turning over Fraction Cards and try to find matching cards that show equivalent fractions.

Fraction Top-It

Players turn over two Fraction Cards and compare the shaded parts of the cards. The player with the larger fraction keeps both cards. The player with more cards at the end wins!

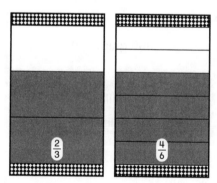

Name That Number

Each player turns over a card to find a number that must be renamed using any combination of five faceup cards.

Number-Grid Difference Game

Players subtract 2-digit numbers using the number grid.

Unit 9: Family Letter *cont.*

As You Help Your Child with Homework

As your child brings home assignments, you may want to go over the instructions together, clarifying them as necessary. The answers listed below will guide you through this unit's Home Links.

Home Link 9·1

5. 115   **6.** 791

7. 46   **8.** 325

Home Link 9·2

3. 12 inches   **4.** 3 feet

5. 10 centimeters   **6.** 100 centimeters

7. 24 inches   **8.** 9 feet

9. 40 centimeters   **10.** 700 centimeters

11. 69   **12.** 85

13. 48   **14.** 37

Home Link 9·3

1. $2\frac{1}{2}$ inches   **2.** 4 inches

3. 3 centimeters   **4.** 9 centimeters

10. 290   **11.** 397

Home Link 9·4

1. Perimeter: 6 or 7 inches

2. Perimeter: $4\frac{1}{2}$ or 5 inches

3. Answer: 47 feet. Sample number models:

$14 + 14 + 9\frac{1}{2} + 9\frac{1}{2} = 47$ or

$2 \times 14 + 2 \times 9\frac{1}{2} = 47$

Home Link 9·5

1. 214   **2.** 113

Home Link 9·6

2.

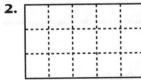

15 square centimeters   8 square centimeters

3. 359   **4.** 794

5. 400   **6.** 401

Home Link 9·7

1. 9 sq cm   **2.** 11 sq cm

3. 10 sq cm   **4.** l: 20 cm

                         U: 24 cm

                         J: 22 cm

5. 95   **6.** 92

7. 162   **8.** 103

Home Link 9·8

Rule
1 gal = 4 qt

gal	qt
2	8
4	16
6	24
10	40

Answers vary.

1. 83   **2.** 34

Home Link 9·9

1. 159   **2.** 177

HOME LINK 9·1

Using Measurement

> **Family Note** In class today, your child measured distances by using a yardstick. Talk with your child about measurements that you use at your job, around the house, in sports, or in other activities. If you don't have measuring tools to show your child, you might find pictures of measuring tools in a catalog, magazine, or book. Discuss with your child how these tools are used.
>
> *Please return this Home Link to school tomorrow.*
>
> **MRB** 64–66

1. Talk with people at home about how they use measurements at home, at their jobs, or in other activities.

2. Ask people at home to show you the tools they use for measuring. Write the names of some of these tools. Be ready to talk about your list in class.

   _____   _____

   _____   _____

   _____   _____

3. Look for measures in pictures in newspapers or magazines. For example, an ad might name the height of a bookcase or tell how much a container holds. Ask an adult if you may bring the pictures to school for our Measures All Around Museum. Circle the measures.

4. Bring one or two small boxes shaped like rectangular prisms to school. The boxes should be small enough to fit on a sheet of paper. **You will need these for Lesson 9-4.**

| **Practice** |

5. 86
   + 29

6. 770
   + 21

7. 60
   − 14

8. 350
   − 25

LESSON 9·1 Measuring Length with Paper Clips

Materials ☐ small paper clips

☐ large paper clips

Directions

1. Use small paper clips to measure the line below.

_____

About how many small paper clips? _____

Now, use large paper clips to measure the same line.

About how many large paper clips? _____

2. Try again. Measure this line with small and large paper clips.

_____

About how many small paper clips? _____

About how many large paper clips? _____

3. Why are the measurements different for the **same** line?

_____

_____

_____

_____

_____

253

LESSON 9·1 | Comparing Crooked Paths

1. Plan how you can compare the length of the crooked paths without using measuring tools.

   Describe your plan below.

   _____

   _____

   _____

   _____

2. Carry out your plan. Compare the lengths of the crooked paths. Write the letter for the path that is

   the longest path: _____

   the shortest path: _____

3. Estimate the length of each path in yards. Use words like *about, a little more than, a little less than.*

   I estimate that Path A is _____.

   I estimate that Path B is _____.

   I estimate that Path C is _____.

4. Now measure the lengths and check your estimates.

   Path A is about _____.

   Path B is about _____.

   Path C is about _____.

LESSON 9·2 | A Foot and a Decimeter

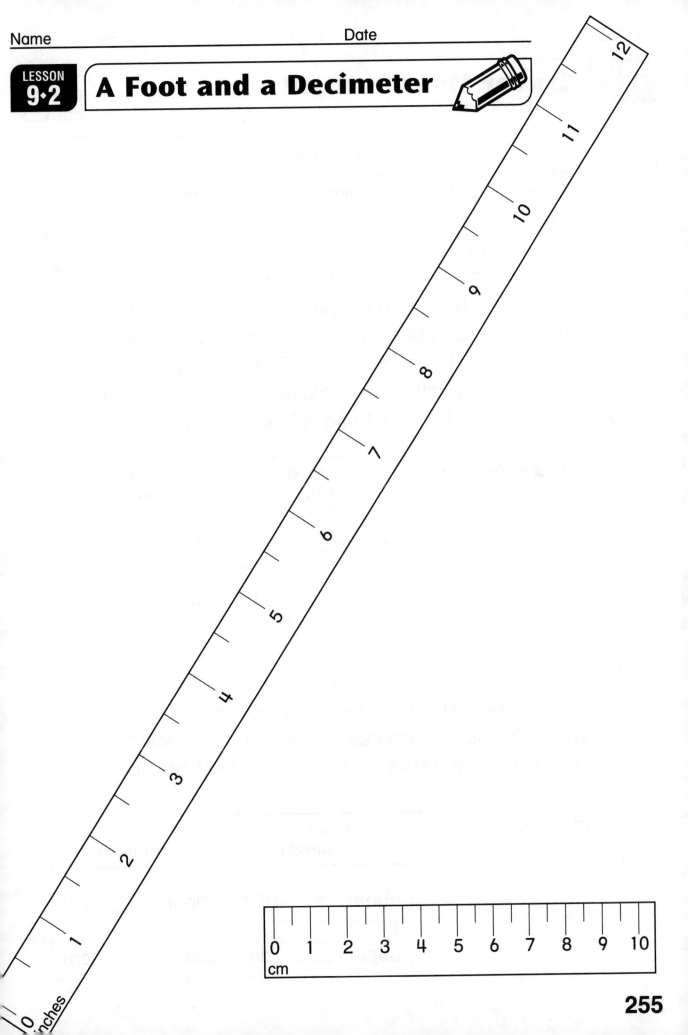

inches
0
1
2
3
4
5
6
7
8
9
10
11
12

0 1 2 3 4 5 6 7 8 9 10
cm

HOME LINK 9·2

Linear Measurements

Family Note Today your child reviewed how to use a ruler to measure objects and distances in inches and feet and in centimeters and decimeters. Your child's class also began making a Table of Equivalent Measures for the U.S. customary and metric systems. Ask your child to show you how to measure some of the objects or distances that he or she selects to complete the tables below.

Please return this Home Link to school tomorrow.

MRB
64–67

1. Cut out the 6-inch ruler on the next page. Measure two objects or distances. Measure to the nearest foot. Then measure again to the nearest inch. Some things you might measure are the width of the refrigerator door, the length of the bathtub, or the height of a light switch from the floor.

Object *or* Distance	Nearest Foot	Nearest Inch
	about _____ ft	about _____ in.
	about _____ ft	about _____ in.

2. Cut out the 10-centimeter ruler on the next page. Measure the same objects or distances. Measure to the nearest decimeter. Then measure again to the nearest centimeter.

Object *or* Distance	Nearest Decimeter	Nearest Centimeter
	about _____ dm	about _____ cm
	about _____ dm	about _____ cm

Linear Measurements *continued*

HOME LINK
9·2

Complete each sentence.

3. One foot is equal to _____ inches.

4. One yard is equal to _____ feet.

5. One decimeter is equal to _____ centimeters.

6. One meter is equal to _____ centimeters.

7. Two feet are equal to _____ inches.

8. Three yards are equal to _____ feet.

9. Four decimeters are equal to _____ centimeters.

10. Seven meters are equal to _____ centimeters.

Practice

11. $23 + 46 =$ _____

12. $38 + 47 =$ _____

13. $84 - 36 =$ _____

14. $76 - 39 =$ _____

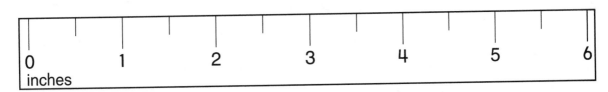

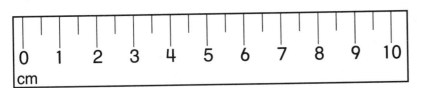

LESSON 9·2

Foot-Long Foot

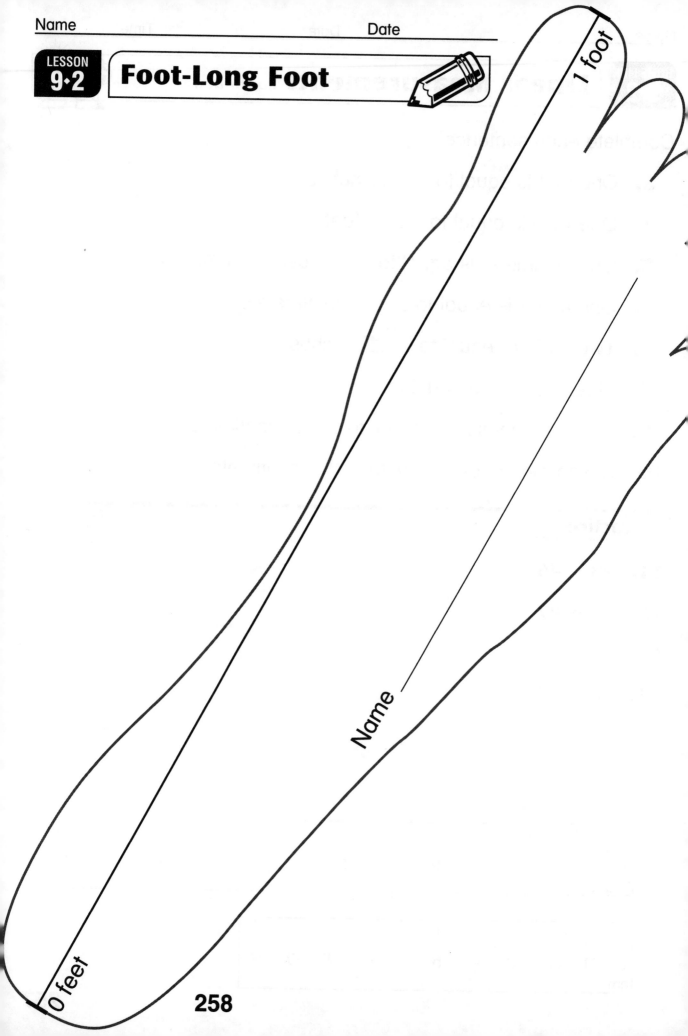

1 foot

Name

0 feet

LESSON 9·2   **Fish Poster**

Fish A
1 lb
12 in.

Fish B
3 lb
14 in.

Fish C
4 lb
18 in.

Fish D
5 lb
24 in.

Fish E
6 lb
24 in.

Fish F
8 lb
30 in.

Fish G
10 lb
30 in.

Fish H
14 lb
30 in.

Fish I
15 lb
30 in.

Fish J
24 lb
36 in.

Fish K
35 lb
42 in.

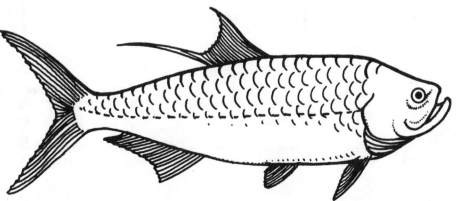

Fish L
100 lb
72 in.

259

LESSON 9·3 | **An Inch**

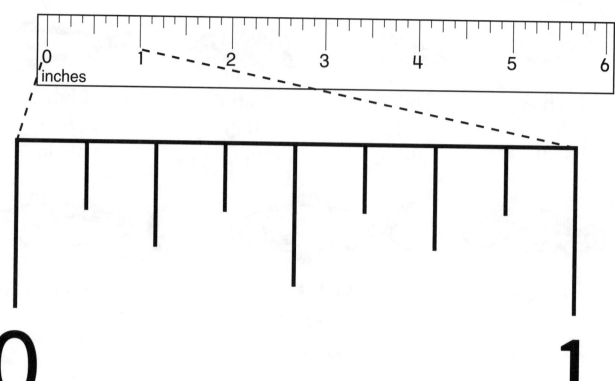

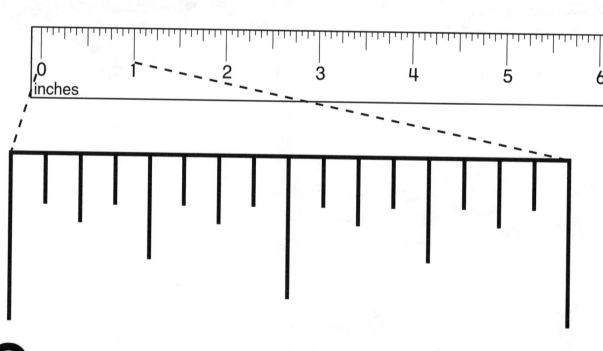

LESSON 9·3

A Centimeter

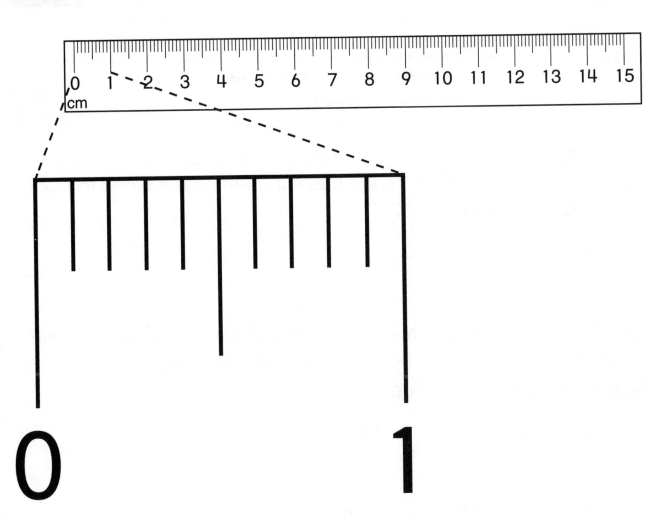

HOME LINK 9·3   # Measuring Lengths

Family Note   Today your child measured life-size pictures of objects to the nearest half-inch and half-centimeter. Take turns with your child measuring objects to the nearest half-inch and half-centimeter. Check to see if your measurements are the same.

Please return this Home Link to school tomorrow.

Cut out the 6-inch ruler on the next page. Measure each line segment to the nearest half-inch. Write the measurement in the blank to the right of each segment.

1. _____   _____ inches

2. _____   _____ inches

Cut out the 15-centimeter ruler on the next page. Measure each line segment to the nearest half-centimeter. Write the measurement in the blank to the right of each segment.

3. _____   _____ centimeters

4. _____   _____ centimeters

Measure some objects in your home to the nearest half-inch or half-centimeter. List the objects and their measurements below.

Object	**Measurement**
5. _____	_____
6. _____	_____
7. _____	_____
8. _____	_____

HOME LINK 9·3 | Measuring Lengths *continued*

9. Draw pictures of two things you measured. Mark the
parts you measured. Record the measurements under
the pictures.

Practice

10. 231
       + 59
       ____

11. 452
       − 55
       ____

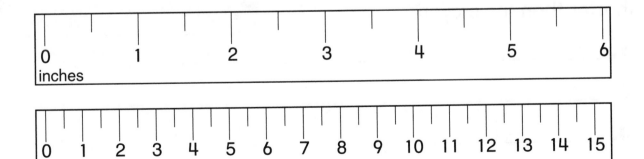

LESSON 9·3 | Comparing Lengths of Objects

Take a paper strip from your teacher. Use your 12-inch ruler to measure the paper strip to the nearest inch. Record the length on the paper strip, including the units.

Find 5 objects in the room that are about the same length as the paper strip. List the names or draw pictures of your objects.

1. _____

2. _____

3. _____

4. _____

5. _____

Are all your objects **about** the same size? _____

Are all your objects **exactly** the same size? _____

Write 5 sentences that compare the objects. Use words like *longer, shorter, about, a little more than,* and so on.

Example:
The crayon and the eraser are **about** 3 inches long. The eraser is **a little shorter than** the crayon.

```
CRAYON
```

```
ERASER
```

1. _____

2. _____

3. _____

4. _____

5. _____

264

LESSON 9·3 | Metric Units of Linear Measure

Work with 1 or 2 people.

Materials ☐ tape measure

☐ meterstick

☐ string or ribbon from your teacher

Directions

1. Check your measuring tools. Look for these units:

   ◆ 1 meter (100 centimeters)

   ◆ decimeters (10 centimeters each)

   If the units are hard to see, mark them with a crayon.

2. Measure the string or ribbon you get from your teacher. Measure it 3 times.

   Use meters the first time you measure. Use decimeters the next time. Use centimeters the last time.

_____ meters

_____ decimeters

_____ centimeters

LESSON 9·3

Metric Units *continued*

3. Choose a different item to measure, such as:

- ◆ the width of a door, the classroom, or a window

- ◆ the length of someone's arm or leg

- ◆ the length and width of a rug, a table, or the hall

Measure the item 3 times. Use meters the first time you measure, decimeters the next time, and centimeters the last time.

_____ meters

_____ decimeters

_____ centimeters

4. Discuss the measurements in Problems 2 and 3. Can anyone see any patterns among the 3 measurements? Explain the patterns you see.

_____

_____

_____

_____

_____

5. Name some things that would best be measured in these units:

a. meters _____

b. centimeters _____

c. decimeters _____

LESSON 9·4 **Thumb and Wrist Measurements**

Name _____

Work with a partner.

Measure, to the nearest centimeter, the distance around:

your thumb   **your wrist**

_____   _____
centimeters   centimeters

Name _____

Work with a partner.

Measure, to the nearest centimeter, the distance around:

your thumb   **your wrist**

_____   _____
centimeters   centimeters

Name _____

Work with a partner.

Measure, to the nearest centimeter, the distance around:

your thumb   **your wrist**

_____   _____
centimeters   centimeters

Name _____

Work with a partner.

Measure, to the nearest centimeter, the distance around:

your thumb   **your wrist**

   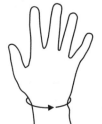

_____   _____
centimeters   centimeters

HOME LINK 9·4 Perimeter

Family Note Today your child found the perimeter of different shapes and the distance around his or her thumb, wrist, neck, and ankle. Perimeter is the measure around something. Finding perimeters also gives your child practice in measuring to the nearest inch and centimeter.

Please return this Home Link to school tomorrow.

MRB
68

Cut out the 6-inch ruler on the next page. Measure the side of each figure to the nearest inch. Write the length next to each side. Then find the perimeter.

1.

Perimeter: _____ inches

2.

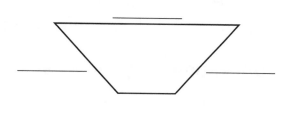

Perimeter: _____ inches

268

HOME LINK 9·4

Perimeter *continued*

Solve the number story. Write a number model.

3. Mr. Lopez is putting a fence around his vegetable garden. The garden is shaped liked a rectangle. The longer sides are 14 feet long, and the shorter sides are $9\frac{1}{2}$ feet long. How much fencing should Mr. Lopez buy?

Answer: _____ feet

Number model: _____

4. Draw a quadrangle below. Measure the sides to the nearest $\frac{1}{2}$-inch. Write the length next to each side. Find the perimeter.

The perimeter of my quadrangle is _____ inches.

LESSON 9·4 | **Measuring Perimeter in Paces**

Your teacher will put two lines of tape on the floor that are 18 feet apart.

1. Start with your toes on one line. Count the number of paces you take to reach the other line. Each time your foot hits the floor counts as 1 pace.

Number of paces: _____

2. Use this table to find out how long your pace is.

Number of Steps Taken	Length of Your Pace Is About . . .
15 or more	1 foot
11 to 14	$1\frac{1}{2}$ feet
8 to 10	2 feet
7	$2\frac{1}{2}$ feet
6	3 feet

The length of my pace is about _____ feet.

LESSON 9·4 | **Measuring Perimeter in Paces** *cont.*

3. Mrs. Dean's garden is square.
Each side is 30 feet long.

a. How many paces would
you take to walk along
one side of the garden?

_____ paces

b. How many paces would
you take to walk around
the whole garden?

_____ paces

c. The perimeter of the garden is _____ feet.

d. The perimeter of the garden is _____ of my paces.

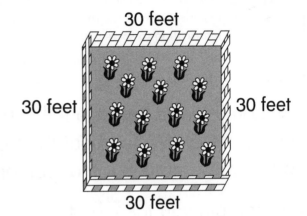

30 feet

30 feet

30 feet

30 feet

HOME LINK 9·5 Travel Interview

> **Family Note** Our class is studying measurement of longer distances. If the traveler your child talks to had experiences with the metric system in another country, have your child include this information to share with the class.
>
> *Please return this Home Link to school tomorrow.*

Ask someone at home to tell you about the longest trip he or she ever took. Write about the trip. Here are some questions you might want to ask that person:

◆ When did you take the trip?

◆ Where did you go?

◆ What interesting or unusual things did you see or do?

◆ How did you travel? By car? By plane? By train?

◆ How long did the trip take?

◆ How far did you travel?

_____

_____

_____

_____

_____

_____

_____

Practice

1. 136 + 78 = _____

2. 172 − 59 = _____

LESSON 9·5 | How Many Days?

Use the map on journal page 218. Solve the problem below.
Explain your work.

The Chang family drove from Seattle to Los Angeles by way of
Butte, Billings, Cheyenne, Denver, and Albuquerque. They
drove about 400 miles per day. About how many days did the
trip take them?

_____

_____

_____

_____

_____

_____

_____

_____

_____

_____

_____

LESSON 9·5 ## Units of Measure

All the items below may be measured with any of the given units. Some units are best for measuring short distances, and some units are better for measuring long distances.

Decide which unit is best for each situation.

Circle the unit that you would use to measure each of them.

1. distance from Orlando, Florida, to Boston, Massachusetts

inch   foot   mile

2. length of a paper clip

centimeter   meter   kilometer

3. height of your teacher

yard   foot   mile

4. perimeter of your bedroom

centimeter   meter   kilometer

5. width of a deck of cards

inch   foot   yard

6. length of a bus

inch   foot   mile

LESSON 9·6 | **Which Cylinder Holds More?**

Work with a small group.

Materials
- ☐ *Math Journal 2,* p. 221
- ☐ rulers; masking tape; macaroni
- ☐ pieces of cardboard
- ☐ 2 sheets of $8\frac{1}{2}$" by 11" construction paper

Directions

1. Draw a line 1 inch from a long edge on one construction paper rectangle.

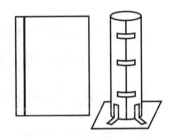

  ◆ Roll the rectangle into a long cylinder and tape the paper along the line.

  ◆ Then tape the cylinder to a piece of cardboard.

2. Draw a line 1 inch from a short edge on the other rectangle.

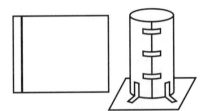

  ◆ Roll the rectangle into a short cylinder and tape the paper along the line.

  ◆ Then tape the cylinder to a piece of cardboard.

LESSON 9·6 | **Which Cylinder Holds More?** *continued*

3. Talk about these questions with your group.

◆ Suppose that you fill both containers with macaroni. Will one of the cylinders hold more macaroni than the other?

◆ If so, which one? Why? Record your prediction on journal page 221.

4. Find out. Fill the tall cylinder with macaroni.

Then carefully pour the macaroni from the tall cylinder into the short cylinder.

Record what happened on journal page 221.

LESSON 9·6 Measuring Area

Work in a small group.

Materials □ centimeter grid paper

□ inch grid paper

□ Everything Math Deck, if available

□ for tracing: slate, Pattern-Block Template, crayon box, and other objects

□ *Math Journal 2,* p. 221

Directions

1. Place the deck of cards on the centimeter grid paper.

Trace around the deck. The tracing shows the border of the deck.

2. Count the squares that cover the space inside the border.

◆ If more than half of a square is inside the border, count the whole square.

◆ If less than half of a square is inside the border, do not count the square at all.

3. The amount of space inside the border is called the **area.**

The number of squares you counted is a measurement of the area in **square centimeters.**

LESSON 9·6 | **Measuring Area** *continued*

4. Repeat Steps 1 and 2 using inch grid paper.

5. Find the area of four or five more objects.

You might trace things like …

- ◆ a Pattern-Block Template

- ◆ pattern blocks

- ◆ a crayon box

- ◆ objects from the Measures All Around Museum

6. Record the areas you measured on journal page 221.

Follow-Up

Work together as a group. Explain why your results are estimates and not exact measurements. How are the units used to measure area different from those used to measure perimeter?

LESSON 9·6 **Things to Measure**

Work with a small group.

Materials ☐ *Math Masters,* p. 280

☐ ruler; tape measure; meterstick; yardstick; scale; measuring cup; measuring spoon

Directions

1. Explore and discuss how to use each of the measuring tools.

2. Sort the measuring tools into the following three groups:

linear measures: tools that measure length, width, height, distance between, distance around (perimeter)

measures of weight: how heavy a thing is; how hard it is to move

measures of volume and capacity: how much of something there is; how much a container will hold

3. Complete *Math Masters,* page 280. List things you can measure with tools from each group. Write the unit that would be used to measure each item.

Follow-Up

Discuss other measuring tools you know about.

List them on the back of *Math Masters,* page 280.

LESSON 9·6 | **Things to Measure** *continued*

1. List 4 things you can measure with a ruler, a tape measure, a meterstick, or a yardstick. Write the unit that you would use to make each measurement.

Object	**Unit**
Example: _Math Journal_	_Inches_
_____	_____
_____	_____
_____	_____
_____	_____

2. List 4 things you can weigh with a scale.

Object	**Unit**
_____	_____
_____	_____
_____	_____
_____	_____

3. List 4 things you can measure with a measuring cup, a measuring spoon, or some other container.

Object	**Unit**
_____	_____
_____	_____
_____	_____

HOME LINK
9·6

Capacity and Area

Family Note   Today your child explored the ideas of *capacity* and *area*. Before your child is exposed to formal work with these measures (such as equivalent units of capacity or formulas for finding area), it is important that he or she have an informal understanding of these measures.

In Problem 1, help your child see that although the glasses may have different dimensions, they can still hold about the same amount of water. In Problem 2, the number of squares that your child counts is the area in square centimeters.

Please return this Home Link to school tomorrow.

MRB
69 70

1. Find two different glasses at home that you think hold about the same amount of water. Test your prediction by pouring water from one glass into the other. Do they hold about the same amount of water? Does one glass hold more than the other? Explain to someone at home how you know.

2. Count squares to find the area of each figure.

_____ square centimeters   _____ square centimeters

Practice

3. 459 − 100 = _____   4. 594 + 200 = _____

5.   350
   + 50
   _____

6.   460
   −   59
   _____

LESSON 9·6 | **Area**

Guess how many cubes are needed to cover each square with no gaps or overlaps. Cover each square with cubes to check your guess.

1. I think it will take

_____ cubes to cover this square.

It took _____ cubes to cover this square.

2. I think it will take

_____ cubes to cover this square.

It took _____ cubes to cover this square.

HOME LINK 9·7 | Area and Perimeter

Family Note Today children discussed the concept of finding the area of a surface. Area is measured by finding the number of square units needed to cover the surface inside a shape. Make sure your child understands that, when he or she is finding the perimeter of the letters in Problem 4, he or she is finding the distance around the outside of the letters.

Please return this Home Link to school tomorrow.

MRB
69

Find the area of each letter.

1.

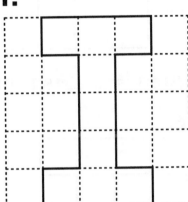

Area = _____ sq cm

2.

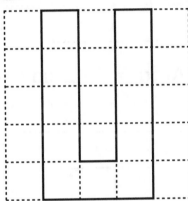

Area = _____ sq cm

3.

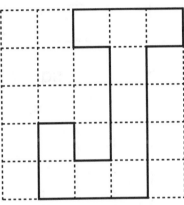

Area = _____ sq cm

4. What is the perimeter of each letter?

I: _____ cm   U: _____ cm   J: _____ cm

Practice

5. 67 + 28 = _____

6. 154 − 62 = _____

7. 88
      + 74
     _____

8. 126
     − 23
     _____

LESSON 9·7 | **Letter Areas**

Find the area of each letter.

1.

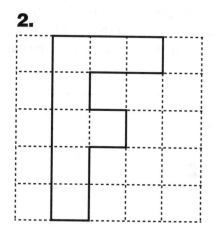

Area = _____ sq cm

2.

Area = _____ sq cm

3.

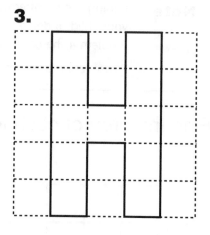

Area = _____ sq cm

4.

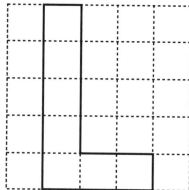

Area = _____ sq cm

5.

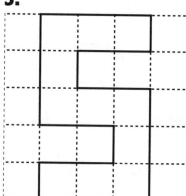

Area = _____ sq cm

6.

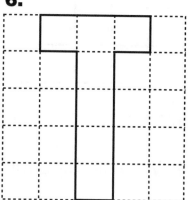

Area = _____ sq cm

Try This

An 8-by-8 checkerboard has 64 squares. Some squares on a checkerboard are white. Some are black. Squares of the same color are never next to each other.

7. How many white squares are in each row? _____

How many black squares? _____

8. If the square in one corner is black, what color is the square in the diagonal corner? _____

HOME LINK 9·8 | Capacity

Ask someone at home to help you find a recipe that uses units of capacity. Copy those ingredients and the amounts that are used in the recipe. Bring your list to school.

Example: $\frac{3}{4}$ *cup of milk*

_____

_____

_____

"What's My Rule?"

Rule
1 gal = 4 qt

gal	qt
2	
	16
6	
10	

Practice

1. 27
      + 56
      _____

2. 92
      − 58
      _____

LESSON 9·8 | Measuring Capacity

Materials ☐ half-gallon container

☐ tape

☐ measuring cup

☐ pitcher of water

1. Make a measuring container.

◆ Attach a piece of tape from the bottom to the top of an empty half-gallon container.

◆ Fill a measuring cup with a half-cup of water.

◆ Pour the water into the container. Do all of your pouring on a tray to catch the drips.

◆ Mark the tape to show how high the water is inside the container.

◆ Write $\frac{1}{2}$ **c** next to the mark.

◆ Pour another half-cup of water into the container.

◆ Mark the tape and write **1 c** next to the mark.

◆ Continue. Mark the tape $1\frac{1}{2}$ **c** to show 3 half-cups, **2 c** for 4 half-cups, and so on. Fill the container.

◆ Pour the water back into the pitcher.

LESSON 9·8 **Measuring Capacity** *continued*

2. In the first column of the table below, write the names or draw pictures of several containers in the Measures All Around Museum. In the second column, estimate the capacity of each container.

Container (description or picture)	Estimated Capacity	Measured Capacity
	_____ c	_____ c
	_____ c	_____ c
	_____ c	_____ c
	_____ c	_____ c

3. Measure the capacity of each container.

   ◆ Fill the container with water.

   ◆ Pour the water into your measuring container.

   ◆ See how high the water is on the tape. Write the number of the nearest mark in the third column above.

   ◆ Pour the water back into the pitcher.

HOME LINK 9·9

Weight

> **Family Note**
>
> Today children discussed U.S. customary units of weight (pounds, ounces) and metric units of weight (grams, kilograms). Your child weighed different objects using a variety of scales. Help your child weigh items using scales in your home or find items with weights written on them.
>
> *Please return this Home Link to school tomorrow.*

Find out what kinds of scales you have at home—for example, a bath scale, a letter scale, or a package scale. Weigh a variety of things on the scales, such as a person, a letter, or a book. Record your results below.

If you don't have any scales, look for cans and packages of food with weights written on them. Record those weights below. Remember that ounces (oz) measure weight and that fluid ounces (fl oz) measure capacity.

Object	**Weight** (include unit)
_____	_____
_____	_____
_____	_____
_____	_____
_____	_____
_____	_____

Practice

1. 86 + 73 = _____

2. 132 + 45 = _____

HOME LINK 9·10

Unit 10: Family Letter

Decimals and Place Value

In this unit, children will review money concepts, such as names of coins and bills, money exchanges, and equivalent amounts. They will pretend to pay for items and to make change.

The unit also focuses on extending work with fractions and money by using decimal notation. Children will use calculators for money problems and estimation.

Later in this unit, children will work with place-value notation for 5-digit numbers. Here, as previously, the focus remains on strategies that help children automatically think of any digit in a numeral in terms of its value as determined by its place. For example, children will learn that in a number like 7,843, the 8 stands for 800, not 8, and the 4 for 40, not 4.

50¢

50 cents

$\frac{1}{2}$ of a dollar

$0.50

fifty cents

Ⓓ Ⓓ Ⓓ Ⓓ Ⓓ

Please keep this Family Letter for reference as your child works through Unit 10.

289

Vocabulary

Important terms in Unit 10:

decimal point A mark used to separate the ones and tenths places in decimals. A decimal point separates dollars from cents in money notation. The mark is a dot in the U.S. customary system and a comma in Europe and some other countries.

flat In *Everyday Mathematics,* the base-10 block consisting of one hundred 1-centimeter cubes.

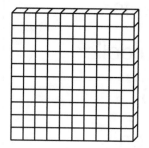

long In *Everyday Mathematics,* the base-10 block consisting of ten 1-centimeter cubes.

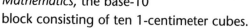

cube In *Everyday Mathematics,* the smaller cube of the base-10 blocks, measuring 1 centimeter on each edge.

place value A system that gives a digit a value according to its position in a number. In our standard *base-10* (decimal) system for writing numbers, each place has a value 10 times that of the place to its right and one-tenth the value of the place to its left. The chart below illustrates the place value of each digit in 7,843.

thousands	,	hundreds	tens	ones
7	,	8	4	3

Building Skills through Games

In Unit 10, your child will build his or her understanding of fractions and money by playing the following games:

Fraction Top-It

Players turn over two fraction cards and compare the shaded parts of the cards. The player with the larger fraction keeps both cards. The player with more cards wins.

Money Exchange Game

Players roll a die and put that number of $1 bills on their Place-Value Mats. Whenever possible, they exchange ten $1 bills for one $10 bill. The first player to make an exchange for one $100 bill wins.

Pick-a-Coin

Players create coin collections based on rolls of a die. Players try to get the largest possible values for their collections.

Spinning for Money

Players "spin the wheel" to find out which coins they will take from the bank. The first player to exchange his or her coins for a dollar wins.

Equivalent Fractions Game

Players take turns turning over Fraction Cards and try to find matching cards that show equivalent fractions.

Do-Anytime Activities

To work with your child on the concepts taught in this unit and in previous units, try these interesting and rewarding activities:

1. Collect a variety of coins and help your child count them. Discuss what other coin combinations would equal the same amount. For example, each group of coins shown on this page equals $1.00.

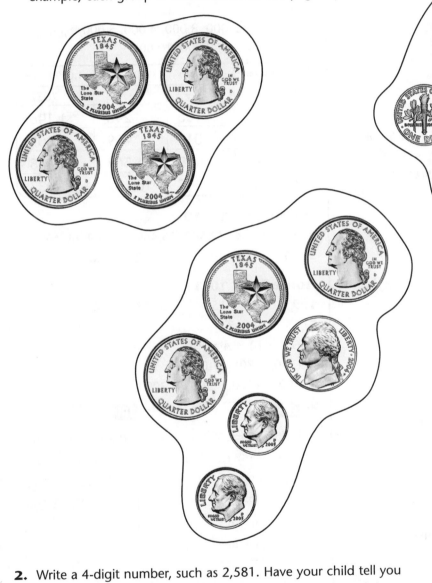

2. Write a 4-digit number, such as 2,581. Have your child tell you the place value of each digit. Rearrange the digits several times, pointing out the change in place value for each of the new number's digits. In 2,581, the 2 stands for 2,000; the 5, 500; the 8, 80; and the 1, 1.

3. Ask your child to add up grocery receipts by using a calculator.

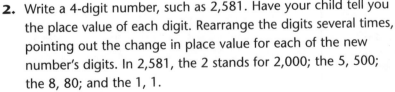

As You Help Your Child with Homework

As your child brings home assignments, you may want to go over the instructions together, clarifying them as necessary. The answers listed below will guide you through this unit's Home Links.

Home Link 10·1

1. 10 pennies = 10¢, or $0.10
10 nickels = 50¢, or $0.50
10 dimes = $1.00
10 quarters = $2.50
10 half-dollars = $5.00
Total = $9.10

Home Link 10·2

1. $3.57   **2.** $3.55   **3.** $0.52   **4.** $0.08
5. Sample answers: $1 $1 Q Q D P P P P or
$1 Q Q Q Q D D D N N N N P P P
6. 180   **7.** 55

Home Link 10·3

1. $0.06; $0.50; $1.30; $1.50; $3.36
3. 303   **4.** 197

Home Link 10·4

1. 1.09; 2.5; 0.98; 3.18; 0.06
3. 76   **4.** 72   **5.** 44   **6.** 18

Home Link 10·5

1. $0.70   **2.** $2.60   **3.** $1.00
4. $1.30   **5.** $4.00   **6.** $1.20
7. $2.30   **8.** $1.30 + $0.50 = $1.80
9. $0.80 + $0.40 = $1.20
10. $0.70 + $0.90 = $1.60
11. $1.40 + $0.80 = $2.20

Home Link 10·7

1. 17 sq cm   **2.** 23 cm²   **3.** 11 square cm
4. 9 cm²   **5.** 85   **6.** 29

Home Link 10·8

1. ④62   **2.** 1,③26   **3.** 5,⓪06   **4.** ⑧69
5. 2,③04   **6.** 4,⑤67   **9.** 1,183   **10.** 1,204
11. 158   **12.** 188   **13.** 29

Home Link 10·9

1. 0; 100; 200; 300; 400; 500; 600; 700; 800; 900; 1,000
2. 0; 1,000; 2,000; 3,000; 4,000; 5,000; 6,000; 7,000; 8,000; 9,000; 10,000

3.

Number	10 More	100 More	1,000 More
32	42	132	1,032
146	156	246	1,146
309	319	409	1,309
1,468	1,478	1,568	2,468
10,037	10,047	10,137	11,037

Home Link 10·10

3. 72,469   **4.** 72,569; 75,469; 72,369; 69,469
5. 76   **6.** 49   **7.** 225   **8.** 170

Home Link 10·11

1. 9   **2.** 15   **3.** 13   **4.** 6
5. 13 − (9 + 2) = 2
6. (28 − 8) − 4 = 16
7. (150 − 70) − 40 = 40
8. 800 − (200 + 300) = 300
9.
15
~~25 = (15 + 5)~~
(25 − 15) + 5
(17 − 9) + 7
~~17 = (9 + 7)~~
(3 + 6) + 6
3 + (6 + 6)

10.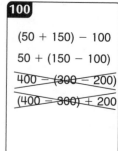
100
(50 + 150) − 100
50 + (150 − 100)
~~400 = (300 + 200)~~
~~(400 − 300) + 200~~

HOME LINK 10·1

Coin Combinations

Family Note

In today's lesson, your child practiced writing amounts of money. For example, in Problem 1, 10 pennies can be written as 10¢ or $0.10. Your child also showed different groups of coins that have the same monetary value. For example, your child could show 62¢ with 2 quarters, 1 dime, and 2 pennies; or 4 dimes, 4 nickels, and 2 pennies. For Problem 2, help your child find items in newspaper or magazine ads and think of different combinations of coins and bills to pay for the items.

MRB
88 89

Please return this Home Link to school tomorrow.

1. Pretend that you have 10 of each kind of coin. How much is that in all?

10 pennies = _____

10 nickels = _____

10 dimes = _____

10 quarters = _____

10 half-dollars = _____

Total = _____

2. Find two ads in a newspaper or magazine for items that cost less than $3.00 each.

◆ Ask for permission to cut out the ads.

◆ Cut them out and glue them onto the back of this page.

◆ Draw coins to show the cost of each item.

(If you can't find ads, draw pictures of items and prices on the back of this page.)

293

LESSON 10·1   Ways to Make a Dollar

Use Ⓠ, Ⓓ, Ⓝ, and Ⓟ.

1. Show $1.00 using 4 coins.

2. Show $1.00 using 6 coins.

3. Show $1.00 using 7 coins.

LESSON 10·1 | Plan a Picnic

You and two friends are planning a picnic for yourselves. You will be really hungry!

Use the Good Buys Poster on journal page 230.

Select **at least** 3 different items to buy. Find the total.

Items	**Cost**
_____	_____
_____	_____
_____	_____
_____	_____
_____	_____

Total cost _____

You and your friends are equally sharing the total cost. About how much does each of you owe? _____

Show your work.

LESSON
10·2 **Many-Name Scramble**

Cut out the names of 🖳, 🪙, and 🪙 from *Math Masters*, page 297. Then paste them in the proper columns below.

Many-Name Scramble *continued*

$1.00	$\frac{1}{100}$ of a dollar
$0.01	100 pennies
a dollar	10 dimes
one-tenth of a dollar	$\frac{1}{10}$ of a dollar
10¢	one-hundredth of a dollar
a dime	1¢
$0.10	a penny

HOME LINK 10·2 | **How Much?**

Family Note In today's lesson, your child practiced reading and writing money amounts using dollars and cents. Ask your child to read each amount aloud. Remind your child that the digits before the decimal point stand for whole dollars; the digits after the decimal point stand for cents. When reading amounts such as "3 dollars and fifty-seven cents," the word "and" is used to denote the decimal point.

Please return this Home Link to school tomorrow.

MRB 90

How much money? Write your answer in dollars-and-cents notation.

1. $1 $1 $1 Q Q N P P $____._____

2. $1 $1 Q Q Q Q D D D N N N N N $____._____

3. Q D D P P P P P P P P $____._____

4. N P P P $____._____

5. Use $1, Q, D, N, and P to draw $2.64 in two different ways.

Practice

Solve.

6. 123 + 57 = _____   **7.** 84 − 29 = _____

LESSON 10·2

10 × 5 Grid

Paste/tape to here to create a 10 × 10 grid.

HOME LINK 10·3 Coin Values

Family Note In today's lesson, your child used a calculator to enter amounts of money and find totals. For Problem 2, help your child collect and find the total value of each type of coin. Then find the grand total. If you wish to use a calculator, help your child enter the amounts. Remind your child that amounts like $1.00 and $0.50 will be displayed on the calculator as "1." and "0.5" because the calculator doesn't display ending zeros.

Please return this Home Link to school tomorrow.

1. Complete the table.

Coins	Number of Coins	Total Value
Ⓟ	6	$___ . ___
Ⓝ	10	$___ . ___
Ⓓ	13	$___ . ___
Ⓠ	6	$___ . ___
Grand Total		$___ . ___

2. Ask someone at home to help you collect pennies, nickels, dimes, quarters, and, if possible, half-dollars. Use the coins in your collection to complete the table below.

Coins	Number of Coins	Total Value
Ⓟ		
Ⓝ		
Ⓓ		
Ⓠ		
Half-dollar		
Grand Total		

Practice

Solve.

3. 250 + 53 = _____

4. 250 − 53 = _____

LESSON 10·3 | **Money Calculator Counts**

1. Count on your calculator to determine the value of collections of dimes (10s). Complete the table below.

Number of Dimes	1	2	3	4	5	6	7	8	9	10	11
Calculator Display	.1	.2	.3								1.1

Record the total value of 11 dimes in dollars-and-cents notation: $__.__

Show the value using Q, D, N, and P. _____

2. Clear your calculator. Count on your calculator to determine the value of collections of pennies (1s). Complete the table below.

Number of Pennies	1	2	3	4	5	6	7	8	9	10	11
Calculator Display	.01	.02	.03								.11

Record the total value of 11 pennies in dollars-and-cents notation: $__.__

Show the value using Q, D, N, and P. _____

3. Clear your calculator. Count on your calculator to determine the value of collections of nickels (5s). Complete the table below.

Number of Nickels	3	4	5	6	7	8	9	10	11
Calculator Display	.15					.4			

Record the total value of 11 nickels in dollars-and-cents notation: $__.__

Show the value using Q, D, N, and P. _____

LESSON 10·3 | **Displaying Money on the Calculator**

Lily bought a pencil and an eraser. She had her calculator with her. When she added up the price of the two items, the calculator displayed

How much could each item cost? Show your work.

_____

Explain how you found your answer.

_____

_____

Lily had a $5-bill. She wanted to buy a pen. When she added its cost to the calculator total of 1.3, it displayed

Did Lily have enough money? Explain your answer.

_____

_____

How much did the pen cost? Show your work.

_____

_____

LESSON 10·4 Then-and-Now Poster

Now

Grape Jelly
2 lb
$2.29

20-Inch Girl's Bicycle
$119.99

Harmonica
Ten Double Holes
$17.50

Crackers
1 lb
$2.49

Raisins
1 lb
$2.39

Cheddar Cheese
8 oz ($\frac{1}{2}$ lb)
$2.99

Catsup
32 oz/1 qt
$2.79

Child's Wagon
Medium Size—15$\frac{1}{2}$" × 34"
$47.99

1897

Grape Jelly
2 lb
28¢

20-Inch Girl's Bicycle
$29.00

Harmonica
Ten Double Holes
45¢

Crackers
1 lb
6¢

Cheddar Cheese
$\frac{1}{2}$ lb
6¢

Raisins
1 lb
10¢

Catsup
32 oz/1 qt
25¢

Child's Wagon
Large Size—15" × 30"
$1.65

303

HOME LINK 10·4 | **Calculators and Money**

Family Note In today's lesson, your child used a calculator to solve problems with money. In Problem 2, your child will ask you or another adult to compare the cost of an item when you were a child to its current cost. There are two ways to make this type of comparison. You might describe a *difference comparison*. For example: "A bicycle costs about $90.00 more now than it did then." You might also use a *ratio comparison*. For example, "A bicycle costs about 4 times as much now as it did then." You do not need to share the terms *difference comparison* and *ratio comparison* with your child, but it is important that your child be exposed to both types of comparisons.

Please return this Home Link to school tomorrow.

1. Enter the following amounts into your calculator. What does your calculator show?

Enter	**Calculator Shows**
$1.09	_____
$2.50	_____
98¢	_____
$3.18	_____
6¢	_____

2. Ask an adult to think about an item that he or she remembers from when he or she was a child. Ask the adult to compare how much the item cost then and now. Record what you find out.

_____

_____

Practice

Solve.

3. 37 + 39 = _____

4. 49 + 23 = _____

5. 73 − 29 = _____

6. 56 − 38 = _____

LESSON 10·4 | Solving a Money Problem

Mr. Evans buys a newspaper every Monday, Tuesday, Wednesday, Thursday, Friday, and Saturday for $0.50 each. On Sunday, he buys a magazine for $1.25. Use your calculator to find out how much Mr. Evans spends in 1 week.

Record your display each time you add another day. Add coins each time you enter another day to help you show and write the amount. Clear your calculator before you start. Do not clear your calculator again until you get your 1 week total.

Day	Enter	Display	Amount
Monday	.50 +	0.50	$0.50
Tuesday	.50 +	1.	$1.00
Wednesday	.50 +		
Thursday	.50 +		
Friday	.50 +		
Saturday	.50 +		
Sunday	1.25 =		
1 Week Total			

Mr. Evans spends $____.____ per week.

How much does Mr. Evans spend in 2 weeks? Use your calculator. Show what keys you press, record your display and write your dollars-and-cents amount.

Keys You Press	Display	Money Amount
		$____.____

305

LESSON 10·4 | **That Was Then**

In 1897, grape jelly was about 30¢.
Now the grape jelly is about $2.30.

30¢ + 30¢ + 30¢ + 30¢ + 30¢ + 30¢ + 30¢ = $2.10.

For 1 jar of grape jelly today, you could have bought 7 jars in 1897.

Use the Then-and-Now Poster (*Math Masters,* page 303). Could you have bought more bottles of catsup or bicycles in 1897 for today's cost? Show your work. You can use ballpark estimates.

Name	Date	Time

Estimation to the Nearest 10¢

Family Note

In today's lesson, your child estimated sums by first finding the nearest ten cents for each amount of money being added and then adding the amounts for the nearest ten cents together. For Problems 1–7, ask your child how she or he arrived at each answer. If needed, use coins to show which amount is actually closer. For Problems 8–11, help your child find the totals by thinking of a problem like $1.20 + $0.60 as 12 + 6 or as 120 cents + 60 cents.

Please return this Home Link to school tomorrow.

Write the correct answer to each question.
Talk with someone at home about your answers.

1. Is $0.69 closer to $0.60 or $0.70? _____

2. Is $2.59 closer to $2.50 or $2.60? _____

3. Is $0.99 closer to $0.90 or $1.00? _____

4. Is $1.31 closer to $1.30 or $1.40? _____

5. Is $3.99 closer to $3.90 or $4.00? _____

6. Is $1.17 closer to $1.10 or $1.20? _____

7. Is $2.34 closer to $2.30 or $2.40? _____

Fill in the blanks and estimate the total cost in each problem.

Example:

$1.19 + $0.59 is about _$1.20_ + _$0.60_ = _$1.80_ .

8. $1.29 + $0.48 is about _____ + _____ = _____.

9. $0.79 + $0.39 is about _____ + _____ = _____.

10. $0.69 + $0.89 is about _____ + _____ = _____.

11. $1.41 + $0.77 is about _____ + _____ = _____.

LESSON 10·5 | **Rounding Numbers**

When we round a number, we find a number that is close to it.

1. Here is one strategy for rounding a number:

   To round 27, put your finger on 27 on the number grid.
   Move it up or down to the nearest multiple of 10.

   a. Is it fewer steps from 27 to 30 or from 27 to 20? _____

   Use your number grid to round these numbers:

   b. 22 _____   **c.** 38 _____   **d.** 51 _____   **e.** 75 _____

   (Hint: If a number is halfway between, we always round to
   the higher number.)

2. Here is another way to think of rounding numbers:

   a. To round 17, think: What would be multiples of 10
   that are close to 17? _____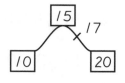

   b. What number would be at the top of the hill? _____

   c. Would 17 be heading toward 10 or toward 20? _____

3. Draw a picture to show how you would round 63.

4. Draw a picture to show how you would round 234.

LESSON 10·5 Tic-Tac-Toe Addition

Draw a line through any three numbers whose sum is the target number in the square. The numbers may be in a row, in a column, or on a diagonal. Draw a line for each correct sum.

Example:

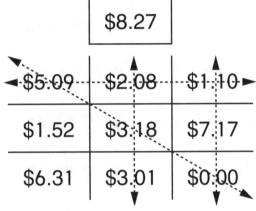

	$8.27	
$5.09	$2.08	$1.10
$1.52	$3.18	$7.17
$6.31	$3.01	$0.00

1.

	$14.62	
$3.40	$4.15	$7.07
$1.75	$8.22	$6.00
$5.00	$2.25	$3.00

2.

	$18.05	
$6.25	$3.75	$3.05
$6.10	$8.50	$4.90
$6.50	$5.80	$9.10

Try This

Write a target number in the box. Fill in the rest of the spaces to reach the target.

3.

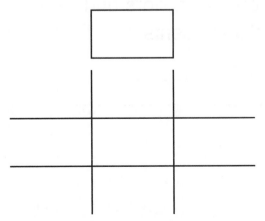

4.

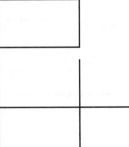

309

LESSON 10·6 Math Message

Name: _____

Write in dollars-and-cents notation:

1. 29 cents = $_____

2. 59¢ = $_____

3. 9 cents = $_____

4. a dollar forty-seven

= $_____

5. 10 dollars and 2 cents

= $_____

6. nine hundred thirty-three
dollars and thirty cents

= $_____

Try This

7. three thousand five hundred
forty-six dollars and
sixteen cents

= $_____

Name: _____

Write in dollars-and-cents notation:

1. 29 cents = $_____

2. 59¢ = $_____

3. 9 cents = $_____

4. a dollar forty-seven

= $_____

5. 10 dollars and 2 cents

= $_____

6. nine hundred thirty-three
dollars and thirty cents

= $_____

Try This

7. three thousand five hundred
forty-six dollars and
sixteen cents

= $_____

HOME LINK 10·6 Making Change

> **Family Note**
>
> In today's lesson, your child made change by counting up. When counting out change, encourage your child to begin with the cost of the item and count up to the amount of money that the customer has given to the clerk. For the example listed in the table below, your child could do the following:
>
> **1.** Say "89 cents"—the price of the item.
>
> **2.** Put a penny on the table and say "90 cents."
>
> **3.** Put a dime on the table and say "$1.00."
>
> **4.** Count the coins on the table. 1¢ + 10¢ = 11¢. The change is 11¢.
>
> *Please return this Home Link to school tomorrow.*

Materials ☐ coins and bills (You can make bills out of paper.)

☐ items with prices marked

Practice making change with someone at home. Pretend you are the clerk at a store and the other person is a customer. The customer buys one of the items and pays with a bill. You count out the change.

Record some purchases here.

Item	Price	Amount Used to Pay	Change
can of black beans	$0.89	$1.00	$0.11

If possible, go to the store with someone. Buy something and get change. Count the change. Is it correct?

311

LESSON 10·6 | What Did They Buy?

Using the Good Buys Poster, find the items each child could have bought with the total they spent.

1. Peter went shopping for his mom. He bought ground beef, tuna, mayonnaise, hamburger buns, and wheat bread. If he spent a total of $9.73, what are two other items that he could have bought? Show your work.

2. Sarah had $10.00. She spent $9.45 at the market. What could Sarah have bought? Show your work.

Try This

3. Kevin had $12.00 when he went to the market. He left the store with $2.37 in change. What might he have bought? Show your work.

Name _____ Date _____ Time _____

 LESSON 10·7 ## Math Message

Name: _____

Count squares to find the area of each shaded figure.

1.
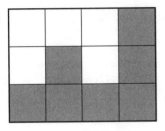 _____ square centimeters

2.
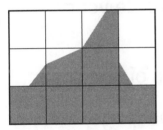 _____ sq cm

---

Name: _____

Count squares to find the area of each shaded figure.

1.
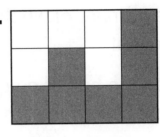 _____ square centimeters

2.
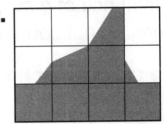 _____ sq cm

---

Name: _____

Count squares to find the area of each shaded figure.

1.
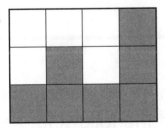 _____ square centimeters

2.
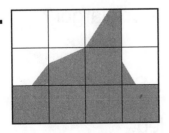 _____ sq cm

---

Name: _____

Count squares to find the area of each shaded figure.

1.
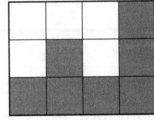 _____ square centimeters

2.
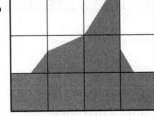 _____ sq cm

313

LESSON 10·7 | My Handprint and Footprint Areas

Work with a partner.

1. Trace your partner's hand onto his or her journal page 248. When your hand is traced, keep your fingers close together.

2. Count the number of whole square centimeters inside your handprint.

   ◆ If more than half of a square centimeter is inside your handprint, count the whole square.

   ◆ If less than half of a square centimeter is inside your handprint, do not count the square.

3. Record the area of your handprint at the bottom of that page.

4. Trace your partner's foot onto his or her journal page 249. (Keep your sock on your foot.)

5. Count to find the area of your footprint. Record the area of your footprint at the bottom of that page.

6. Exchange journals and check each other's counts. Count again if you don't agree with your partner.

Follow-Up

Work in a small group. Compare your hand to other group members' hands. Then compare your foot to others'. Predict the following:

◆ Whose hand areas are about the same? Whose are larger? Smaller?

◆ Whose foot areas are about the same? Larger? Smaller?

Compare your predictions to the areas you recorded.

LESSON 10·7 — Worktables

Work in a group.

Materials ☐ trapezoid pattern blocks

☐ Pattern-Block Template (1 per person)

☐ *Math Journal 2*, p. 250

Pretend that each red trapezoid pattern block
is a small table.

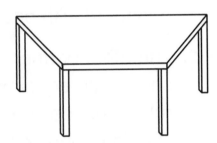

Your teacher wants to make larger worktables
by fitting these small tables together.

Try each of the following problems. Use a Pattern-Block
Template to record the tables you make on journal page 250.

1. Make a worktable shaped like a hexagon.

2. Make a worktable shaped like a triangle.

3. Use more than 1 block to make a worktable
   shaped like a trapezoid.

4. Make a worktable shaped like a parallelogram.

5. Make another parallelogram worktable that has
   twice the area of the one you just made.

6. Make any other worktable shapes that you can with
   the trapezoids.

Follow-Up

Compare your reports. Find all the different-size and
different-shape worktables that your group made.

LESSON 10·7 | **Geoboard Fractions**

Materials ☐ geoboard ☐ rubber bands

☐ *Math Journal 2,* p. 251

Work with a partner.

1. One partner makes a shape on the geoboard with one rubber band.

2. The other partner tries to divide the shape into equal parts using other rubber bands. The equal parts should be the same size and shape.

Example:

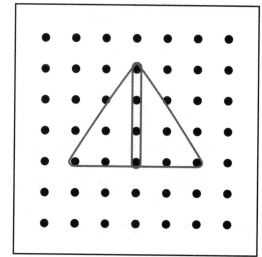

3. Take turns until each partner has made 3 shapes.

4. Record some of the shapes you divided on journal page 251. Show the equal parts.

5. Record some shapes on the journal page that you could not divide into equal parts.

Work in a group.

6. Check one another's work.

7. Discuss these questions:

♦ Are shapes that can be divided equally special in some way?

♦ What about the shapes that cannot be divided equally?

HOME LINK 10·7 | **Area**

Family Note In today's lesson, your child found the area of shapes by counting square centimeters. As you observe your child finding the areas below, check that he or she is counting squares that are more than $\frac{1}{2}$ shaded as 1 square centimeter and not counting squares that are less than $\frac{1}{2}$ shaded. For Problem 4, see if your child has a suggestion for what to do if exactly $\frac{1}{2}$ of a square is shaded. Remind your child that area is reported in square units. Other ways to write square centimeters are **sq cm** and **cm²**.

Please return this Home Link to school tomorrow.

MRB 69

Count squares to find the area of each shaded figure.

1.

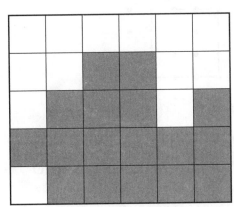

_____ sq cm

2.

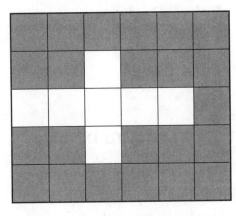

_____ cm²

3.

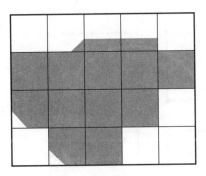

_____ square cm

4.

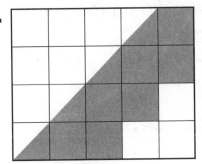

_____ cm²

Practice

5. $\begin{array}{r} 56 \\ + 29 \\ \hline \end{array}$

6. $\begin{array}{r} 88 \\ - 59 \\ \hline \end{array}$

LESSON 10·7 | Equal Parts

Use a geoboard to solve each problem. Record what you
did below.

1. Make the square below on
your geoboard. Divide the
square in half with a rubber
band. Record what you did
on the square below.

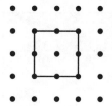

2. Make the square below on
your geoboard. Divide the
square into 3 equal parts with
rubber bands. Record what
you did on the square below.

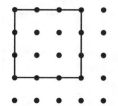

3. Make the square below
on your geoboard.
Divide the square into
4 equal parts with
rubber bands. Record
what you did on the
square below.

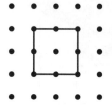

4. Show four ways you can
divide this rectangle into
equal parts on a
geoboard. Record
your work below.

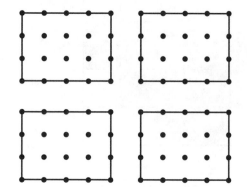

LESSON 10·7 | Fractional Parts

Find the WHOLE for each fractional part shown. Record your work on the geoboards for each problem.

1. This shape is worth
$\frac{1}{2}$ of the whole shape.
Draw the rest of the shape.

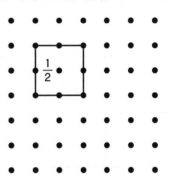

2. This shape is worth $\frac{1}{3}$ of
the whole shape.
Draw the rest of the shape.

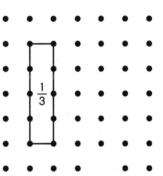

3. This shape is worth $\frac{1}{4}$ of
the whole shape. Draw the
rest of the shape.

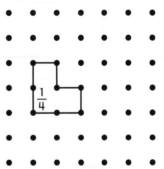

LESSON 10·8 · Place-Value Chart

Ten-Thousands	Thousands	Hundreds	Tens	Ones

LESSON 10·8 | **Place-Value Mat**

Ⓟ pennies	Ⓓ dimes	💲1 dollars	💲10
▫ 1s	▭ 10s	▦ 100s	▦ 1,000s

HOME LINK 10·8 | **Place Value**

> **Family Note** In this lesson, your child has been studying place value, or the value of digits in numbers. Listen as your child reads the numbers in Problems 1–6. You might ask your child to pick a few of the numbers and tell you the place value of each of the digits. For example, in 462, the value of 4 is 400, the value of 6 is 60, and the value of 2 is 2.
>
> *Please return this Home Link to school tomorrow.*

In each number: ◆ Circle the digit in the hundreds place.

◆ Underline the digit in the thousands place.

Example: 9̲,③4 2

1. 4 6 2

2. 1 , 3 2 6

3. 5 , 0 0 6

4. 8 6 9

5. 2 , 3 0 4

6. 4 , 5 6 7

7. Read the numbers in Problems 1–6 to someone at home.

Write the numbers represented by the base-10 blocks.

8. 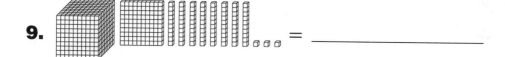 = _____ 247 _____

9. _____ = _____

10. _____ = _____

Practice

Solve.

11. $134 + 24 =$ _____

12. $152 + 36 =$ _____

13. $67 - 38 =$ _____

LESSON 10·9   Place-Value Book

You will make a Place-Value Book that looks like the one below.

Place-Value Book

Tool-Kit Number _____

Ten-Thousands	Thousands	Hundreds	Tens	Ones

Cut out the pages of the Place-Value Book on *Math Masters,* pages 323–326. Cut on the dashed lines. Your teacher will show you how to make the book.

Place-Value Book

Tool-Kit Number _____

Page 1

LESSON 10·9

Place-Value Book *continued*

Page 2

0	0	0	0	0

Page 3

1	1	1	1	1

Page 4

2	2	2	2	2

Page 5

3	3	3	3	3

Place-Value Book *continued*

Page 6

| 4 | 4 | 4 | 4 | 4 |

Page 7

| 5 | 5 | 5 | 5 | 5 |

Page 8

| 6 | 6 | 6 | 6 | 6 |

Page 9

| 7 | 7 | 7 | 7 | 7 |

Place-Value Book *continued*

Page 10

8	8	8	8	8

Page 11

9	9	9	9	9

Page 12

Ten-Thousands	Thousands	Hundreds	Tens	Ones

LESSON 10·9 | Digit Cards

✂

4   9

3   8

2   7

1   6

0   5

Place-Value Labels

| Ten-Thousands |
| Thousands |
| Hundreds |
| Tens |
| Ones |

| Ten-Thousands |
| Thousands |
| Hundreds |
| Tens |
| Ones |

| Ten-Thousands |
| Thousands |
| Hundreds |
| Tens |
| Ones |

| Ten-Thousands |
| Thousands |
| Hundreds |
| Tens |
| Ones |

| Ten-Thousands |
| Thousands |
| Hundreds |
| Tens |
| Ones |

| Ten-Thousands |
| Thousands |
| Hundreds |
| Tens |
| Ones |

LESSON 10·9   **Place-Value Card Holder**

Ones

Tens

← Fold back on dotted line. →

Hundreds

Thousands

Ten-Thousands

LESSON 10·9 Place-Value Book Cover

Page 1

Place-Value Book

Tool-Kit Number _____

Place-Value Book 0 and 1

Page 2

0

0

0

0

0

Page 3

1

1

1

1

1

LESSON 10·9 | Place-Value Book 2 and 3

Page 4

2

2

2

2

2

Page 5

3

3

3

3

3

LESSON 10·9   **Place-Value Book 4 and 5**

Page 6

| 4 |
| 4 |
| 4 |
| 4 |
| 4 |

Page 7

| 5 |
| 5 |
| 5 |
| 5 |
| 5 |

LESSON 10·9 | Place-Value Book 6 and 7

Page 8

6

6

6

6

6

Page 9

7

7

7

7

7

LESSON 10·9

Place-Value Book 8 and 9

Page 10

8

8

8

8

8

Page 11

9

9

9

9

9

LESSON 10·9 | Place Values for the Place-Value Book

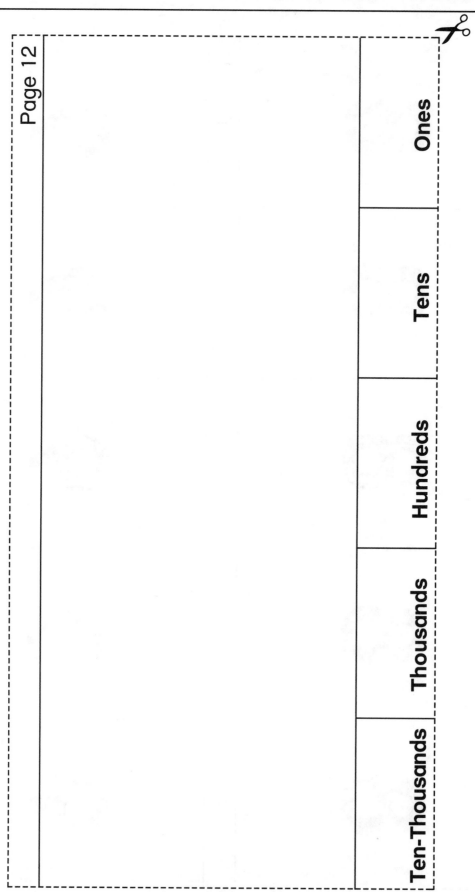

Page 12

Ten-Thousands	Thousands	Hundreds	Tens	Ones

Counting by 10s, 100s, and 1,000s

Family Note In this lesson, your child used place value to count by 10s, 100s, and 1,000s. For Problems 1 and 2, listen carefully to find out if your child counts quickly and accurately. Help your child complete the table in Problem 3. If necessary, have your child use a calculator to find the answers. Ask your child to describe any patterns he or she sees in the completed table.

Please return this Home Link to school tomorrow.

MRB
162 163

1. Show someone at home how to count by 100s from 0 to 1,000. Record your counts.

_____

_____

2. Now count by 1,000s from 0 to 10,000. Record your counts.

_____

_____

3. Complete the table.

Number	10 More	100 More	1,000 More
32	42	132	1,032
146			
309			
1,468			
Try This			
10,037			

LESSON 10·9 | Doing Digit Discovery

For each problem, use your number cards to model and solve the problem. Record your answers in the spaces at the bottom of the page.

Hundreds (100s)	Tens (10s)	Ones (1s)

1. Use your cards to make the number that has a 4 in the tens place, a 6 in the ones place, and a 3 in the hundreds place. Record the number you made: _____

2. Replace one digit and make a number that is 30 more than the number you made in Problem 1. Record the new number you made: _____ Circle the new digit. What place is this digit in? _____

3. Replace one digit and make a number that is 30 more than the number you made in Problem 2. Record the new number you made: _____ Circle the new digit. What place is this digit in?

_____

___ Try This ___

4. Make up your own riddle. Record the answer to your riddle: _____

4-Digit and 5-Digit Numbers

Family Note In this lesson, your child read and displayed 4- and 5-digit numbers. Listen to your child read numbers to you. Remind your child not to say "and" when reading numbers such as the ones below. (In reading numbers, "and" indicates a decimal point. For example, 7.9 is read as "seven and nine tenths.") However, do not overcorrect your child if he or she inserts "and" occasionally.

Please return this Home Link to school tomorrow.

1. Read these numbers to someone at home.

3,426;   6,001;   9,864;   13,400;   29,368;   99,999

2. Write other 4- and 5-digit numbers. Read your numbers to someone at home. _____

Try This

3. Write a number that has:

4 in the hundreds place.

6 in the tens place.

2 in the thousands place.

7 in the ten-thousands place.

9 in the ones place.

___ ___ , ___ ___ ___

4. Use the number in Problem 3.

What number is

100 more? _____

3,000 more? _____

100 less? _____

3,000 less? _____

Practice

5. 24 + 52 = _____

6. 78 − 29 = _____

7. 136
    + 89
   _____

8. 244
    − 74
   _____

LESSON 10·10 Areas of States

List the states in the table from largest area to smallest area.

State	Area (sq miles)
Arkansas	53,182
Florida	59,928
Georgia	58,977
Illinois	57,918
Iowa	56,276
New York	53,989

State	Area (sq miles)
largest:	
smallest:	

Name   Date   Time

LESSON 10·10 Areas of States

List the states in the table from largest area to smallest area.

State	Area (sq miles)
Arkansas	53,182
Florida	59,928
Georgia	58,977
Illinois	57,918
Iowa	56,276
New York	53,989

State	Area (sq miles)
largest:	
smallest:	

HOME LINK
10·11 **Grouping with Parentheses**

Family Note In this lesson, your child has solved problems and puzzles involving parentheses. For Problems 1–4, 9, and 10, remind your child that the calculations inside the parentheses need to be done first. In Problem 1, for example, your child should first find $7 - 2$ and then add that answer (5) to 4. For Problems 5–8, observe as your child adds parentheses. Ask your child to explain what to do first to obtain the number on the right side of the equal sign.

Please return this Home Link to school tomorrow.

Solve problems containing parentheses.

1. $4 + (7 - 2) =$ _____

2. $(9 + 21) - 15 =$ _____

3. $6 + (12 - 5) =$ _____

4. $(15 + 5) - 14 =$ _____

Put in parentheses to solve the puzzles.

5. $13 - 9 + 2 = 2$

6. $28 - 8 - 4 = 16$

7. $150 - 70 - 40 = 40$

8. $800 - 200 + 300 = 300$

Cross out the names that don't belong in the name-collection boxes.

9.

15
$25 - (15 + 5)$
$(25 - 15) + 5$
$(17 - 9) + 7$
$17 - (9 + 7)$
$(3 + 6) + 6$
$3 + (6 + 6)$

10.

100
$(50 + 150) - 100$
$50 + (150 - 100)$
$400 - (300 - 200)$
$(400 - 300) + 200$

LESSON 10·11   **Exploring the Order of Operations**

Julio and Marissa were both working on the following problem:

$7 + 2 - 3 + 4 = $ _____

Julio said the answer is 10.

Marissa said the answer is 2.

How do you think each person found the answer to the problem?

_____

_____

_____

_____

_____

LESSON 10·11 **Number Sentences with Parentheses**

Sue and Lee were playing *Name That Number.*
Here were the cards they drew and the target number.

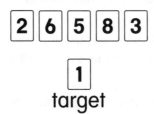

target

Try to write at least 3 different number sentences that "hit" the
target. Use both addition and subtraction in each number
sentence.

Insert parentheses to show what step to do first.

Unit 11: Family Letter

Whole-Number Operations Revisited

In the beginning of Unit 11, children will solve addition and subtraction stories with dollars and cents. Children will use estimation to examine their answers and determine whether the answers make sense.

Children will also review the uses of multiplication and division and begin to develop multiplication and division fact power, or the ability to automatically recall the basic multiplication and division facts.

Children will work with shortcuts, which will help them extend known facts to related facts. For example, the **turn-around rule for multiplication** shows that the order of the numbers being multiplied (the factors) does not affect the product; 3×4 is the same as 4×3. Children will also learn what it means to multiply a number by 0 and by 1. Working with patterns in a Facts Table and in fact families will also help children explore ways of learning multiplication and division facts.

×, ÷	1	2	3	4	5	6	7	8	9	10
1	1	2	3	4	5	6	7	8	9	10
2	2	4	6	8	10	12	14	16	18	20
3	3	6	9	12	15	18	21	24	27	30
4	4	8	12	16	20	24	28	32	36	40
5	5	10	15	20	25	30	35	40	45	50
6	6	12	18	24	30	36	42	48	54	60
7	7	14	21	28	35	42	49	56	63	70
8	8	16	24	32	40	48	56	64	72	80
9	9	18	27	36	45	54	63	72	81	90
10	10	20	30	40	50	60	70	80	90	100

Multiplication/Division Facts Table

Please keep this Family Letter for reference as your child works through Unit 11.

Vocabulary

Important terms in Unit 11:

multiplication diagram A diagram used in *Everyday Mathematics* to model situations in which a total number is made up of equal-sized groups. The diagram contains a number of groups, a number in each group, and a total number.

rows	_____ per row	_____ in all

Number model: _____ × _____ = _____

factor Each of the two or more numbers in a product.

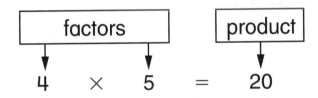

$$4 \times 5 = 20$$

product The result of multiplying two numbers, called *factors*.

quotient The result of dividing one number by another.

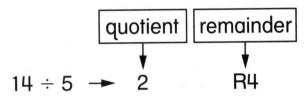

$$14 \div 5 \rightarrow 2 \qquad R4$$

turn-around rule A rule for solving addition and multiplication problems saying it doesn't matter in which order the numbers are written. For example, if you know that $6 + 8 = 14$, then, by the turn-around rule, you also know that $8 + 6 = 14$.

range The difference between the largest (maximum) and smallest (minimum) numbers in a set of data. For example, the range of the data below is $38 - 32 = 6$.

32   32   34   35   35   37   38

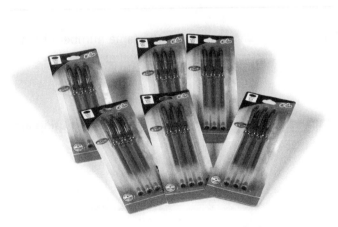

Do-Anytime Activities

To work with your child on the concepts taught in this unit and in previous units, try these interesting and rewarding activities:

1. Review common multiplication shortcuts. Ask, for example: *What happens when you multiply a number by 1? By 0? By 10?* Use pennies to show that 2×3 pennies is the same as 3×2 pennies.

2. At a restaurant or while grocery shopping, work together to estimate the bill.

3. Take turns making up multiplication and division number stories to solve.

Building Skills through Games

In Unit 11, your child will practice multiplication skills, mental arithmetic, and predicting the outcome of events by playing the following games:

Beat the Calculator

A "Calculator" (a player who uses a calculator to solve the problem) and a "Brain" (a player who solves the problem without a calculator) race to see who will be first to solve multiplication problems.

Hit the Target

Players choose a 2-digit multiple of ten as a "target number." One player enters a "starting number" into a calculator and tries to change the starting number to the target number by adding a number to it on the calculator. Children practice finding differences between 2-digit numbers and higher multiples of tens.

Array Bingo

Players roll the dice and find an *Array Bingo* card with the same number of dots. Players then turn that card over. The first player to have a row, column, or diagonal of facedown cards, calls out "Bingo!" and wins the game.

Name That Number

Each player turns over a card to find a number that must be renamed using any combination of five faceup cards.

Soccer Spin

Players pick which spinner will best help them make a goal.

As You Help Your Child with Homework

As your child brings home assignments, you may want to go over the instructions together, clarifying them as necessary. The answers listed below will guide you through this unit's Home Links.

Home Link 11·1

1. $2.22   **2.** $4.06   **3.** $3.34   **4.** $1.64

Home Link 11·2

1. glue stick; $0.14   **2.** glitter; $0.58

3. coloring pencils; $1.12

4. coloring pencils; $1.84

5. $0.11   **6.** $2.22

Home Link 11·3

1. 31; $70 - 40 = 30$ **2.** 23; $50 - 30 = 20$

3. 29; $90 - 60 = 30$ **4.** 17; $30 - 10 = 20$

5. 16; $30 - 20 = 10$

Home Link 11·4

1. 18 tennis balls; $6 \times 3 = 18$

2. 32 buns; $4 \times 8 = 32$

Home Link 11·5

1. 6 packages; $18 \div 3 \rightarrow 6$ R0

2. 6 cards; $25 \div 4 \rightarrow 6$ R1

Home Link 11·6

1. 12   **2.** 12   **3.** 10

4. 9   • • • • • • • • •

5. 14   • • • • • • •
              • • • • • • •

6. 12   • • • •
              • • • •
              • • • •

7. 2 nickels = 10 cents; $2 \times 5 = 10$
6 nickels = 30 cents; $6 \times 5 = 30$

8. 4 dimes = 40 cents; $4 \times 10 = 40$
7 dimes = 70 cents; $7 \times 10 = 70$

9. double 6 = 12; $2 \times 6 = 12$
double 9 = 18; $2 \times 9 = 18$

Home Link 11·7

2. a. 99   **b.** 502   **c.** 0   **d.** 0

4. 55   **5.** 26

Home Link 11·9

1. $5 \times 7 = 35$ **2.** $3 \times 6 = 18$
$7 \times 5 = 35$ $6 \times 3 = 18$
$35 \div 5 = 7$ $18 \div 3 = 6$
$35 \div 7 = 5$ $18 \div 6 = 3$

3. $4 \times 6 = 24$ **4.** $5 \times 6 = 30$
$6 \times 4 = 24$ $6 \times 5 = 30$
$24 \div 4 = 6$ $30 \div 5 = 6$
$24 \div 6 = 4$ $30 \div 6 = 5$

Buying Art Supplies

$0.75

Crayons

$1.47

Glitter

$2.59

Coloring Pencils

$0.89

Glue Stick

Find the total cost of each pair of items.

1. crayons and glitter Total cost: _____	**2.** glitter and coloring pencils Total cost: _____
3. crayons and coloring pencils Total cost: _____	**4.** glue stick and crayons Total cost: _____

LESSON 11·1 Estimating Money with Ten Frames

Use $1 bills, dimes, and a ten frame (*Math Masters,* page 422) to solve these problems.

Example: Is $1.43 closer to $1.00 or $2.00?

- ◆ Forget about the pennies.

- ◆ Make $1.40 with $1 bills and dimes.

- ◆ Place the dimes in the ten frame (one to each box).

- ◆ Look at the ten frame. Is it more than half-filled or less than half-filled? <u>Less</u>

- ◆ Because the ten frame is less than half-filled, $1.43 is closer to $1.00. $1.43 is closer to <u>$1.00</u>.

1. Is $1.78 closer to $1.00 or $2.00?

    - ◆ Forget about the pennies.

    - ◆ Make $1.70 with $1 bills and dimes.

    - ◆ Place the dimes in the ten frame.

    - ◆ Is the ten frame more or less than half-filled? _____

    - ◆ $1.78 is closer to _____.

2. Is $1.62 closer to $1.00 or $2.00? _____

Try This

3. Is $2.25 closer to $2.00 or $3.00? _____

4. Is $4.53 closer to $4.00 or $5.00? _____

LESSON 11·1 | Magic Squares

The sum of each row, column, and diagonal must be the same.
Find the missing numbers. Write them in the blank boxes.
Write the sum above the Magic Square.

1. _____

$6	$7	$2
	$5	$9
$8	$3	

2. _____

	$2.00	$7.50
$5.00	$6.00	
	$10.00	$3.50

3. _____

$4.75	$0.50	
	$3.50	$3.00
	$6.50	

4. $15.75

$8.25		$6.50
$3.50		

HOME LINK 11·2 **Comparing Costs**

Family Note In today's lesson, your child solved subtraction number stories involving money amounts. Ask your child to explain how he or she solved each of the subtraction problems below. Encourage your child to use estimation before solving each problem. Ask such questions as: *Is the difference in cost between the crayons and glitter more or less than $1.00?* (less)

Please return this Home Link to school tomorrow.

$0.75

Crayons

$1.47

Glitter

$2.59

Coloring Pencils

$0.89

Glue Stick

In Problems 1–4, circle the item that costs more.
Then find how much more.

1. glue stick or crayons

How much more? _____

2. glue stick or glitter

How much more? _____

3. glitter or coloring pencils

How much more? _____

4. coloring pencils or crayons

How much more? _____

5. Carlos bought a glue stick. He paid with a $1 bill. How much change should he get?

_____

6. Solve.

$1.47 + $0.75 = _____

351

LESSON 11·2 Differences on the Number Grid

Use *Math Masters*, page 417 to solve the problems below.
Show your work on the number grid.

Example:

Circle 13 and 39. Find the difference between 13 and 39.
Use a pencil to mark the number grid to show what you did.

11	12	(13)	14	15	16	17	18	19	20
21	22	23	24	25	26	27	28	29	30
31	32	33	34	35	36	37	38	(39)	40

The difference between 13 and 39 is ____26____.

1. Circle 12 and 34. Find the difference between 12 and 34.
   Use a pencil to mark the number grid to show what you did.

   The difference between 12 and 34 is _____.

2. Circle 45 and 63. Find the difference between 45 and 63.
   Use a pencil to mark the number grid to show what you did.

   The difference between 45 and 63 is _____.

3. Circle 76 and 91. Find the difference between 76 and 91.
   Use a pencil to mark the number grid to show what you did.

   The difference between 76 and 91 is _____.

HOME LINK 11·3 Trade-First Subtraction

Family Note

Today your child learned about subtracting multidigit numbers using a procedure called the trade-first method. Your child also used "ballpark estimates" to determine whether his or her answers made sense.

The **trade-first** method is similar to the traditional subtraction method that you may be familiar with. However, all the "regrouping" or "borrowing" is done before the problem is solved—which gives the method its name, "trade-first."

Example:

```
longs │ cubes
 10s  │  1s

  4   │  6
- 3   │  9
──────┼──────
```

◆ Are there enough tens and ones to remove exactly 3 tens and 9 ones from 46? *(No; there are enough tens, but there aren't enough ones.)*

◆ Trade 1 ten for 10 ones.

```
longs │ cubes
 10s  │  1s
  3   │ 1 6
  4̶   │  6̶
- 3   │  9
──────┼──────
```

◆ Solve. 3 tens minus 3 tens leaves 0 tens. 16 ones minus 9 ones leaves 7 ones. The answer is 7.

```
longs │ cubes
 10s  │  1s
  3   │ 1 6
  4̶   │  6̶
- 3   │  9
──────┼──────
      │  7
```

◆ Make a ballpark estimate to see whether the answer makes sense: 46 is close to 50, and 39 is close to 40. 50 − 40 = 10. 10 is close to the answer of 7, so 7 is a reasonable answer.

The trade-first method is one of many ways people solve subtraction problems. Your child may choose this method or a different procedure. What is most important is that your child can successfully solve subtraction problems using a method that makes sense to him or her.

*Please return the **second page** of this Home Link to school tomorrow.*

MRB
34

353

Trade-First Subtraction *cont.*

Make a ballpark estimate for each problem and write a number model for your estimate.

Use the trade-first method of subtraction to solve each problem.

Example: Ballpark estimate:

$$30 - 20 = 10$$

longs 10s	cubes 1s
1	16
2̶	6̶
− 1	8
	8

Answer 8

---

1. Ballpark estimate:

_____

longs 10s	cubes 1s
7	3
− 4	2

Answer

---

2. Ballpark estimate:

_____

longs 10s	cubes 1s
4	9
− 2	6

Answer

---

3. Ballpark estimate:

_____

longs 10s	cubes 1s
8	5
− 5	6

Answer

---

4. Ballpark estimate:

_____

longs 10s	cubes 1s
3	2
− 1	5

Answer

---

5. Ballpark estimate:

_____

$$34 - 18$$

Answer

LESSON 11·3   Subtraction with Base-10 Blocks

Use base-10 blocks to help you subtract.

1.

longs 10s	cubes 1s
3	7
− 2	2

2.

longs 10s	cubes 1s
4	3
− 3	1

3.

longs 10s	cubes 1s
2	4
− 1	8

4.

longs 10s	cubes 1s
6	2
− 3	9

5.

longs 10s	cubes 1s
5	5
− 4	6

6.

longs 10s	cubes 1s
4	7
− 2	9

7. Write a problem of your own. Record what you would do with base-10 blocks to solve your problem.

HOME LINK 11·4 | Multiplication Stories

Show someone at home how to solve these multiplication stories.
Fill in each multiplication diagram.
Use counters or draw pictures or arrays to help you.

1. The store has 6 cans of tennis balls.
There are 3 balls in each can.
How many tennis balls are there in all?

cans	tennis balls per can	tennis balls in all

Answer: _____ tennis balls

Number model: _____ × _____ = _____

356

HOME LINK 11·4

Multiplication Stories *continued*

2. Hamburger buns come in packages of 8.
You buy 4 packages.
How many buns are there in all?

packages	buns per package	buns in all

Answer: _____ buns

Number model: _____ × _____ = _____

3. Make up and solve a multiplication number story below.

_____

_____

_____

_____	_____	_____
	per _____	in all

Answer: _____

Number model: _____ × _____ = _____

Equal Groups on a Number Line

Look at the example. Then follow the directions for each problem.

Example: $3 \times 2 = ?$

Start at 0. Show 3 hops of 2.

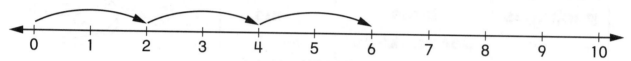

Where did you land? ____6____   Number model: $3 \times 2 = 6$

1. $3 \times 3 = ?$

Start at 0. Show 3 hops of 3.

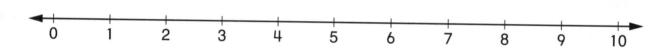

Where did you land? _____   Number model: _____

2. $4 \times 2 = ?$

Start at 0. Show 4 hops of 2.

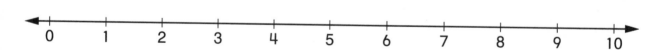

Where did you land? _____   Number model: _____

3. $5 \times 3 = ?$

Start at 0. Show 5 hops of 3.

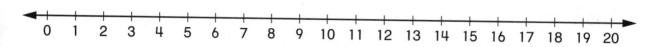

Where did you land? _____   Number model: _____

LESSON 11·4 | Making Multiples

Use base-10 blocks to solve the problems. For each problem, draw the base-10 blocks that come out of the machine and write a number model. Look for a pattern.

Example:

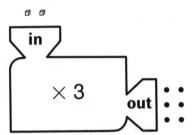

Number model: _2 × 3 = 6_

1.

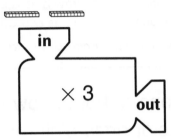

Number model: _____

2.

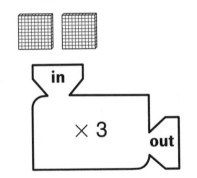

Number model: _____

3.

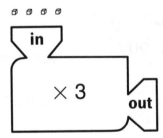

Number model: _____

4.

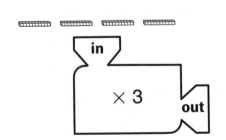

Number model: _____

5.

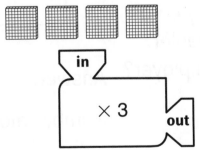

Number model: _____

HOME LINK 11·5 | Division Number Stories

Family Note

Today your child solved division number stories about equal sharing and equal groups. The diagram used for multiplication can also be used for division number stories to identify known and unknown information. Your child will write a number model for each problem below. A number model is the symbolic representation of a number story. For example, in Problem 1, the number model is $18 \div 3 \rightarrow 6$ R0. This model is read as *18 divided by 3 gives 6, remainder 0.* An arrow is used instead of an equals (=) sign because the result of a division problem can be two whole numbers: the quotient and remainder.

Please return this Home Link to school tomorrow.

MRB
112–115

Show someone at home how to solve these division stories.
Use counters or draw pictures or diagrams to help you.

1. Our group needs 18 pens. There are 3 pens in each package. How many packages must we buy?

packages	pens per package	pens in all

Answer: _____ packages

Number model: _____ ÷ _____ → _____ R_____

2. Four children are playing a game with 25 cards. How many cards can the dealer give each player?

children	cards per child	cards in all

Answer: _____ cards

Number model: _____ ÷ _____ → _____ R_____

3. Make up and solve a division story on the back of this sheet.

LESSON 11·5 — Exploring Equal Shares

Use counters and quarter-sheets of paper to solve each problem.
Record your work in the rectangles.

Example:

Nomi had 8 crayons. She gave the crayons to 4 of her friends. Each friend got the same number of crayons. Draw the number of crayons each friend gets.

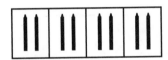

1. Latrell shared 10 marbles with his best friend. Draw the number of marbles each boy had.

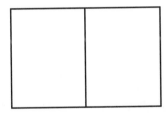

2. Melissa had 6 bags of treats for her birthday party. She had a total of 12 treats in her bags. Draw the number of treats in each bag.

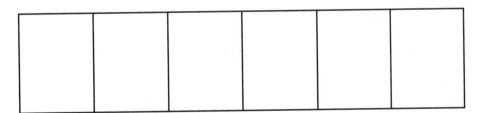

3. Make up your own problem. Draw your solution.

HOME LINK 11·6 Multiplication Facts

Family Note In this lesson, your child has been learning multiplication facts and has used arrays to represent those facts. The first factor in a multiplication fact tells the number of rows in the array, and the second factor tells the number of columns in the array. In Problem 1, for example, an array with 2 rows of 6 dots is used for the multiplication fact 2 × 6 = 12.

Please return this Home Link to school tomorrow.

Show someone at home how you can use arrays to find products. Use •s.

1. 2 × 6 = _____ •••••• ••••••	**2.** 6 × 2 = _____	**3.** 1 × 10 = _____
4. 1 × 9 = _____	**5.** 2 × 7 = _____	**6.** 3 × 4 = _____

7. 2 nickels = _____ cents   2 × 5 = _____

   6 nickels = _____ cents   6 × 5 = _____

8. 4 dimes = _____ cents   4 × 10 = _____

   7 dimes = _____ cents   7 × 10 = _____

9. double 6 = _____   2 × 6 = _____

   double 9 = _____   2 × 9 = _____

362

LESSON 11·6 Calculator Counts

1. Use your calculator to count by 1s. Complete the table below.

Count by 1s.	One	Two	Three	Four	Five	Six	Seven	Eight	Nine	Ten
	1	1s	1s	1s	1s	1s	1s	1s	1s	1s
Display	1									

2. Clear your calculator. Use your calculator to count by 2s. Complete the table below.

Count by 2s.	One	Two	Three	Four	Five	Six	Seven	Eight	Nine	Ten
	2	2s	2s	2s	2s	2s	2s	2s	2s	2s
Display	2									

3. Clear your calculator. Use your calculator to count by 5s. Complete the table below.

Count by 5s.	One	Two	Three	Four	Five	Six	Seven	Eight	Nine	Ten
	5	5s	5s	5s	5s	5s	5s	5s	5s	5s
Display	5									

4. How can counting on your calculator help you learn your multiplication facts?

363

HOME LINK 11·7 | Multiplication Facts

Family Note In today's lesson, your child practiced multiplication facts by using a table and discussed patterns in multiplication facts. For example, any number multiplied by 1 is that number; any number multiplied by 0 is 0; and if the order of the factors in a multiplication fact is reversed, the product remains the same. Observe the strategies your child uses to find the answers below. Counting by 2s, 5s, 10s, and so on is one strategy to look for. Another strategy is drawing pictures. Some children may be able to solve some multiplication facts mentally, but this is not expected until the end of third grade.

Please return this Home Link to school tomorrow.

1. Show someone at home what you know about multiplication facts. You can use arrays or pictures to help solve the problems.

$0 \times 9 =$ _____	$8 \times 0 =$ _____	$4 \times 0 =$ _____	$0 \times 7 =$ _____
$1 \times 3 =$ _____	$3 \times 1 =$ _____	$1 \times 8 =$ _____	$10 \times 1 =$ _____
$2 \times 8 =$ _____	$3 \times 2 =$ _____	$2 \times 7 =$ _____	$4 \times 2 =$ _____
$5 \times 3 =$ _____	$2 \times 5 =$ _____	$6 \times 5 =$ _____	$5 \times 8 =$ _____
$10 \times 4 =$ _____	$3 \times 10 =$ _____	$9 \times 10 =$ _____	$10 \times 6 =$ _____

2. Explain to someone at home why it is easy to solve the following multiplication problems.

a. $\begin{array}{r} 99 \\ \times\ 1 \\ \hline \end{array}$ b. $\begin{array}{r} 502 \\ \times\ 1 \\ \hline \end{array}$ c. $\begin{array}{r} 37 \\ \times\ 0 \\ \hline \end{array}$ d. $\begin{array}{r} 15{,}461 \\ \times\ \ \ \ 0 \\ \hline \end{array}$

3. Make up and solve some multiplication problems of your own on the back of this page.

Practice

4. $84 - 29 =$ _____ **5.** $93 - 67 =$ _____

LESSON 11·7 | Square Products

Work in a small group.

Materials
- ☐ centimeter grid paper (*Math Masters,* p. 434)
- ☐ centimeter cubes or pennies (or both)
- ☐ tape

Directions

1. Each person chooses a different number from 2 to 10.

2. Build an array that shows your number multiplied by itself. Use pennies or centimeter cubes.

3. Draw each array on centimeter grid paper. Write a number model under each array.

Example:

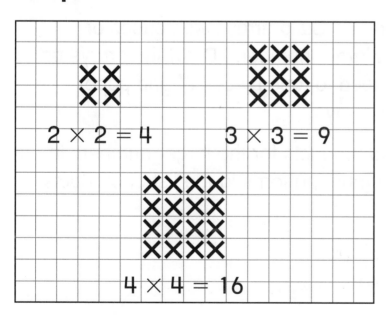

LESSON 11·7 | **Square Products** *continued*

4. Make and record a few more arrays. On a blank sheet of paper, make a table like the one below. Begin with the smallest factors. Record them in order: 2×2, 3×3, 4×4, and so on.

Array (factors)	Total (product)
2×2	4
3×3	9
4×4	16

5. Continue working together. Build arrays with cubes or pennies for larger and larger numbers. Draw the arrays on grid paper. You may need to tape pieces of grid paper together for the larger arrays.

6. Record the factors and products for the larger numbers in your table. Look for number patterns in the list of products.

×, ÷ Fact Triangles

Family Note

Fact Triangles are tools for building mental arithmetic skills. You might think of them as the *Everyday Mathematics* version of the flash cards that you may remember from grade school. Fact Triangles, however, are more effective for helping children memorize facts because they emphasize fact families.

A **fact family** is a collection of related facts made from the same three numbers. For the numbers 4, 6, and 24, the multiplication/division fact family consists of 4 × 6 = 24, 6 × 4 = 24, 24 ÷ 6 = 4, and 24 ÷ 4 = 6.

Please help your child cut out the Fact Triangles attached to this letter.

To use Fact Triangles to practice multiplication with your child, cover the number next to the dot with your thumb. The number you have covered is the product.

Your child uses the numbers that are showing to tell you one or two multiplication facts: 3 × 5 = 15 or 5 × 3 = 15.

To practice division, use your thumb to cover a number without a dot.

Your child uses the numbers that are showing to tell you the division fact 15 ÷ 5 = 3.

Now cover the other number without a dot. Your child tells you the other division fact, 15 ÷ 3 = 5.

If your child misses a fact, flash the other two fact problems on the card and then return to the fact that was missed.

Example: Your child can't answer 15 ÷ 3. Flash 3 × 5, then 15 ÷ 5, and finally 15 ÷ 3 a second time.

Make this activity brief and fun. Spend about 10 minutes each night. The work you do at home will support the work your child is doing at school.

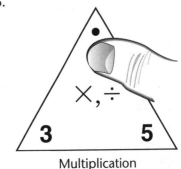

Multiplication

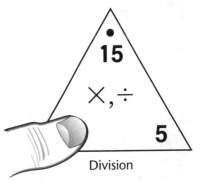

Division

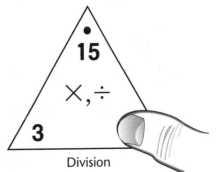

Division

×, ÷ **Fact Triangles** *continued*

Cut out the Fact Triangles. Show someone at home how you can use them to practice multiplication and division facts.

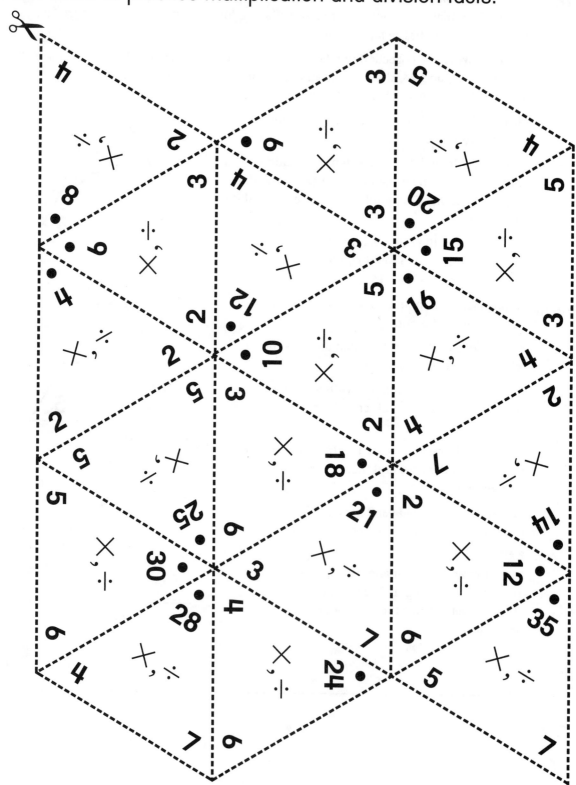

LESSON 11·8

Exploring Fact Triangles

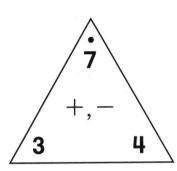
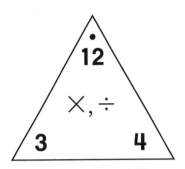

1. Write two ways the Fact Triangles above are alike.

_____

_____

_____

2. Write two ways the Fact Triangles above are different.

_____

_____

_____

3. Fill in the blank addition/subtraction and multiplication/division
Fact Triangles below so that they have the same numbers.
[Hint: Look for numbers that, when added together, have a sum
that is the same as when they are multiplied together. It is a
square number.]

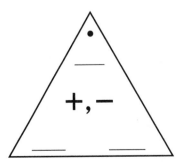
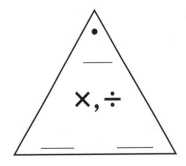

HOME LINK 11·9 — Fact Families

Family Note Today your child continued to practice multiplication and division facts by playing a game called *Beat the Calculator* and by using Fact Triangles. Observe as your child writes the fact family for each Fact Triangle below. Use the Fact Triangles that your child brought home yesterday. Spend about 10 minutes practicing facts with your child. Make the activity brief and fun. The work you do at home will support the work your child is doing at school.

Please return this Home Link to school tomorrow.

MRB
38

Write the fact family for each Fact Triangle.

1.

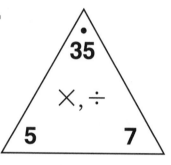

$$\underline{5} \times \underline{7} = \underline{35}$$

$$\underline{} \times \underline{} = \underline{}$$

$$\underline{35} \div \underline{5} = \underline{7}$$

$$\underline{} \div \underline{} = \underline{}$$

2.

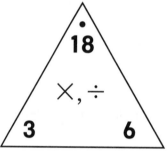

$$\underline{} \times \underline{} = \underline{}$$

$$\underline{} \times \underline{} = \underline{}$$

$$\underline{} \div \underline{} = \underline{}$$

$$\underline{} \div \underline{} = \underline{}$$

3.

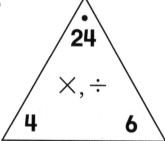

$$\underline{} \times \underline{} = \underline{}$$

$$\underline{} \times \underline{} = \underline{}$$

$$\underline{} \div \underline{} = \underline{}$$

$$\underline{} \div \underline{} = \underline{}$$

4.

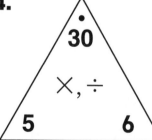

$$\underline{} \times \underline{} = \underline{} \qquad \underline{} \div \underline{} = \underline{}$$

$$\underline{} \times \underline{} = \underline{} \qquad \underline{} \div \underline{} = \underline{}$$

LESSON 11·9   Ten Frames

LESSON 11·9 A Paper-Folding Problem

Imagine folding a piece of paper in half. You would get 2 rectangles.
If you fold it in half again, you would get 4 smaller rectangles.

Predict how many small rectangles you would
get if you fold a piece of paper in half 6 times. _____

After you have made your prediction, try it out and check
your answer.

Keep track of your results after each fold to see if there is a pattern.

_____

_____

✂ -

Name   Date   Time

LESSON 11·9 A Paper-Folding Problem

Imagine folding a piece of paper in half. You would get 2 rectangles.
If you fold it in half again, you would get 4 smaller rectangles.

Predict how many small rectangles you would
get if you fold a piece of paper in half 6 times. _____

After you have made your prediction, try it out and check
your answer.

Keep track of your results after each fold to see if there is a pattern.

_____

HOME LINK 11·10

Unit 12: Family Letter

Year-End Reviews and Extensions

Rather than focusing on a single topic, Unit 12 reinforces some of the main topics covered in second grade.

Children will begin the unit by reviewing time measurements—telling time on clocks with hour and minute hands; naming time in different ways; using larger units of time, such as centuries and decades; and keeping track of time in years, months, weeks, and days.

Children will also work with computation dealing with multiplication facts and the relationship between multiplication and division.

Finally, children will display and interpret measurement data, with special attention to the range, median, and mode of sets of data.

Please keep this Family Letter for reference as your child works through Unit 12.

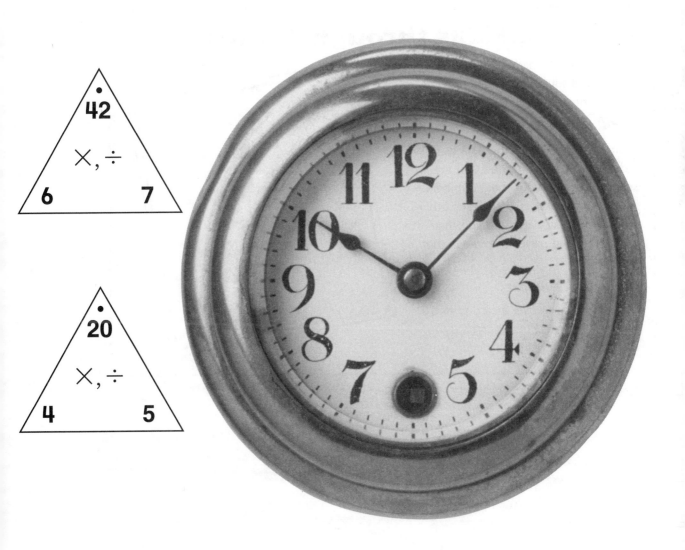

Vocabulary

Important terms in Unit 12:

timeline A *number line* showing when events took place. For example, the timeline below shows when the telephone, radio, and television were invented.

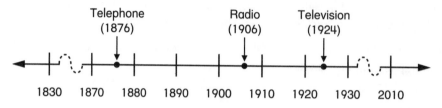

Telephone (1876)   Radio (1906)   Television (1924)

1830   1870   1880   1890   1900   1910   1920   1930   2010

mode The value or values that occurs most often in a set of data.

Building Skills through Games

In Unit 12, your child will practice adding and subtracting numbers by playing the following games:

Addition Card Draw

Each player draws the top 3 cards from a deck, records the numbers on the score sheet, and adds the 3 numbers. After 3 turns, players check each other's work with a calculator and add their 3 answers. The player with the higher total wins.

Name That Number

Each player turns over a card to find a number that must be renamed using any combination of five faceup cards.

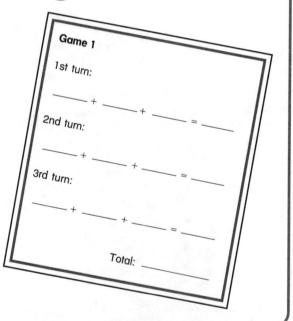

Game 1

1st turn:

_____ + _____ + _____ = _____

2nd turn:

_____ + _____ + _____ = _____

3rd turn:

_____ + _____ + _____ = _____

Total: _____

Do-Anytime Activities

To work with your child on the concepts taught in this unit and in previous units, try these interesting and rewarding activities:

1. Together, make up multidigit addition and subtraction number stories. Solve them. Share solution strategies.

2. Make timelines of your lives. In addition to personal information, mark various dates of events that interest you, such as events in music, art, sports, or politics.

3. Continue to ask the time. Encourage your child to name time in different ways, such as *twenty to nine* for 8:40 and *half-past two* for 2:30.

4. Continue to review and practice basic facts for all operations, emphasizing the multiplication facts.

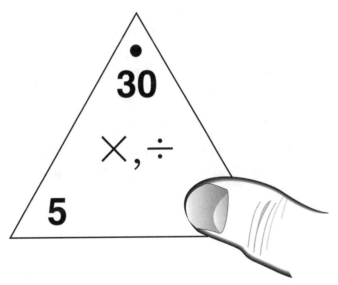

FEBRUARY						
Sun	Mon	Tue	Wed	Thu	Fri	Sat
	1	2	3	4	5	6
7	8	9	10	11	12	13
14	15	16	17	18	19	20
21	22	23	24	25	26	27
28	(29)					

As You Help Your Child with Homework

As your child brings home assignments, you may want to go over the instructions together, clarifying them as necessary. The answers listed below will guide you through this unit's Home Links.

Home Link 12·1

1. $9 \times 2 = 18$

$2 \times 9 = 18$

$18 \div 2 = 9$

$18 \div 9 = 2$

2. $1 \times 8 = 8$

$8 \times 1 = 8$

$8 \div 1 = 8$

$8 \div 8 = 1$

3. $5 \times 8 = 40$

$8 \times 5 = 40$

$40 \div 8 = 5$

$40 \div 5 = 8$

4. 184

5. 60

6. 243

7. 181

Home Link 12·2

1. 4:10　　**2.** 8:15　　**3.** 10:45

4.

5.

6.

7. 169　　**8.** 142　　**9.** 91　　**10.** 47

Home Link 12·3

2. 531　　　　　　**3.** 280

Home Link 12·5

1. 7　　**2.** 6　　**3.** 7　　**4.** 3

5. 4　　**6.** 4　　**7.** 4　　**8.** 5

9. 7　　**10.** 8　　**11.** 7　　**12.** 9

13. 6　　**14.** 9

Home Link 12·6

1. 30 years

2. dolphins and humans

3. 10 years

4. ostrich

5. squirrel, house cat, lion, horse, ostrich, dolphin, human

6. 30 years　**7.** 130　**8.** 156　**9.** 29　**10.** 87

Home Link 12·7

1. a. 1,450　**b.** 1,750

2. a. 2,000　**b.** 1,300　**c.** 700

3. 1,450

4. 1,450

LESSON 12·1 | Math Message

Name _____

Math Message

There are:

_____ days in 1 week.

_____ hours in 1 day.

_____ months in 1 year.

_____ weeks in 1 year.

_____ seconds in 1 minute.

_____ minutes in 1 hour.

Name _____

Math Message

There are:

_____ days in 1 week.

_____ hours in 1 day.

_____ months in 1 year.

_____ weeks in 1 year.

_____ seconds in 1 minute.

_____ minutes in 1 hour.

Name _____

Math Message

There are:

_____ days in 1 week.

_____ hours in 1 day.

_____ months in 1 year.

_____ weeks in 1 year.

_____ seconds in 1 minute.

_____ minutes in 1 hour.

Name _____

Math Message

There are:

_____ days in 1 week.

_____ hours in 1 day.

_____ months in 1 year.

_____ weeks in 1 year.

_____ seconds in 1 minute.

_____ minutes in 1 hour.

HOME LINK 12·1 | **Fact Triangles**

Family Note In class today, your child reviewed the calendar and continued to practice multiplication and division facts. Please spend a few minutes with your child as often as possible practicing facts. You can use Fact Triangles, or you can play a game like *Multiplication Top-It* or *Beat the Calculator.*

Please return this Home Link to school tomorrow.

MRB 38

Fill in the missing number in each Fact Triangle. Then write the fact family for the triangle.

1.

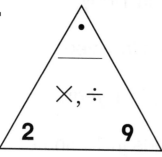

____ × ____ = ____

____ × ____ = ____

____ ÷ ____ = ____

____ ÷ ____ = ____

2.

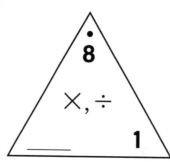

____ × ____ = ____

____ × ____ = ____

____ ÷ ____ = ____

____ ÷ ____ = ____

3.

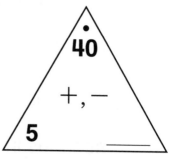

____ × ____ = ____

____ × ____ = ____

____ ÷ ____ = ____

____ ÷ ____ = ____

Practice

4.
$$\begin{array}{r} 231 \\ -\ 47 \\ \hline \end{array}$$

5.
$$\begin{array}{r} 85 \\ -\ 25 \\ \hline \end{array}$$

6.
$$\begin{array}{r} 156 \\ +\ 87 \\ \hline \end{array}$$

7.
$$\begin{array}{r} 94 \\ +\ 87 \\ \hline \end{array}$$

LESSON 12·1

Telling Time to the Nearest Five Minutes

Start at 0. Count by 5s. Fill the numbers of minutes at the 5-minute intervals around the clock face.

1.

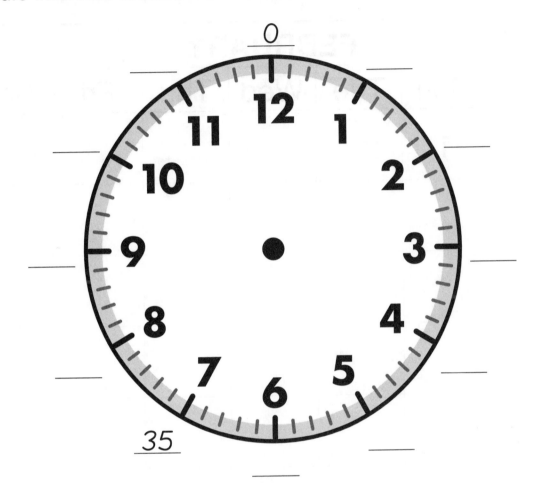

0

35

Draw the minute hands on the clocks to show the times. Use the 5-minute intervals to help.

2.

12:20

3.

1:50

4.

7:25

379

LESSON 12·1 | **Leap Years**

1. Fill in the numbers to show a leap year calendar for February. Circle the date that makes it a leap year.

FEBRUARY

Sun	Mon	Tue	Wed	Thu	Fri	Sat
	1					

2. The year 2000 was a leap year. Fill in the Frames-and-Arrows diagram with the other leap years. Write the rule for figuring out leap years.

Rule

| | 2000 | | |

| | | | |

Many Names for Times

Family Note Because clocks with clock faces were used for centuries before the invention of digital clocks, people often name the time by describing the positions of the hour and minute hands. Observe as your child solves the time problems below.

Please return this Home Link to school tomorrow.

MRB
82 83

What time is it? Write the time shown on the clocks.

1.

____ : ____

2.

____ : ____

3.

____ : ____

Draw the hour hand and the minute hand to show the time.

4.

half-past nine

5.

six fifty

6.

quarter-to two

Practice

7. 126 + 43 =

8. 243 − 101 =

9.   38
      +53

10.   84
       −37

LESSON 12·2 | Military Time

Regular time uses numbers 1 to 12 to identify each of the 24 hours in a day. In military time, the hours are numbered from 00 to 23.

Under this system, midnight is 00; 1 A.M. is 0100 hours; 1 P.M. is 1300 hours; 4 P.M. is 1600 hours.

Complete the table showing regular time and military time.

Regular Time	Military Time (hours)	Regular Time	Military Time (hours)
Midnight	0000	Noon	1200
1:00 A.M.	0100	1:00 P.M.	1300
2:00 A.M.	0200	2:00 P.M.	
3:00 A.M.	0300		
4:00 A.M.			
5:00 A.M.			
6:00 A.M.			
7:00 A.M.			

6 A.M. is the same as _____ hours.

10 P.M. is the same as _____ hours.

Try This

How would you write 3:15 P.M. in military time? Explain your answer.

LESSON 12·2 **Telling Time to Five Minutes**

Write the time shown on each clock.

1.

_____ : _____

2.

_____ : _____

3.

_____ : _____

4.

_____ : _____

5.

_____ : _____

6.

_____ : _____

Draw the hour and minute hands to match the time.

7.

4:55

8.

7:25

9.

8:05

10.

1:50

11.

6:20

12.

10:40

HOME LINK 12·3 Timelines

Emily's Day at the Beach

1. For each event below, make a dot on the timeline and write the letter for the event above the dot.

   A Ate lunch (12:30 P.M.)

   B Went fishing in a boat (10:00 A.M.)

   C Arrived at the beach (9:00 A.M.)

   D Returned from fishing trip (11:30 A.M.)

   E Played volleyball (1:30 P.M.)

   F Went swimming (2:00 P.M.)

   G Drove home (4:00 P.M.)

   H Built sandcastles (3:00 P.M.)

Practice

Solve.

2. 563 − 32 | **Answer** |

3.   263
       + 17 | **Answer** |

5:00 P.M.

4:00 P.M.

3:00 P.M.

2:00 P.M.

1:00 P.M.

A •

12:00 P.M.

11:00 A.M.

10:00 A.M.

9:00 A.M.

8:00 A.M.

7:00 A.M.

384

LESSON 12·3 | Placing Numbers on a Number Line

Draw a mark on the number line to show where each number belongs. Write the number below the mark.

Example: Show 95.

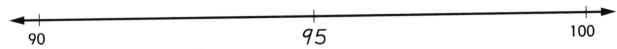

90   *95*   100

1. Use the number line below.

Show 80.

Show 100.

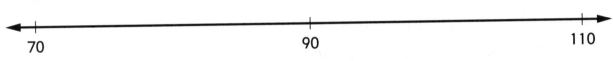

70   90   110

2. Use the number line below.

Show 1900 (the turn of the century).

Show 100 years before you were born.

1850   1950

Try This

3. Use the number line below.

Show the year you were born.

Show this year.

1950   2050

385

LESSON 12·3 | **Interpreting a Timeline**

1. What is the earliest invention on the timeline

on journal page 295? _____

What is the most recent invention? _____

For each pair of inventions:

♦ tell about how many decades there were between inventions.

> **Reminder:** 1 decade is 10 years.
> 1 century is 100 years.
> 1 century is 10 decades.

♦ tell about how many years there were between inventions.

2. typewriter and movie machine

about _____ decades   about _____ years

3. phonograph and videocassette

about _____ decades   about _____ years

4. telegraph and CD player

about _____ decades   about _____ years

About how many years ago were these things invented?

5. CD player: about _____ years ago

6. FM radio: about _____ years ago

7. 3-D movies: about _____ years ago

8. typewriter: about _____ years ago

HOME LINK 12·4

×, ÷ Fact Triangles

Family Note   Your child has been practicing multiplication facts. Today children reviewed shortcuts for solving multiplication problems with the numbers 2, 5, and 10. Encourage your child to practice with the Fact Triangles over the summer in preparation for third grade.

MRB
38

Cut out the Fact Triangles on these pages. Show someone at home how you can use them to practice multiplication facts.

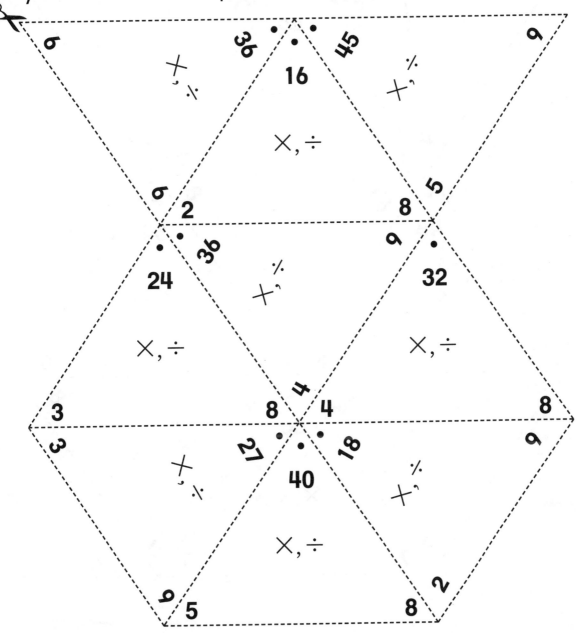

HOME LINK 12·4   ×, ÷ **Fact Triangles** *continued*

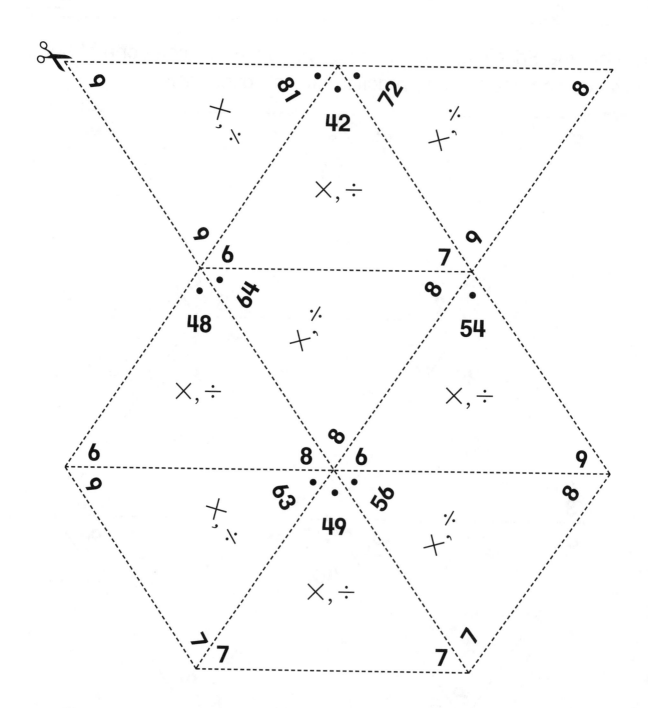

LESSON 12·4   # Multiplication Arrays

Draw the array for each problem. Then fill in the Fact Triangle to match the arrays.

1. Draw an array for 3 groups of 2.

Number model: $3 \times 2 = ?$

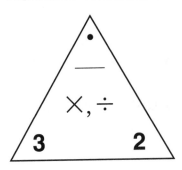

Number model: $3 \times 2 = \underline{\hspace{1cm}}$

Draw an array for 2 groups of 3.

Number model: $2 \times 3 = ?$

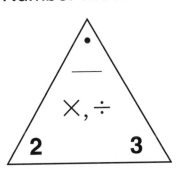

Number model: $2 \times 3 = \underline{\hspace{1cm}}$

2. Draw an array for 3 groups of 4.

Number model: $3 \times 4 = ?$

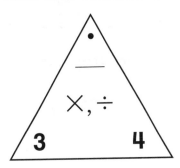

Number model: $3 \times 4 = \underline{\hspace{1cm}}$

Draw an array for 4 groups of 3.

Number model: $4 \times 3 = ?$

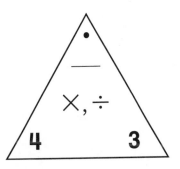

Number model: $4 \times 3 = \underline{\hspace{1cm}}$

Try This

1. Draw an array for 3 groups of 3.

Number model: $3 \times 3 = ?$

Number model: $3 \times 3 = \underline{\hspace{1cm}}$

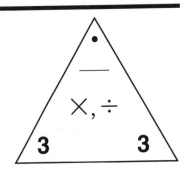

389

LESSON 12·4 | # A Multiplication Strategy

To solve 4 × 3, Briana used two steps.

◆ In her first step, she got 6.

◆ In her second step, she got 12. 12 was the answer.

To solve 4 × 7, Briana again used two steps.

◆ In her first step, she got 14.

◆ In her second step, she got 28. 28 was the answer.

Explain Briana's strategy. Then try solving 4 × 8 using Briana's strategy.

_____

_____

_____

_____

_____

HOME LINK 12·5

×, ÷ **Facts Practice**

Family Note   In this lesson, your child has connected multiplication and division facts by using Fact Triangles and completing fact families. A good way to solve division problems is to think in terms of multiplication. For example, to divide 20 by 5, ask yourself: *5 times what number equals 20?* Since $5 \times 4 = 20$, $20 \div 5 = 4$.

Please return this Home Link to school tomorrow.

Solve these division facts. Think multiplication.

Use the Fact Triangles to help you.

1. $14 \div 2 = $ _____

Think:
$2 \times ? = 14$

14
×, ÷
2   **7**

2. $24 \div 4 = $ _____

Think:
$4 \times ? = 24$

24
×, ÷
4   **6**

3. $21 \div 3 = $ _____

Think:
$3 \times ? = 21$

21
×, ÷
3   **7**

4. $18 \div 6 = $ _____

Think:
$6 \times ? = 18$

18
×, ÷
6   **3**

5. $28 \div 7 = $ _____

Think:
$7 \times ? = 28$

28
×, ÷
7   **4**

6. $16 \div 4 = $ _____

Think:
$4 \times ? = 16$

16
×, ÷
4   **4**

HOME LINK 12·5

×, ÷ **Facts Practice** *continued*

7. 20 ÷ 5 = _____

Think:
5 × ? = 20

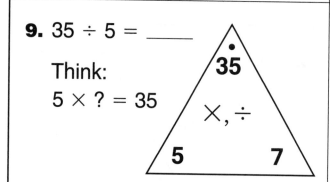

8. 30 ÷ 6 = _____

Think:
6 × ? = 30

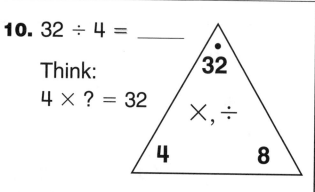

9. 35 ÷ 5 = _____

Think:
5 × ? = 35

10. 32 ÷ 4 = _____

Think:
4 × ? = 32

11. 42 ÷ 6 = _____

Think:
6 × ? = 42

12. 63 ÷ 7 = _____

Think:
7 × ? = 63

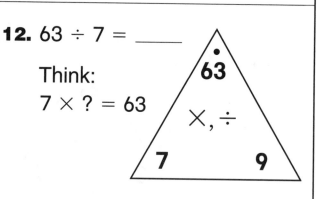

13. 54 ÷ 9 = _____

Think:
9 × ? = 54

14. 81 ÷ 9 = _____

Think:
9 × ? = 81

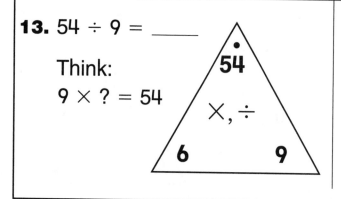
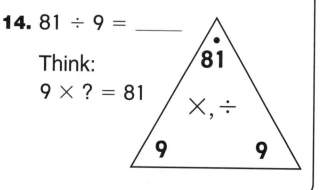

LESSON 12·5 | **Equal Rows**

Use counters to build arrays for each problem. Find the number in each row for the arrays.

1. Use 6 counters. Build an array that has 2 rows. How many are in each row? _____

Write a number model to show how you found the number in each row.

Number Model: _____

2. Use 12 counters. Build an array that has 4 rows. How many are in each row? _____

Write a number model to show how you found the number in each row.

Number Model: _____

3. Use 16 counters. Build an array that has 4 rows. How many are in each row? _____

Write a number model to show how you found the number in each row.

Number Model: _____

Try This

4. Use _____ counters. Build an array that has _____ rows. How many are in each row? _____

Write a number model to show how you found the number in each row.

Number Model: _____

393

LESSON 12·5   **"What's My Rule?"**

Complete the tables in Problems 1–3.

1.

Rule
×2

in	out
3	
5	
	14
8	
	12

2.

Rule
×10

in	out
2	
4	
	50
7	
	100

3.

Rule
×5

in	out
0	
3	
	50
8	
	100

Complete the table and write the rule.

4.

Rule

in	out
1	2
2	4
	6
5	
8	16

Complete the table and write the rule.

5.

Rule

in	out
2	8
3	12
5	
6	24
	40

Write a rule of your own. Fill in the table.

6.

Rule

in	out

HOME LINK 12·6 Typical Life Spans

Family Note In this lesson, your child has been reading, drawing, and interpreting bar graphs. Bar graphs are often useful when one wants to make rough comparisons quickly and easily. Provide your child with additional practice in interpreting a bar graph by asking questions like Problems 1 through 4.

Please return this Home Link to school tomorrow.

MRB
44

Typical Life Spans

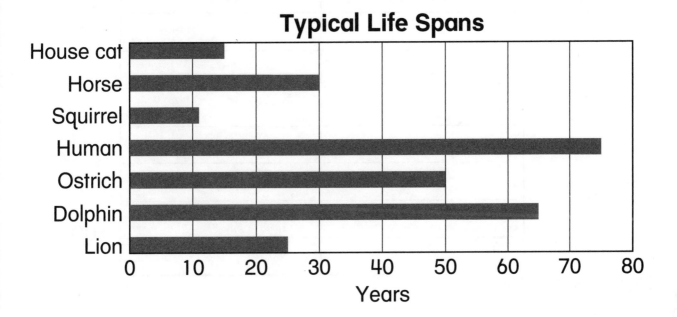

1. About how long do horses live? _____ years

2. Which animals live longer than an ostrich?

   _____

3. About how much longer do lions live than house cats?
   _____ years

4. Which animal lives about twice as long as lions? _____

HOME LINK 12·6 | **Typical Life Spans** *continued*

5. List the animals in order from the shortest life span to the longest life span.

Life Spans	
Animal	**Years**
shortest:	
longest:	

6. What is the middle value? _____ years
This is the **median.**

Practice

7. 71 + 59 =

8. 121
     + 35
    _____

9. 68 − 39 =

10. 125
      − 38
    _____

LESSON 12·6 | Distances

Distances athletic adults can travel in 10 seconds:

Cross-country skiing 200 feet

Ice-skating 450 feet

Walking 125 feet

Swimming 75 feet

Running hurdles 275 feet

Running 325 feet

LESSON 12·6 | **Graphing Information**

1. Complete the graph below with the information on *Math Masters*, page 397.

Distances Athletic Adults Can Travel in 10 Seconds

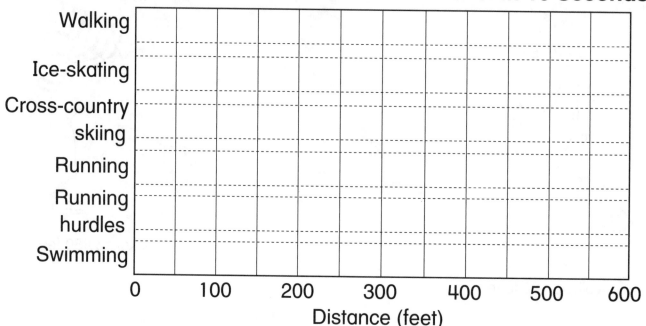

Distance (feet)

Interpret the graph.

2. The longest distance is _____ feet.

   The shortest distance is _____ feet.

   The difference between the
   longest distance and the shortest distance (range) is _____ feet.

3. What is a middle value of the distances on your graph? _____ feet

4. About how much distance can a cross-country skier cover:

   in 20 seconds? _____ feet

   in 30 seconds? _____ feet

   in 1 minute? _____ feet

LESSON 12·6 | **Observing the Sleeping Hours of Animals**

Use the graph below to answer the following questions.

How Much Sleep Does an Animal Need?

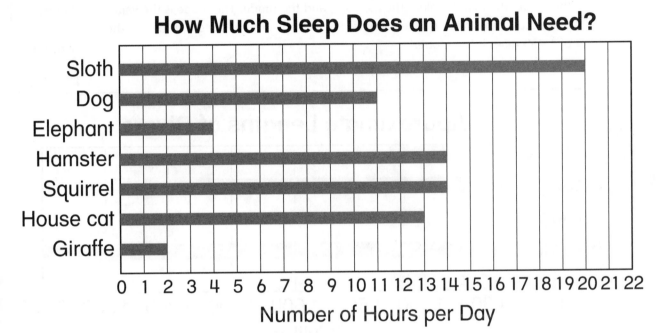

Number of Hours per Day

1. Which animal sleeps the most?

(maximum) _____ How long? _____ hours

2. Which animal sleeps the least?

(minimum)_____ How long? _____ hours

3. What is the range (difference) between the longest and shortest time animals sleep in a day? _____ hours

4. What is the median (middle value) number of hours of sleep? _____

5. What is the mode (number that occurs most often) number of hours of sleep? _____

6. How many hours do you sleep per night?

_____ hours

HOME LINK
12·7

Interpret a Bar Graph

Family Note In class today, your child interpreted graphs and identified the greatest value, the least value, the range, the middle value (the median), and the mode. The mode is the value or category that occurs most often in a set of data. For example, in the bar graph below, the river length of 1,450 miles is the mode.

Please return this Home Link to school tomorrow.

Approximate Lengths of Rivers

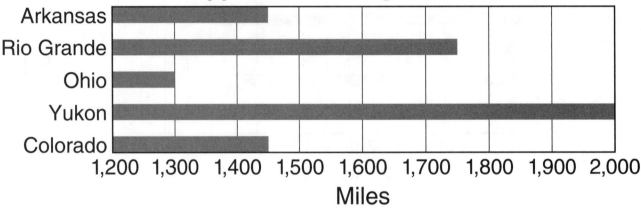

1. a. What is the length of the Colorado River? About _____ miles

   b. Of the Rio Grande? About _____ miles

2. a. What is the length of the longest river? About _____ miles

   b. What is the length of the shortest river? About _____ miles

   c. What is the difference in length between the longest and the

   shortest rivers? About _____ miles. This is the **range.**

3. Which river length occurs most often? About _____ miles
This is the **mode.**

4. What is the middle length of the rivers? About _____ miles
This is the **median.**

LESSON 12·7 | **Landmarks of a Data Set**

The Children's Book Club members went to the library to check out books. Jim recorded the number of books each child checked out. This is what he found:

The minimum number of books is 1.

The maximum number of books is 6.

The mode number of books is 3.

The median number of books is 3.

The range for the number of books children check out is 5.

Explain what each landmark means.

_____

_____

_____

_____

_____

_____

Circle the graph that shows Jim's data.

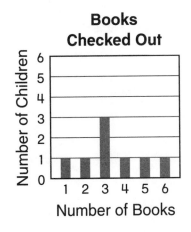

Books Checked Out

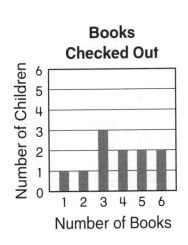

Books Checked Out

HOME LINK 12·8 **Family Letter**

Congratulations!

By completing *Second Grade Everyday Mathematics,* your child has accomplished a great deal. Thank you for your support!

This Family Letter is provided as a resource for you to use throughout your child's vacation. It includes an extended list of Do-Anytime Activities, directions for games that can be played at home, an Addition/Subtraction Facts Table, and a sneak preview of what your child will be learning in *Third Grade Everyday Mathematics.* Enjoy your vacation!

Do-Anytime Activities

Mathematics concepts are more meaningful when they are rooted in real-life situations. To help your child review some of the concepts he or she has learned in second grade, we suggest the following activities for you and your child to do together over vacation. These activities will help your child build on the skills learned this year and help prepare him or her for *Third Grade Everyday Mathematics.*

1. Fill in blank calendar pages for the vacation months, including special events and dates. Discuss the number of weeks of vacation, days before school starts, and so on.

2. Continue to ask the time. Encourage alternate ways of naming time, such as *twenty to nine* for 8:40 and *quarter-past five* for 5:15.

3. Continue to review and practice basic facts for all operations, especially those for addition and subtraction.

4. Use Fact Triangle cards to practice basic multiplication and division facts, such as the following:

$2 \times 2 = 4$	$4 \div 2 = 2$
$2 \times 3 = 6$	$6 \div 2 = 3$
$2 \times 4 = 8$	$8 \div 2 = 4$
$2 \times 5 = 10$	$10 \div 2 = 5$
$3 \times 4 = 12$	$12 \div 3 = 4$
$3 \times 3 = 9$	$9 \div 3 = 3$
$4 \times 4 = 16$	$16 \div 4 = 4$
$3 \times 5 = 15$	$15 \div 3 = 5$
$4 \times 5 = 20$	$20 \div 4 = 5$

Building Skills through Games

The following section describes games that can be played at home. The number cards used in some games can be made from 3" by 5" index cards or from a regular playing-card deck.

Addition Top-It

Materials   ☐ 4 cards for each of the numbers 0–10 (1 set for each player)

Players   2 or more

Skill   Add, subtract, or multiply two numbers

Object of the Game To have the most cards

Directions

Players combine and shuffle their cards and place them in a deck, facedown. Each player turns up a pair of cards from the deck and says the sum of the numbers. The player with the greater sum takes all the cards that are in play. The player with the most cards at the end of the game is the winner. Ties are broken by drawing again—winner takes all.

Variation: *Subtraction Top-It*

Partners pool and shuffle their 0–20 number cards. Each player turns up a pair of cards from the facedown deck and says the difference between them. The player with the greater difference gets all four cards. The player with more cards at the end of the game is the winner.

Variation: *Multiplication Top-It*

Players find the product of the numbers instead of the sum or difference. Use the 0–10 number cards.

Pick-a-Coin

Materials   ☐ regular die

                 ☐ record sheet (see example)

                 ☐ calculator

Players   2 or 3

Skill   Add coin and dollar amounts

Sample Record Sheet						
	Ⓟ	Ⓝ	Ⓓ	Ⓠ	$1	Total
1st turn	2	1	4	5	3	$ 4.72
2nd turn						$ ___
3rd turn						$ ___
4th turn						$ ___
					Grand Total	$ ___

Object of the Game To have the highest total

Directions

Players take turns. At each turn, a player rolls a die five times. After each roll, the player records the number that comes up on the die in any one of the empty cells for that turn on his or her Record Sheet. Then the player finds the total amount and records it in the table.

After four turns, each player uses a calculator to find his or her grand total. The player with the highest grand total wins.

Multiplication Draw

Materials
- ☐ number cards 1, 2, 3, 4, 5, 10 (4 of each)
- ☐ record sheet (1 for each player)
- ☐ calculator

Players 2–4

Skill Multiply two numbers

Object of the Game To have the highest total

Multiplication Draw Record Sheet

1st Draw: _____ × _____ = _____

2nd Draw: _____ × _____ = _____

3rd Draw: _____ × _____ = _____

4th Draw: _____ × _____ = _____

5th Draw: _____ × _____ = _____

Sum of products: _____

Directions

Shuffle the cards and place the deck facedown on the playing surface. At each turn, players draw two cards from the deck to make up a multiplication problem. They record the problem on a record sheet and write the answer. If the answer is incorrect, it will not be counted. After five turns, players use a calculator to find the total of their correct answers. The player with the highest total wins.

Name That Number

Materials
- ☐ number cards 0–10 (4 of each)
- ☐ number cards 11–20 (1 of each)

Players 2 or 3

Skill Add, substract, multiply, or divide two numbers to reach a target number

Object of the Game To have the most cards

Directions

Shuffle the deck of cards and place it facedown on the table. Turn the top five cards faceup and place them in a row. Turn over the next card. This is the target number for the round.

In turn, players try to name the target number by adding, subtracting, multiplying, or dividing the numbers on 2 or more of the 5 cards that are number-side up. A card may be used only once for each turn. If you can name the target number, take the cards you used to name it. Also take the target-number card. Then replace all the cards you took by drawing from the top of the deck. If you cannot name the target number, your turn is over. Turn over the top card of the deck and lay it down on the target-number pile. The number on this card is the new target number.

Play continues until there are not enough cards left in the deck to replace the players' cards. The player who has taken the most cards at the end wins. Sample turn:

Mae's turn:

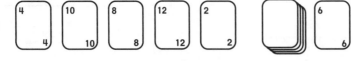

The target number is 6. Mae names it with 12 − 4 − 2. She also could have used 4 + 2 or 8 − 2.

Mae takes the 12, 4, 2, and 6 cards. She replaces them by drawing cards from the facedown deck and then turns over and lays down the next card to replace the 6. Now it is Mike's turn.

Fact Power

Addition/subtraction fact families can also be practiced by using the Addition/Subtraction Facts Table. This table can be used to keep a record of facts that have been learned as well.

+,−	0	1	2	3	4	5	6	7	8	9
0	0	1	2	3	4	5	6	7	8	9
1	1	2	3	4	5	6	7	8	9	10
2	2	3	4	5	6	7	8	9	10	11
3	3	4	5	6	7	8	9	10	11	12
4	4	5	6	7	8	9	10	11	12	13
5	5	6	7	8	9	10	11	12	13	14
6	6	7	8	9	10	11	12	13	14	15
7	7	8	9	10	11	12	13	14	15	16
8	8	9	10	11	12	13	14	15	16	17
9	9	10	11	12	13	14	15	16	17	18

Looking Ahead:
Third Grade Everyday Mathematics

Next year, your child will …

◆ Explore the relationship between multiplication and division

◆ Extend multiplication and division facts to multiples of 10, 100, and 1,000

◆ Use parentheses in writing number models

◆ Record equivalent units of length

◆ Use number models to find the areas of rectangles

◆ Explore 2- and 3-dimensional shapes and other geometric concepts

◆ Read and write numbers up to 1,000,000

◆ Work with fractions and decimals

◆ Collect data for yearlong sunrise/sunset and high/low temperature projects

◆ Use map scales to estimate distances

Again, thank you for your support this year. Have fun continuing your child's mathematics experiences throughout the vacation!

Project Masters

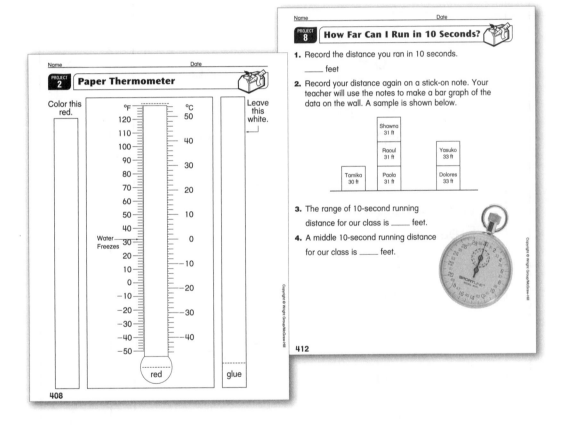

Paper Thermometer

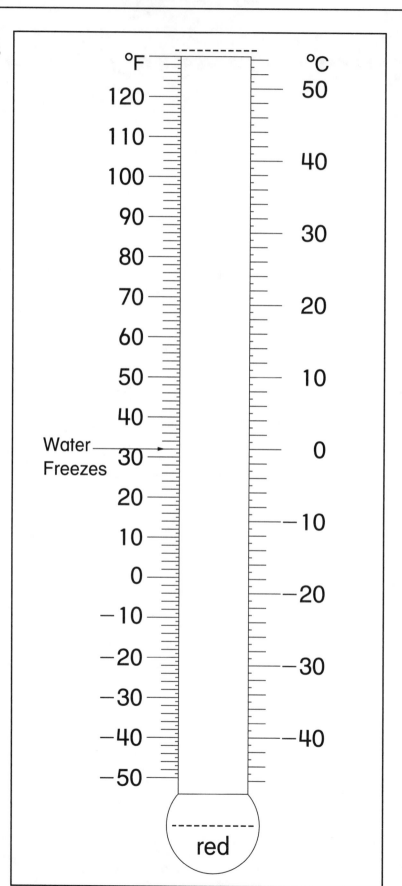

Color this red.

°F
120
110
100
90
80
70
60
50
40
Water Freezes → 30
20
10
0
−10
−20
−30
−40
−50

°C
50
40
30
20
10
0
−10
−20
−30
−40

red

Leave this white.

glue

Name _____   Date _____

A Week of Weather Observations

Temp.		Cloudy	Windy	Rainy	Snowy	Foggy	Icy	Other
Monday Mon.	A.M. P.M.							
Tuesday Tues.	A.M. P.M.							
Wednesday Wed.	A.M. P.M.							
Thursday Thurs.	A.M. P.M.							
Friday Fri.	A.M. P.M.							
Totals	**A.M.** High ___ Low ___ **P.M.** High ___ Low ___	Clear ○ ___ Partly Cloudy ◑ ___ Cloudy ● ___						

Chinese Calendar Animals

Order of the animals beginning with the year of the rat: rat, ox, tiger, rabbit, dragon, snake, horse, sheep, monkey, rooster, dog, pig.

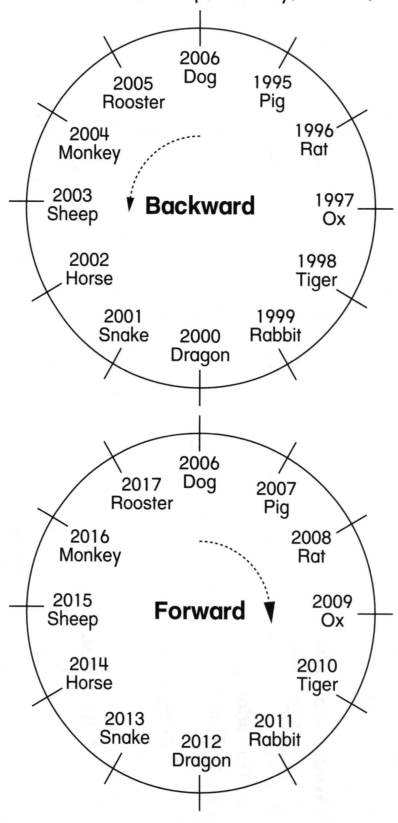

Top circle (Backward):
- 2006 Dog
- 1995 Pig
- 2005 Rooster
- 1996 Rat
- 2004 Monkey
- 1997 Ox
- 2003 Sheep
- 1998 Tiger
- 2002 Horse
- 1999 Rabbit
- 2001 Snake
- 2000 Dragon
- **Backward**

Bottom circle (Forward):
- 2006 Dog
- 2007 Pig
- 2017 Rooster
- 2008 Rat
- 2016 Monkey
- 2009 Ox
- 2015 Sheep
- 2010 Tiger
- 2014 Horse
- 2011 Rabbit
- 2013 Snake
- 2012 Dragon
- **Forward**

PROJECT 3

Chinese Calendar

Year of the

_____

_____

_____

_____

_____

_____

_____

_____

_____

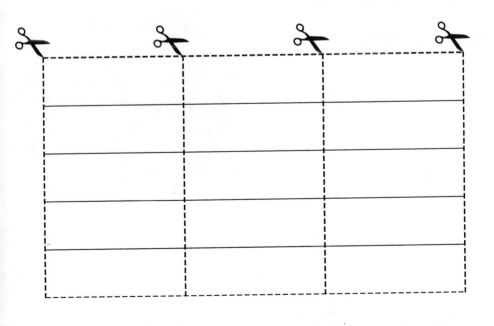

How Far Can I Run in 10 Seconds?

1. Record the distance you ran in 10 seconds.

_____ feet

2. Record your distance again on a stick-on note. Your teacher will use the notes to make a bar graph of the data on the wall. A sample is shown below.

	Shawna 31 ft	
	Raoul 31 ft	Yasuko 33 ft
Tamika 30 ft	Paola 31 ft	Dolores 33 ft

3. The range of 10-second running distance for our class is _____ feet.

4. A middle 10-second running distance for our class is _____ feet.

412

Teaching Aid Masters

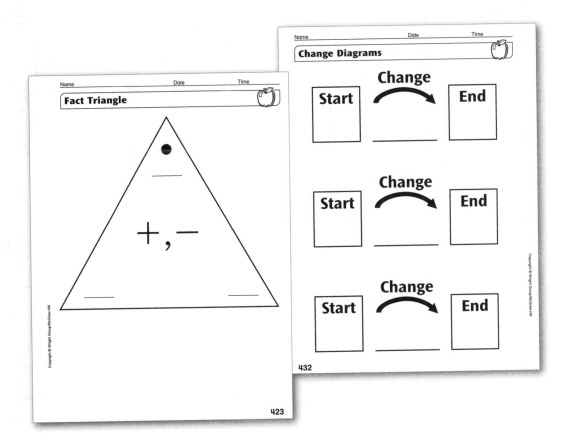

Name _____ Date _____ Time _____

Fact Triangle

●

—

$+, -$

Copyright © Wright Group/McGraw-Hill

423

Name _____ Date _____ Time _____

Change Diagrams

Change

Start	→	End

Change

Start	→	End

Change

Start	→	End

Copyright © Wright Group/McGraw-Hill

432

Blank Calendar Grid

						Sunday
						Monday
						Tuesday
						Wednesday
						Thursday
						Friday
						Saturday

Month _____

My Exit Slip

✂ -

My Exit Slip

Number Grid

−9	−8	−7	−6	−5	−4	−3	−2	−1	0
1	2	3	4	5	6	7	8	9	10
11	12	13	14	15	16	17	18	19	20
21	22	23	24	25	26	27	28	29	30
31	32	33	34	35	36	37	38	39	40
41	42	43	44	45	46	47	48	49	50
51	52	53	54	55	56	57	58	59	60
61	62	63	64	65	66	67	68	69	70
71	72	73	74	75	76	77	78	79	80
81	82	83	84	85	86	87	88	89	90
91	92	93	94	95	96	97	98	99	100
101	102	103	104	105	106	107	108	109	110

−9	−8	−7	−6	−5	−4	−3	−2	−1	0
1	2	3	4	5	6	7	8	9	10
11	12	13	14	15	16	17	18	19	20
21	22	23	24	25	26	27	28	29	30
31	32	33	34	35	36	37	38	39	40
41	42	43	44	45	46	47	48	49	50
51	52	53	54	55	56	57	58	59	60
61	62	63	64	65	66	67	68	69	70
71	72	73	74	75	76	77	78	79	80
81	82	83	84	85	86	87	88	89	90
91	92	93	94	95	96	97	98	99	100
101	102	103	104	105	106	107	108	109	110

Number Grid

-9	-8	-7	-6	-5	-4	-3	-2	-1	0
1	2	3	4	5	6	7	8	9	10
11	12	13	14	15	16	17	18	19	20
21	22	23	24	25	26	27	28	29	30
31	32	33	34	35	36	37	38	39	40
41	42	43	44	45	46	47	48	49	50
51	52	53	54	55	56	57	58	59	60
61	62	63	64	65	66	67	68	69	70
71	72	73	74	75	76	77	78	79	80
81	82	83	84	85	86	87	88	89	90
91	92	93	94	95	96	97	98	99	100
101	102	103	104	105	106	107	108	109	110

Number Grid

-9	-8	-7	-6	-5	-4	-3	-2	-1	0
1	2	3	4	5	6	7	8	9	10
11	12	13	14	15	16	17	18	19	20
21	22	23	24	25	26	27	28	29	30
31	32	33	34	35	36	37	38	39	40
41	42	43	44	45	46	47	48	49	50
51	52	53	54	55	56	57	58	59	60
61	62	63	64	65	66	67	68	69	70
71	72	73	74	75	76	77	78	79	80
81	82	83	84	85	86	87	88	89	90
91	92	93	94	95	96	97	98	99	100
101	102	103	104	105	106	107	108	109	110

A Number Story

Unit

Grid Paper

Facts Table

+,−	0	1	2	3	4	5	6	7	8	9
0	0	1	2	3	4	5	6	7	8	9
1	1	2	3	4	5	6	7	8	9	10
2	2	3	4	5	6	7	8	9	10	11
3	3	4	5	6	7	8	9	10	11	12
4	4	5	6	7	8	9	10	11	12	13
5	5	6	7	8	9	10	11	12	13	14
6	6	7	8	9	10	11	12	13	14	15
7	7	8	9	10	11	12	13	14	15	16
8	8	9	10	11	12	13	14	15	16	17
9	9	10	11	12	13	14	15	16	17	18

Ten-Frame Card

Fact Triangle

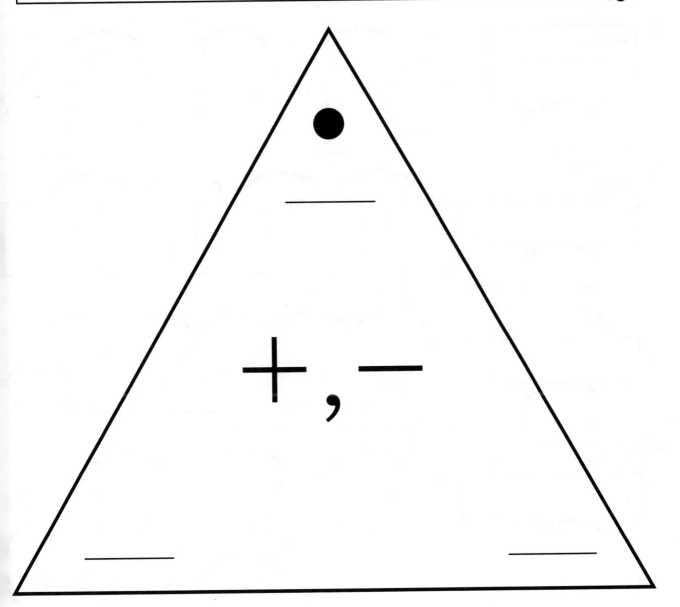

Frames-and-Arrows Problems

1.

Rule

2.

Rule

   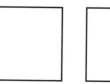

3.

Rule

 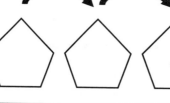 

4.

Rule

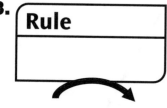 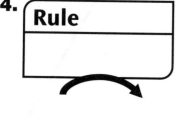

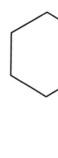 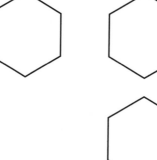 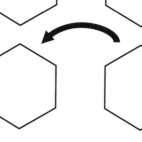 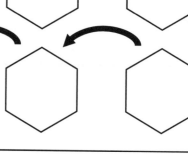

5.

Rule

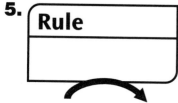 

Function Machine

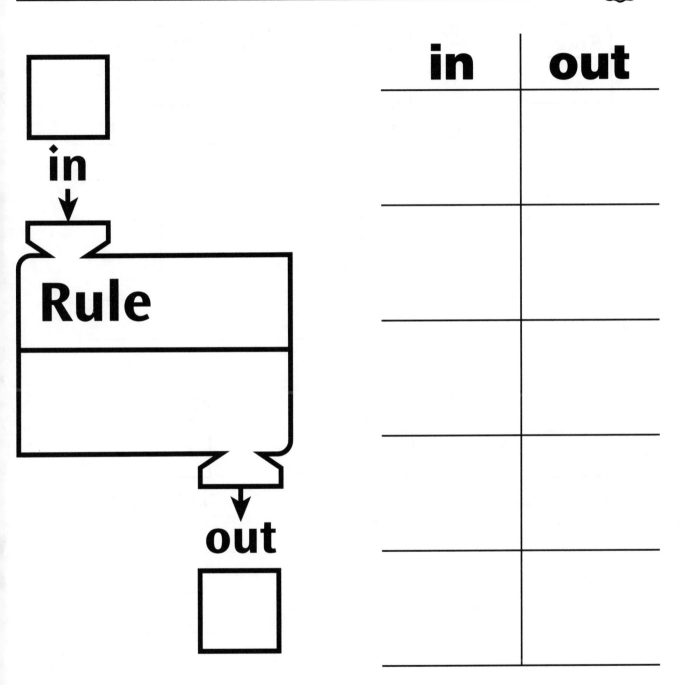

in	out

"What's My Rule?"

1.

Rule

in	out

2.

Rule

in	out

3.

Rule

in	out

4.

Rule

in	out

5.

Rule

in	out

6.

Rule

in	out

Place-Value Mat

ones	tens	hundreds

Place-Value Mat

Pennies 1s Cubes

$0.01
1¢

Dimes 10s Longs

$0.10
10¢

Dollars 100s Flats

$1.00
100¢

Geoboard Dot Paper (5 × 5)

1.

2.

3.

4.

5.

6.

Geoboard Dot Paper (7 × 7)

1.

2.

3.

4.

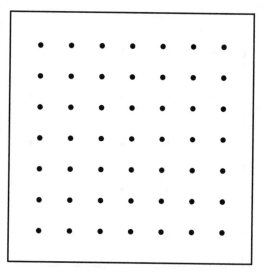

5.

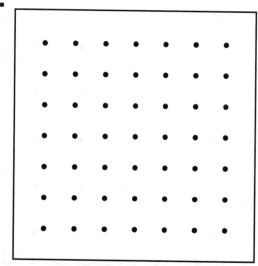

6.

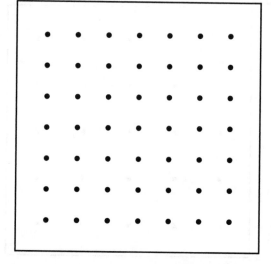

Two-Rule Frames and Arrows

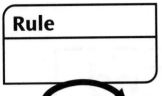

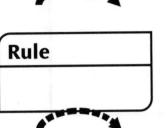

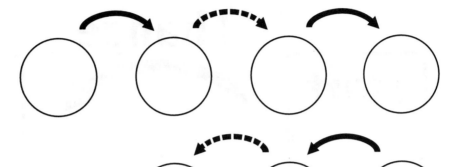

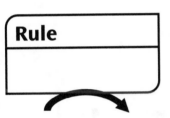

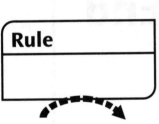

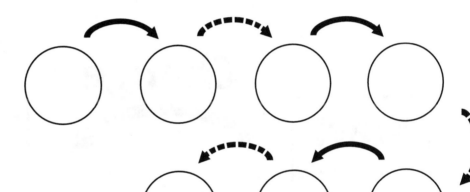

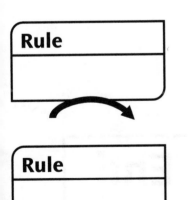

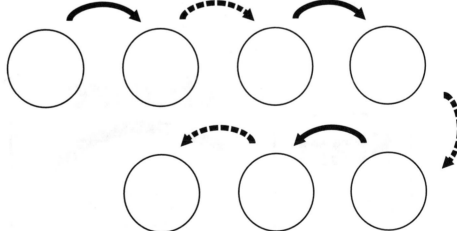

Change Diagrams

Start   Change   End

_____

Start   Change   End

_____

Start   Change   End

_____

Parts-and-Total Diagram

Total

Part

Part

Centimeter Grid Paper

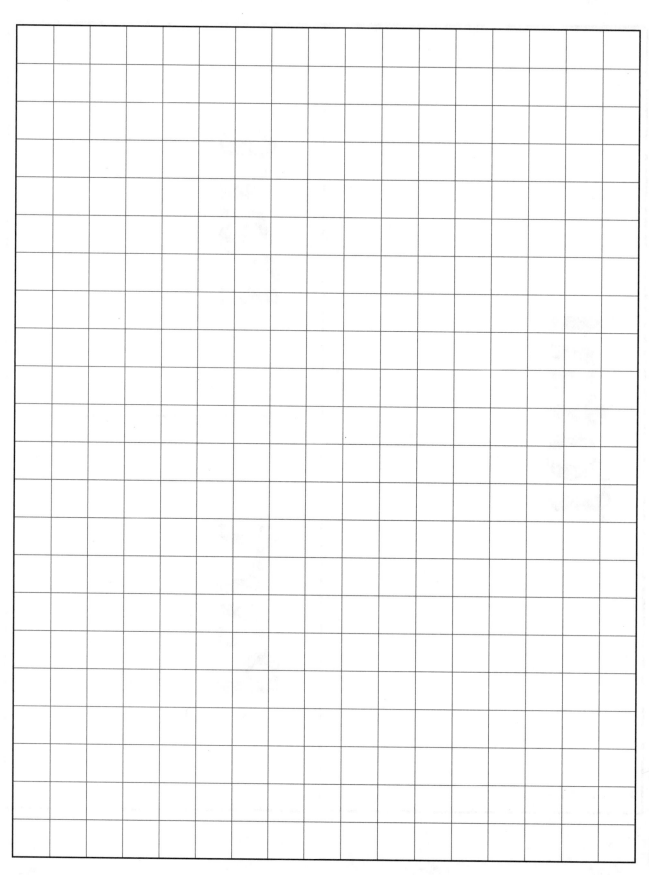

Base-10 Flat

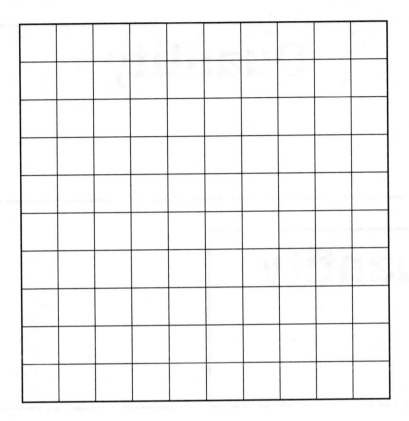

Comparison Diagram

Quantity

Quantity

_____
Difference

Diagram for Number Stories

Change

1.

Start

Change

End

2.

Start

Change

End

Parts-and-Total

Total	
Part	Part

Total	
Part	Part

Comparison

Quantity

Quantity

Difference

Quantity

Quantity

Difference

Array Multiplication

Array

```
O   O   O   O   O   O   O   O   O   O

O   O   O   O   O   O   O   O   O   O

O   O   O   O   O   O   O   O   O   O

O   O   O   O   O   O   O   O   O   O

O   O   O   O   O   O   O   O   O   O

O   O   O   O   O   O   O   O   O   O

O   O   O   O   O   O   O   O   O   O

O   O   O   O   O   O   O   O   O   O
```

Multiplication Diagram

rows	_____ per row	_____ in all

Number model: _____ × _____ = _____

Making Patterns

Make designs by coloring the grids. Use more than one color in each design.

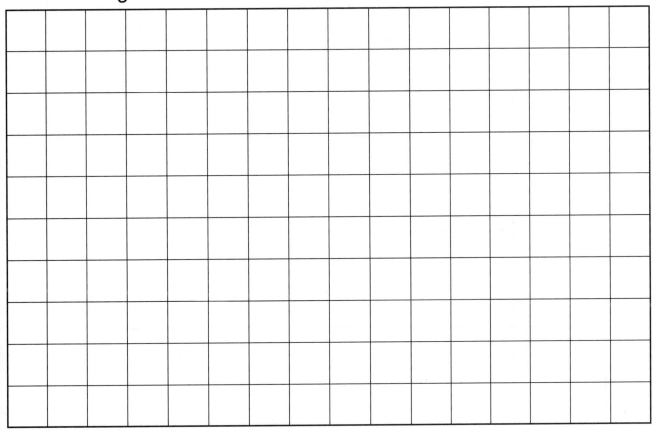

Name   Date   Time

Inch Grid Paper

Good Buys Poster

Fruit/Vegetables Group

Seedless Grapes
99¢ lb

Carrots
1-lb bag
3/$1.00

Plums
69¢ lb

Oranges
$1.49 lb

Bananas
59¢ lb

Watermelons
$2.99 ea.

Celery
59¢ lb

Meat Group

Pork & Beans
16 oz
2/89¢

Peanut Butter
18-oz jar
$1.29

Ground Beef
$1.99 lb

Chunk Light
Tuna
6.5 oz
69¢

Lunch Meat
1-lb package
$1.39

Milk Group

Gallon
Milk
$2.39

American
Cheese
8 oz
$1.49

6-pack
Yogurt
$2.09

Grain Group

Wheat Bread
16 oz
99¢

Saltines
1 lb
69¢

Hamburger
Buns
16 oz
69¢

Miscellaneous Items

Mayonnaise
32 oz
$1.99

Catsup
32 oz
$1.09

Grape Jelly
2-lb jar
$1.69

441

Multiplication/Division Diagram

_____	_____	_____ in all
	per _____	

_____	_____	_____ in all
	per _____	

_____	_____	_____ in all
	per _____	

Products Table

0×0 $= 0$	0×1 $=$	0×2 $=$	0×3 $=$	0×4 $=$	0×5 $=$	0×6 $=$	0×7 $=$	0×8 $=$	0×9 $=$	0×10 $=$
1×0 $=$	1×1 $= 1$	1×2 $=$	1×3 $=$	1×4 $=$	1×5 $=$	1×6 $=$	1×7 $=$	1×8 $=$	1×9 $=$	1×10 $=$
2×0 $=$	2×1 $=$	2×2 $= 4$	2×3 $=$	2×4 $=$	2×5 $=$	2×6 $=$	2×7 $=$	2×8 $=$	2×9 $=$	2×10 $=$
3×0 $=$	3×1 $=$	3×2 $=$	3×3 $= 9$	3×4 $=$	3×5 $=$	3×6 $=$	3×7 $=$	3×8 $=$	3×9 $=$	3×10 $=$
4×0 $=$	4×1 $=$	4×2 $=$	4×3 $=$	4×4 $= 16$	4×5 $=$	4×6 $=$	4×7 $=$	4×8 $=$	4×9 $=$	4×10 $=$
5×0 $=$	5×1 $=$	5×2 $=$	5×3 $=$	5×4 $=$	5×5 $= 25$	5×6 $=$	5×7 $=$	5×8 $=$	5×9 $=$	5×10 $=$
6×0 $=$	6×1 $=$	6×2 $=$	6×3 $=$	6×4 $=$	6×5 $=$	6×6 $= 36$	6×7 $=$	6×8 $=$	6×9 $=$	6×10 $=$
7×0 $=$	7×1 $=$	7×2 $=$	7×3 $=$	7×4 $=$	7×5 $=$	7×6 $=$	7×7 $= 49$	7×8 $=$	7×9 $=$	7×10 $=$
8×0 $=$	8×1 $=$	8×2 $=$	8×3 $=$	8×4 $=$	8×5 $=$	8×6 $=$	8×7 $=$	8×8 $= 64$	8×9 $=$	8×10 $=$
9×0 $=$	9×1 $=$	9×2 $=$	9×3 $=$	9×4 $=$	9×5 $=$	9×6 $=$	9×7 $=$	9×8 $=$	9×9 $= 81$	9×10 $=$
10×0 $=$	10×1 $=$	10×2 $=$	10×3 $=$	10×4 $=$	10×5 $=$	10×6 $=$	10×7 $=$	10×8 $=$	10×9 $=$	10×10 $= 100$

✕,÷ **Fact Triangle**

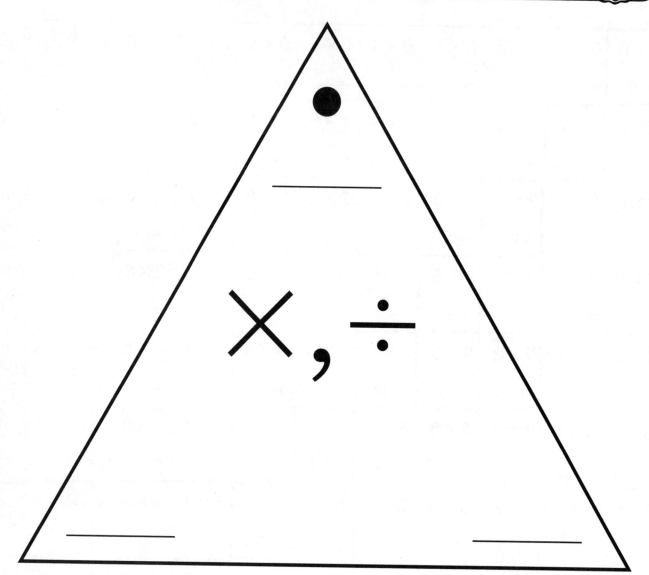

Game Masters

Hit the Target Record Sheet

Round 1

Target number: _____

Starting Number	Change	Result	Change	Result	Change	Result

Round 2

Target number: _____

Starting Number	Change	Result	Change	Result	Change	Result

Round 3

Target number: _____

Starting Number	Change	Result	Change	Result	Change	Result

Round 4

Target number: _____

Starting Number	Change	Result	Change	Result	Change	Result

Copyright © Wright Group/McGraw-Hill

457

Name Date Time

Name That Number Record Sheet

Target
Card

Number Sentence Solution

_____ **Reminder:** Write each step separately.

Copyright © Wright Group/McGraw-Hill

Name Date Time

Name That Number Record Sheet

Target
Card

Number Sentence Solution

_____ **Reminder:** Write each step separately.

462

Copyright © Wright Group/McGraw-Hill

Addition Card Draw Score Sheet

Game 1

1st turn:

____ + ____ + ____ = ____

2nd turn:

____ + ____ + ____ = ____

3rd turn:

____ + ____ + ____ = ____

Total: _____

Game 2

1st turn:

____ + ____ + ____ = ____

2nd turn:

____ + ____ + ____ = ____

3rd turn:

____ + ____ + ____ = ____

Total: _____

Game 3

1st turn:

____ + ____ + ____ = ____

2nd turn:

____ + ____ + ____ = ____

3rd turn:

____ + ____ + ____ = ____

Total: _____

Game 4

1st turn:

____ + ____ + ____ = ____

2nd turn:

____ + ____ + ____ = ____

3rd turn:

____ + ____ + ____ = ____

Total: _____

Addition Spin Spinners

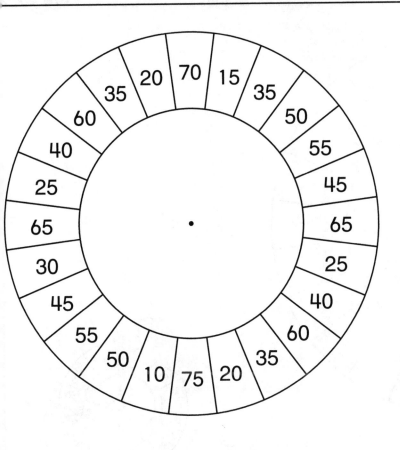

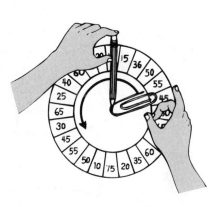

Use a pencil and paper clip to make a spinner.

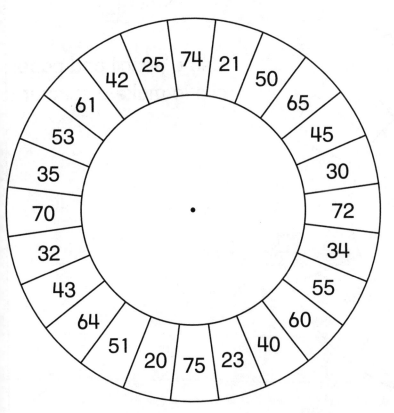

447

Addition Spin **Spinners (Blank)**

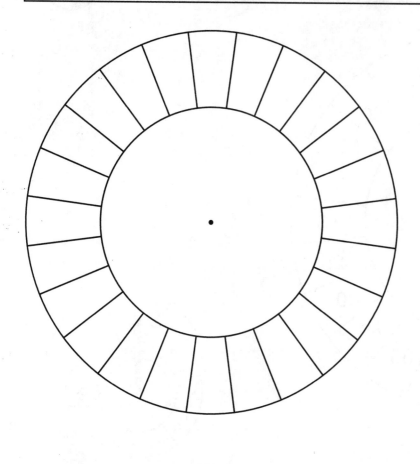

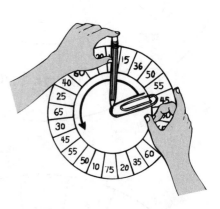

Use a pencil and paper clip to make a spinner.

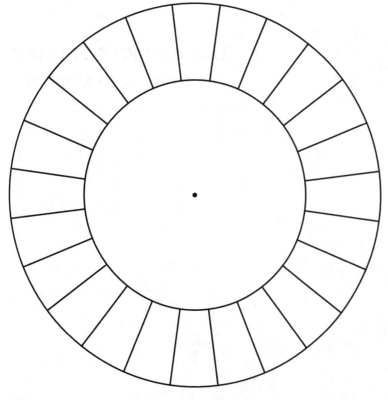

Addition Top-It Record Sheet

Write a number model for each player's cards.

Then write <, >, or = in the box.

_____ = _____   ☐   _____ = _____

_____ = _____   _____ = _____

_____ = _____   ☐   _____ = _____

_____ = _____   ☐   _____ = _____

_____ = _____   ☐   _____ = _____

_____ = _____   _____ = _____

_____ = _____   ☐   _____ = _____

_____ = _____   ☐   _____ = _____

_____ = _____   _____ = _____

_____ = _____   ☐   _____ = _____

_____ = _____   ☐   _____ = _____

_____ = _____   _____ = _____

_____ = _____   ☐   _____ = _____

_____ = _____   ☐   _____ = _____

_____ = _____   ☐   _____ = _____

_____ = _____   _____ = _____

449

Array Bingo Cards

A	**A**	**A**	
2 by 2	2 by 3	2 by 4	4 by 4

A	**A**		
2 by 5	2 by 6	3 by 5	6 by 3

A	**A**	**A**	
3 by 3	1 by 7	4 by 3	3 by 6

	A		
5 by 3	6 by 1	4 by 5	5 by 4

450

Basketball Addition Scoreboard

	Points Scored			
	Team 1		Team 2	
	1st Half	2nd Half	1st Half	2nd Half
Player 1				
Player 2				
Player 3				
Player 4				
Player 5				
Team Score				

Final Score

Coin Top-It Coin Combinations

⒟ ⒟ Ⓝ		Ⓠ Ⓝ Ⓟ Ⓟ Ⓟ Ⓟ	Ⓠ ⒟ Ⓟ Ⓟ Ⓟ
	Ⓠ ⒟ ⒟ Ⓟ Ⓟ		Ⓠ Ⓠ Ⓝ Ⓟ
Ⓠ Ⓠ ⒟	Ⓠ ⒟ ⒟ ⒟ ⒟		Ⓠ Ⓠ Ⓠ
Ⓠ Ⓠ Ⓠ Ⓝ Ⓟ Ⓟ	Ⓠ Ⓠ Ⓠ ⒟ Ⓟ	Ⓠ Ⓠ Ⓠ ⒟ Ⓝ Ⓟ	Ⓠ Ⓠ Ⓠ Ⓠ

Coin Top-It **Combinations** *continued*

Ⓝ Ⓝ Ⓟ Ⓟ Ⓟ		Ⓓ Ⓝ Ⓟ Ⓟ Ⓟ	
Ⓠ Ⓟ Ⓟ Ⓟ		Ⓓ Ⓓ Ⓓ Ⓓ	Ⓓ Ⓓ Ⓓ Ⓝ Ⓝ Ⓟ Ⓟ Ⓟ
	Ⓠ Ⓠ Ⓓ	Ⓠ Ⓓ Ⓓ Ⓝ Ⓝ Ⓝ Ⓝ Ⓟ	Ⓠ Ⓠ Ⓓ Ⓓ Ⓟ Ⓟ
Ⓓ Ⓓ Ⓠ Ⓝ Ⓠ Ⓠ	Ⓠ Ⓠ Ⓝ Ⓟ Ⓓ Ⓠ Ⓝ	Ⓓ Ⓓ Ⓓ Ⓓ Ⓓ Ⓓ Ⓓ Ⓠ	Ⓓ Ⓠ Ⓓ Ⓝ Ⓓ Ⓠ Ⓓ Ⓝ

Dollar Rummy Cards

✂

10¢	10¢	20¢	30¢
Dollar Rummy	Dollar Rummy	Dollar Rummy	Dollar Rummy
10¢	10¢	20¢	30¢
40¢	50¢	50¢	50¢
Dollar Rummy	Dollar Rummy	Dollar Rummy	Dollar Rummy
40¢	50¢	50¢	50¢
60¢	70¢	80¢	90¢
Dollar Rummy	Dollar Rummy	Dollar Rummy	Dollar Rummy
60¢	70¢	80¢	90¢

Dollar Rummy Cards (Advanced)

5¢ Dollar Rummy 5¢	**5¢** Dollar Rummy 5¢	**5¢** Dollar Rummy 5¢	**15¢** Dollar Rummy 15¢
25¢ Dollar Rummy 25¢	**25¢** Dollar Rummy 25¢	**35¢** Dollar Rummy 35¢	**45¢** Dollar Rummy 45¢
55¢ Dollar Rummy 55¢	**65¢** Dollar Rummy 65¢	**85¢** Dollar Rummy 85¢	**95¢** Dollar Rummy 95¢

Doubles or Nothing **Record Sheet**

Round 1

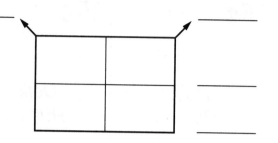

Total _____

Round 2

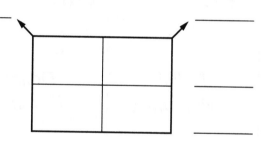

Total _____

Round 3

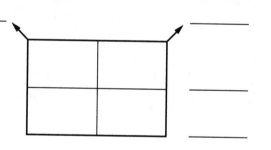

Total _____

Grand Total _____

Name   Date   Time

Hit the Target Record Sheet

Round 1

Target number: _____

Starting Number	Change	Result	Change	Result	Change	Result

Round 2

Target number: _____

Starting Number	Change	Result	Change	Result	Change	Result

Round 3

Target number: _____

Starting Number	Change	Result	Change	Result	Change	Result

Round 4

Target number: _____

Starting Number	Change	Result	Change	Result	Change	Result

457

Money Exchange Game Mat

One Hundred Dollars $100	Ten Dollars $10	One Dollar $1

Money Exchange Game $1 Bills

Name   Date   Time

Money Exchange Game $10 Bills

Money Exchange Game Bills

Name Date Time

Name That Number Record Sheet

Target Card

Number Sentence Solution

Reminder: Write each step separately.

Name Date Time

Name That Number Record Sheet

Target Card

Number Sentence Solution

Reminder: Write each step separately.

Number-Grid Difference Game Record Sheet

My Record Sheet

Round	My Number	My Partner's Number	Difference (Score)
1			
2			
3			
4			
5			
			Total _____

Round	My Number	My Partner's Number	Difference (Score)
1			
2			
3			
4			
5			
			Total _____

Number-Line Squeeze Directions

Materials ☐ *Math Masters*, p. 464

☐ 2 counters

Players 2 or more

Skill Compare and order numbers

Object of the Game To guess a mystery number on the number line

Directions

1. Place the counters on both ends of the number line.

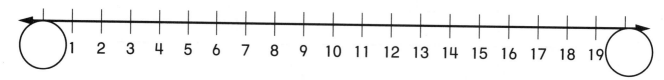

2. One player thinks of a mystery number on the number line.

3. The other players guess the mystery number. If the guess is too high, the first player moves the right counter over to cover the guess. If the guess is too low, the first player moves the left counter over to cover the guess.

4. Repeat Step 3 until the mystery number is guessed.

5. Switch roles and play again.

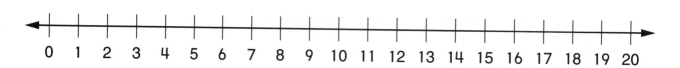

Number Top-It **Place-Value Mat**

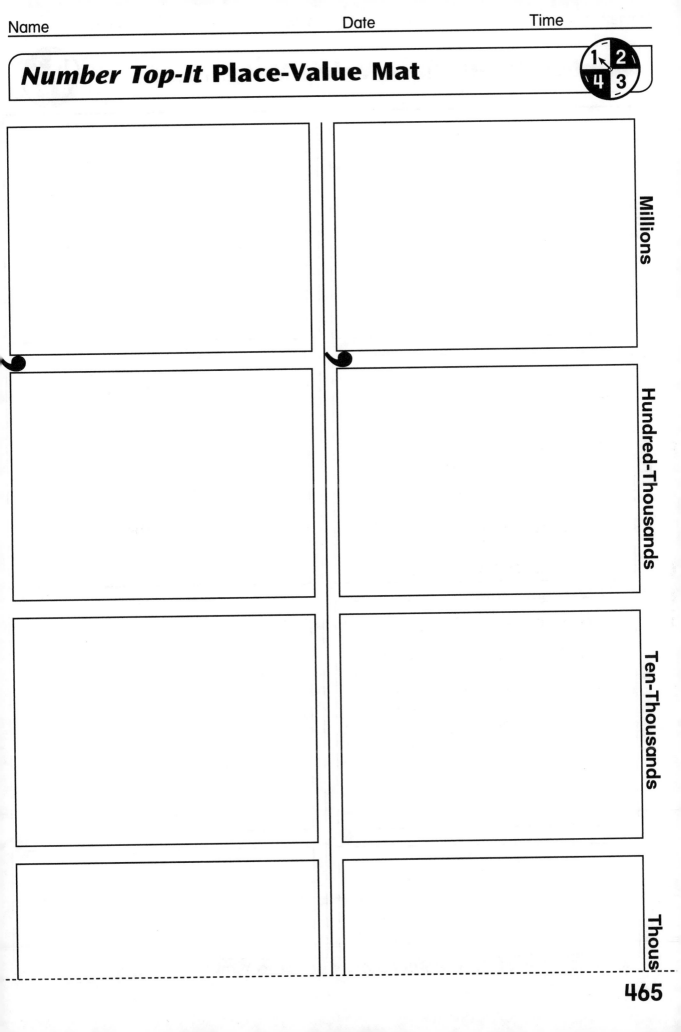

Millions

Hundred-Thousands

Ten-Thousands

Thous

465

Number Top-It **Place-Value Mat** *continued*

1 2
4 3

Ones

Tens

Hundreds

ands

Do not cut. Paste or tape to *Math Masters*, page 465.

466

One-Dollar Exchange **Place-Value Mat**

Dollars 100s **Flats**	Dimes 10s **Longs**	Pennies 1s **Cubes**
$1.00 100¢	$0.10 10¢	$0.01 1¢

Penny Plate Record Sheet

Example:

We started with __20__ pennies.

We could see __6__ pennies on top.

We figured there were __14__ pennies inside.

We counted __14__ pennies inside.

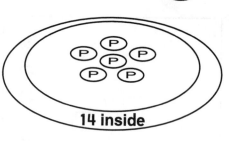

14 inside

Round 1

We started with _____ pennies.

We could see _____ pennies on top.

We figured there were _____ pennies inside.

We counted _____ pennies inside.

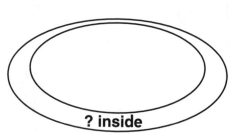

? inside

Round 2

We started with _____ pennies.

We could see _____ pennies on top.

We figured there were _____ pennies inside.

We counted _____ pennies inside.

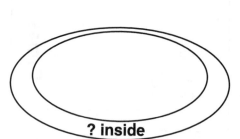

? inside

Round 3

We started with _____ pennies.

We could see _____ pennies on top.

We figured there were _____ pennies inside.

We counted _____ pennies inside.

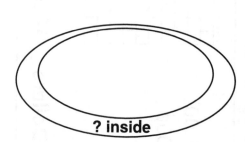

? inside

Pick-a-Coin Record Tables

If you wish, cut apart the 3 tables.

	Ⓟ	Ⓝ	Ⓓ	Ⓠ	$1	Total
1st turn						$____ . ____
2nd turn						$____ . ____
3rd turn						$____ . ____
4th turn						$____ . ____
					Grand Total	$____ . ____

	Ⓟ	Ⓝ	Ⓓ	Ⓠ	$1	Total
1st turn						$____ . ____
2nd turn						$____ . ____
3rd turn						$____ . ____
4th turn						$____ . ____
					Grand Total	$____ . ____

	Ⓟ	Ⓝ	Ⓓ	Ⓠ	$1	Total
1st turn						$____ . ____
2nd turn						$____ . ____
3rd turn						$____ . ____
4th turn						$____ . ____
					Grand Total	$____ . ____

Soccer Spin **Spinners**

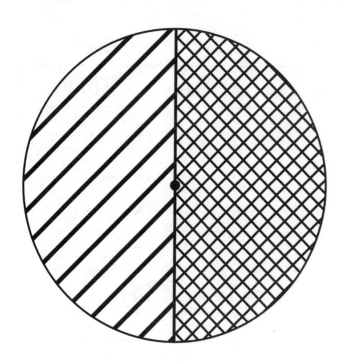

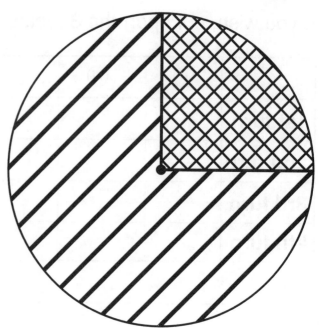

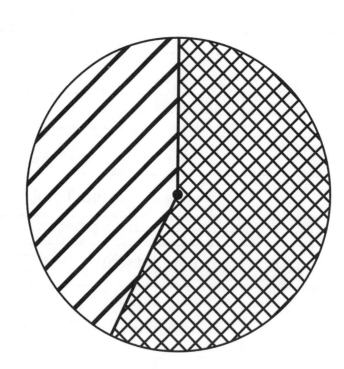

Soccer Spin Gameboard

Stripes Win!

Checks Win!

Spinning for Money Spinner

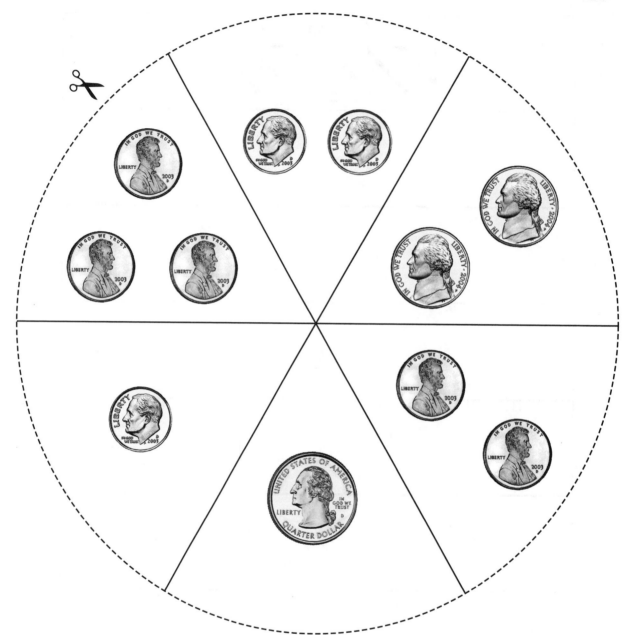

Before beginning the game, cut out this **Spinning for Money Spinner** on the dashed lines.

Three-Addends **Record Sheet**

For each turn:

◆ Write the 3 numbers.

◆ Add the numbers.

◆ Write a number model to show the order in which you added.

1. Numbers: ____, ____, ____

Number model:

____ + ____ + ____ = ____

2. Numbers: ____, ____, ____

Number model:

____ + ____ + ____ = ____

3. Numbers: ____, ____, ____

Number model:

____ = ____ + ____ + ____

4. Numbers: ____, ____, ____

Number model:

____ = ____ + ____ + ____

5. Numbers: ____, ____, ____

Number model:

____ + ____ + ____ = ____

6. Numbers: ____, ____, ____

Number model:

____ + ____ + ____ = ____

7. Numbers: ____, ____, ____

Number model:

____ + ____ + ____ = ____

8. Numbers: ____, ____, ____

Number model:

____ + ____ + ____ = ____

9. Numbers: ____, ____, ____

Number model:

____ = ____ + ____ + ____

10. Numbers: ____, ____, ____

Number model:

____ = ____ + ____ + ____

Time Match Cards

Time Match **Cards** *continued*

3:00	**6:00**	**11:30**
4:30	**2:30**	**10:30**
9:15	**5:15**	**6:45**
2:45	**8:30**	**8:00**

Time Match **Cards** *continued*

2:10	5:25	10:35

4:55	7:20	9:40

Tric-Trac Game Mat